THE SCIENCE OF SEEING

THE
SCIENCE OF SEEING

BY

MATTHEW LUCKIESH, D.SC., D. E.
DIRECTOR, LIGHTING RESEARCH LABORATORY, GENERAL ELECTRIC COMPANY
NELA PARK, CLEVELAND

and

FRANK K. MOSS, E. E.
PHYSICIST, LIGHTING RESEARCH LABORATORY

19 37

D. VAN NOSTRAND COMPANY, INCORPORATED
250 FOURTH AVENUE, NEW YORK

PRESS OF
BRAUNWORTH & COMPANY, INC.
BUILDERS OF BOOKS
BRIDGEPORT • CONNECTICUT

Preface

Seeing is more than visual function. It is an activity of the human being. As such it is subtly, intimately and almost universally woven into the complexity of civilization. It is not only an important part of the foundation of modern life, but it extends prominently throughout this structure and ramifies into much of the embellishment of living. It is a vast panorama including external physical factors, phenomena of the visual sense, psychophysiological effects, and human limitations, abilities and achievements. The science of seeing encompasses controllable aids and hindrances to seeing, internal penalties and rewards to the human seeing-machine, characteristics and requirements of performance, and eventual efficiency, comfort, welfare and experience through the activity of seeing. It includes various sciences or aspects of organized knowledge as well as meagerly explored realms. Its boundaries in the external physical world are obvious but they also extend unobviously and deeply into the complexity of the human being.

In presenting such a comprehensive subject within a reasonable compass, it is necessary to confine the treatment to aspects not primarily developed in the various sciences included. It was decided that the course would be charted chiefly by the new concepts and knowledge of seeing; and that the discussions would deal largely with controllable factors which can contribute toward quick, certain, and easy seeing. This is the only avenue available for reducing the penalties of poor seeing conditions and for improving the quality and quantity of human achievements through this most important human activity. This approach is relatively new in its concepts and objectives both from fundamental and practical viewpoints. It should be of interest to anyone concerned with vision, with any aid to seeing, or with any activity involving seeing in relation to human efficiency, progress, and welfare.

228712

We gratefully acknowledge the helpfulness of Dr. E. Q. Adams in discussing certain aspects of theory and interpretation; of S. K. Guth, A. A. Eastman, L. L. Holladay, and A. H. Taylor in assembling certain data; of T. Knowles and H. E. Wachs in illustrating; and of Margaret Callow and Marjorie Seymour in proofreading.

May 5, 1937

MATTHEW LUCKIESH
FRANK K. MOSS

Contents

THE SCIENCE OF SEEING

CHAPTER I

Seeing

Civilization is an artificial world created by human beings in the pursuit of greater safety, convenience, comfort and enjoyment. For thousands of years since its hazy beginning, practices have commonly preceded knowledge of their effects. Knowledge advanced slowly by the often painful process of accidental experience or by the groping method of trial and error. Many forces have been at work in the construction of this artificial world and for obvious reasons there is much inconsistency and conflict among the artificialities and their ultimate effects upon human beings. It was inevitable that many practices were created and developed before much knowledge of them and of their effects was available. This is a characteristic of civilization even since the recent advent of scientific method inaugurated the era of modern science. Notwithstanding the marvelous contributions of science, we still live in an unscientific world. Only a century has elapsed since modern science definitely enlisted in intimate service to mankind. In that brief period the spirit and method of science has not penetrated much beyond its own sphere of activity and on every hand practices continue to precede knowledge of their effects. Even the applications of scientific knowledge introduce new artificialities which may create hazards or penalties that are not obvious.

It was natural for the artificial world to be built largely for human senses and abilities. It was inevitable that seeing became the important human activity in the construction and operation of this artificial world and in its appeal to human beings. Certainly vision is the most important human sense and seeing is the most universally important controllable activity of human beings. Thus civilization has become largely a complexity of opportunities for seeing, of responsibilities of seeing, and of achievements through seeing. All this complex world of seeing grew and ramified without much knowledge of seeing and even without a proper and adequate concept of seeing. Wherever knowledge is meager or far from complete, misconceptions flourish and erroneous assumptions are commonly false guides. To acquire an adequate conception of seeing as a human activity it is necessary to appreciate human vagaries, abilities and limitations as well as those of the visual sense. Therefore, a proper appreciation, conception and understanding of seeing cannot be attained without tracing man and the visual sense backward far beyond the dawn of civilization or even of the human race. They have their roots deep in the evolution of life in the outdoor environment of Nature. The beginning of seeing lies eons back in the realm of biology. Here we are not interested in the intricate details of evolution and adaptation, but in the philosophy which provides an appropriate background for understanding the vast complexity of seeing.[1]

EVOLUTION OF VISION

Environment, function and organism are now generally accepted as constituting the fundamental biological triad. They must be contemplated together if one is to gain a fair or proper conception of any of them. There can be no life apart from environment. One cannot conceive living matter, as we know it, in complete isolation. Environment apart from life is a futile conception. Certainly it would be meaningless and of no importance to us. The interchange between living matter and its surroundings represents the functioning of the organism. When this functioning ceases the organism dies. Changes in the rate of this functioning or interchange are continually occurring. In some such manner adaptation is called upon and changes in the organism take place. The fittest survive and evolution proceeds upon its way. These changes in the rate of functioning or of interchange between the environment and the living organism are due to many things. Over the course of eons we see written in the permanent language of fossils great chapters in the evolution of living things. This evolution is going on about us ever so slowly as measured by our life-time which is only a tick of the cosmical clock. But it has been plainly recorded in the history of time in which each chapter of life or each branch in the tree of evolution generally spans millions of years.

Environment includes at least everything outside the individual plant or animal between which and the living thing there is an interchange of energy. Most consideration is usually given to factors of the physical environment such as altitude, climate, temperature, rainfall, humidity, winds, radiant energy, nature of the earth's surface, cloudiness or clarity of the atmosphere and character and fertility of the soil. But there is also the living environment as well as the non-living. Plants influence one another as is evidenced by life in a forest or in the open. Also all kinds of living things leave their imprint on plant life. Plants do not migrate as animals do and they have little control over their environment. Animals are mobile and have much effect upon their immediate surroundings. They range for food, burrow for protection from the elements, hide from enemies and even store supplies. Other animals are part of their environment.

The importance of function as a connecting link between the environment and the animal is very greatly affected by the almost infinitely greater mobility of animals compared with plants. They can readily change from one environment to another, for better or for worse as accident or possibly instinct may determine. In general, plant life had to precede animal life because animals cannot manufacture food—excepting for other animals. Plants on the other hand manufacture food by synthesizing salts from the soil and gases from the air with the aid which solar energy gives to their life processes. Animals that eat other animals are indirectly living on plant life. All are living on solar energy indirectly. It is "stored" in the plant structure, in vitamin D in animals of the sea, and contributes to the life processes of all. Everywhere throughout the environment of living things, now and back through the eons of time since life began, solar energy has been an ever-present factor.

The foregoing is a fleeting glimpse of the importance of sunlight in life and on the evolution of life. Throughout biology life is dealt with as an interchange of energy. And as the processes of analysis and synthesis of this science continue to yield more facts and more correlations of them, radiant energy becomes more conspicuous not merely as an environmental factor, but as a vital factor in cellular life and function. Physical science first established laws relating matter and energy, then later revealed the interchangeability between these components of the material world, and finally indicates energy as the sole constituent. The science of living matter reveals more and more of the dominance of energy in life and life processes.

Certainly no one familiar with the modern facts and generalizations in physics, chemistry, biology and ecology would contend that more than a glimpse of the importance of solar energy to life-processes has been revealed as yet. Doubtless most thoughtful persons would prefer to assume that solar energy is intricately interwoven throughout the complex pattern of the living world. It is difficult to conceive that this radiant energy throughout all its wavelengths is not involved at least here and there throughout important processes upon which life and health depend. Certainly ultraviolet radiation, undiscovered until early last century, has been shown in the present century to possess beneficence in curative and preventive values. Its relation to vitamin D is now well known. In contemplating sunlight it is essential to consider its composition and duration as well as merely itself without analysis and measurement. Still, analysis by means of measurements is often neglected in biological, ecological, physiological and ophthalmological considerations notwithstanding its obviously great importance in many cases.

Regardless of ultimate revelations of still greater importance of solar energy in the tangled skein of living matter, sunlight is intricately involved in the evolution and function of the visual sense and in the entire process of seeing. Biology is perhaps still a long way from the answer to the question, What is life? However, it has developed two clear decisions. One of these is the conviction that the principle of evolution is of universal eminence.

The other is the realization that each individual cell of living matter lives and acts independently, to a degree at least. This atom of living matter finally is the focus of much attention as an individual and as an association of millions which constitute a living organism—even a human being. With this single cell in mind let us look back over eons of time when the simplest living organisms were the highest order of life. No one can prove as yet that there was such a time, but it fits the known facts as well as an enlightening philosophy. Such a simple organism lived in contact with much of its necessary environment. It enveloped food and might be considered to be all stomach. It felt food and other things and might be considered to be all a sense of touch. It did not see as we see, but to continue the analogy, it might be considered to be all eye.

Over the course of millions of years these living organisms were altered by changes in the environment. Glacial ages came and the climate changed. The earth's surface may have raised or lowered. Even a tilt to the north or south alters the climate as a change in latitude or altitude does. Deserts or perpetual rainy seasons came and went. Changes in the functioning between the organism and the environment produced a slow adaptation to new conditions. Evolution began and was continued by the same processes and forces. Differentiation in functions began to take place low in the scale of living things. Crude senses began to be separated from one to another. Higher and higher organisms appeared as the eons passed. Various branches of the tree of life developed. All this time the sense of touch was evolving. But touch alone limited the organism to detecting only that part of the external world which it could physically reach. The sense of smell extended the contact or exploration of the environment, but this in principle was still a sense of touch. That is, actual particles of the environment out of actual reach came to this sense of smell and gave the organism information of something at a distance. Taste is in the same category—contact with a part of the substance.

Another sense developed upon an entirely different principle. Radiant energy from the sun and sky was showering over the earth vitalizing plant and animal life, entering into their life processes, and storing itself in living things and eventually in non-living substances. Life was already utilizing it in many ways. Why should not a sense develop which utilized radiant energy which is emitted or reflected or transmitted by all objects? If appropriate eyes were available, the radiant energy from objects of various forms would come to the organism in corresponding patterns. This did happen. Eyes and a visual sense eventually became differentiated. They used radiant energy which is just as invisible and of the same fundamental nature as the energy sent out by our modern wireless and radio stations. Thus objects everywhere were sending-stations and eyes and visual senses evolved as receiving-sets. In the course of eons of time many kinds of eyes were developed. In the process of evolution man and long lines of ancestors acquired two eyes along with other highly differentiated senses and functions. Binocular vision eventually added advantages over monocular vision and over the stationary manifold eyes of insects. With two movable eyes the ability to perceive depth, to estimate distance and to achieve other refinements became possible.

As these and other abilities were being added to the marvelously developing eyes and visual sense, color vision was also evolving. This was not only a refinement of high order, but to the mind and intellect which were evolving human beings high above the level of other animal life, it was something more than the ability to discriminate another characteristic of objects. The gift of color vision made it possible for man to enjoy a magical drapery of color which, by virtue of his color vision and color sense, was spread over all creation. Thus man's visual sense became a tool for seeing which greatly aided the physical being. It also became a doorway through which the external world of light, shade and color could impress the mental being.

LEARNING TO SEE

Evolution did not stop with the development of the visual sense as a super-tool and super-connection between human beings and the external world. The human being still had to develop the ability to see. When this accomplishment was added to other human endowments human beings possessed great powers compared to those of lower animals. It became possible for mobile man, tool-using man, seeing man, thinking man, impressive man, and expressive man to increase control over his environment very greatly and to alter it radically. This alteration results in man's own artificial world being superposed upon or substituted for the natural environment. In making these alterations human beings have not been all-knowing. In fact, they have been grossly ignorant of that overwhelming part of the natural environment which is hidden from their senses. What penalties they have paid or may be paying for their ignorance! Actually they may be hastening their exit from the stage of life. Unless knowledge grows apace with "improvements" of civilization, human beings may be on their way to the fossil stage. As yet man's sojourn has been brief. Chapters in the history of life on earth are measured in eons. Knowledge of hidden causes and effects is the only possible guarantee of his perpetuity. Certainly he must continue to remodel as well as to build new additions to his artificial world according to the dictates of new knowledge.

In the process of the development of vision as the most highly organized and differentiated sense we find physical factors, physiological functions, and mental processes intricately interwoven. Learning to use the visual sense and other senses and to coordinate muscles, mind and other endowments of the human being required a greater period of infancy for such schooling. Seeing in the case of the complex human being is no more merely a matter of radiant energy from the object, of the physical optics of the eyes, and of the other uncontrollable factors such as the physiological and psychological functions in the chain from the object to the consciousness. The ability to see and to get the most out of this activity involves a great deal of learning and some forgetting during the long period of infancy necessary for human beings to master their potential endowments. In the first place we must learn to see objects out in the external world where they are. Their images are inside us, actually on our retinae. Why do we not see them there?

Fortunately our first impressions through the visual sense take place while we are infants, before we have organized our thinking or have developed much analytical ability. Simultaneously with these first impressions we touch the objects with our hands or other parts of our bodies. Gradually we learn that the objects are where our sense of touch or hearing tells us they are. Thus the greatest achievement of seeing is accomplished. Nothing among all the complex abilities of a human being can outrank the ability to see things out in the material world where they actually are.

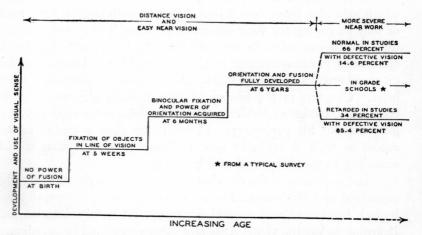

FIG. 1.—Illustrating the development of binocular vision and the use of vision in early childhood. An example of the penalty of defective vision in school work is included.

A diagram of the growth in the development and use of binocular vision [2] is presented in Fig. 1. From birth to six years of age is a period of learning to fixate objects, to orient the eyes, and to fuse the two images into satisfactory binocular vision. At six years of age begins a lifetime of slavery to near-vision. From then on, year after year the prevalence of eye-defectiveness increases quite rapidly. The right-hand portion of the diagram illustrates the influence of defective vision upon progress in studies. Similar influences are found throughout the activities of adults. It is reasonable to consider these as penalties of civilization.

Early in infancy we get our first lessons in interpreting the stresses and strains of the eye-muscles. By convergence we learn

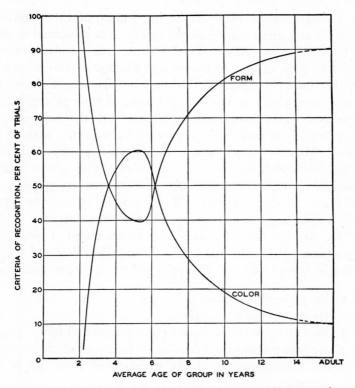

Fig. 2.—The relative potency of color and form perception at various ages. (After Brian and Goodenough.)

something of the distance of nearby objects. By learning the sizes of some objects we learn to estimate the size or distance of distant objects. We learn to concentrate upon form and to ignore color in much of the practice of seeing. Also, we learn to use color when advantageous. We learn to ignore objects in the peripheral or outlying portions of the visual field so as not to distract our attention from the object in the central field upon which our eyes and our consciousness are focused. We learn not to see when the eyes are in motion, or the visual sense has done this for us, in order to avoid blurring. In many ways by learning and by forgetting we add greatly to our ability to see.

A diagrammatic view of the importance of color and form perception at various ages is shown in Fig. 2 as presented by Brian and Goodenough.[3] Much remains to be learned about children under two years of age. However, at the age of two years it appears that form perception is of primary importance. Color appeals to very young children, but little is known of their perception. At two years of age color perception begins to rival form perception and apparently is maximally important between the ages of four and six. After six years of age is reached, form perception becomes very predominantly important and remains so throughout life. Of course, this diagram and analysis refer to average persons. In later years the development of color sensibility or consciousness depends upon a person's training, interest or occupation.

We perceive the third dimension in space and of objects and other aspects of the external world through learning and through practice in interpretation. The principal modes are as follows:

1. By perceiving extent.
2. By appraising perspective.
3. By noting the elevation of objects, near and far.
4. By interpreting the variation of light and shade in objects.
5. By a consciousness of the variation of visual angle with distance.
6. By interpreting muscular effort attending accommodation of the two eyes.
7. By interpreting muscular effort attending convergence of the axes of the two eyes.
8. By interference of near objects with those more distant.
9. By stereoscopic vision.
10. By clearness of brightness or color of distant objects outdoors due to atmospheric haze.

With all our learning, seeing is still deceiving. Many types of visual illusions [4] are present on every hand. In fact, it is probably impossible to conceive a condition in which the appearance of an object—line, area, form, brightness or color—is not affected by something else seen in the immediate environment. For the most part illusions do not interfere seriously with our appraisal of objects through our ability to see them. Still they are ever-present and are to be looked for in any accurate analysis or appraisal. They spring from many causes. Objects and environment mutually affect the appearance of each. Our own experience and knowledge is often at fault. We are more likely to see what we expect to see or are more used to seeing. That is, if two objects have the same form, or nearly so, we are likely to assume that the object is that which is most common in our experience.

Also, there is a wide variation in color vision and sensibility, in retinal sensitivity, in optical defects, in reaction time, in experience, etc. All these produce variations in the interpretation of the external world through the ability to see. In addition, we are mental beings and differ more markedly in psychological reactions than in any other way. All these are factors to be considered in specific cases and in fundamental researches in seeing; but most human beings see sufficiently alike for most practical purposes. Nevertheless, the science of vision is inadequate in scope to include seeing. Even the technique of the eyesight specialist is too much limited to optical and muscle corrections to encompass the entire act of seeing. As a consequence, an extension of their services into the complex realm of seeing provides a new opportunity for further service.

These are brief glimpses of the development of the marvelous human sense and the ability to use it. They provide only a vague conception of seeing as an activity of the entire human being which is of very recent birth. The science of seeing was perfected through necessity for a theory which would rescue experimental research from the dead-end avenue which it entered in its studies of the more restricted aspects such as vision and visibility. It has already inspired researches beyond the physical aspects of eyes and visibility, beyond classical physiological optics, and beyond the

modern ideas and facts of perception. It has led into that realm
of eventual end-products—the costs and values of seeing to human
beings operating as human seeing-machines.

LIGHT AND BRIGHTNESS OUTDOORS

It is an inescapable fact that our eyes, visual sense, physical
body, physiological functions, and everything which constitutes us
as human seeing-machines evolved outdoors through eons of adaptation to the light, brightnesses and colors and to their distributions.
This fact is often carelessly lost sight of or turned aside indiffer-
ently as of no importance even by those who accept the importance
of adaptation to environment in other aspects of life. In the total
absence of knowledge it is far safer to turn to Nature than to trust
in man-made environment; to use Nature as a textbook and guide
than to trust mere opinions implicitly. Certainly there is much
evidence that man was designed by and for Nature. Conversely,
there is no evidence which indicates that Nature was designed for
man regardless of the forces of egoism which would have it so.

Modern science could not have been born until man recognized his insignificance and limitations. The mightiest battles between knowledge and prejudice were fought on this battleground.
Man's ego placed him at the center of the universe and as a consequence had the planets and stars revolving around him. But he
was wrong. Apparently we live on a relatively insignificant speck
of dust that has no significant location in the scheme of the universe.
However, this egoism dies hard. It presents obstacles everywhere
to the true course of thought and action. It remains a nuisance in
the world of seeing because civilization's artificialities are falsely
given some fundamental importance. Biologically speaking, human
beings came indoors only yesterday. Aside from greater comfort
through protection from the obvious discomforts and dangers outdoors, one can scarcely believe that we have escaped the imprint
and modeling by Nature's environment over the course of eons.

Psychological reactions may change rather quickly, but there
is much evidence that Nature impressed deeply in us the fundamentals upon which our esthetic sensibility is based and to which

it bows obediently. We need only contemplate the distributions of brightness which are generally satisfying or natural indoors to know that Nature's impressions are deep within us. We do not live with light floors and dark ceilings, but with the reverse as is prevalent outdoors. To one who appraises lighting without prejudice, a combination of direct and general illumination is found to be most generally satisfying and natural indoors. Outdoors we have direct light from the sun and general illumination from the sky. Of course, man makes special applications for special conditions in the artificial world. Sometimes they may be the best compromise, but here we are discussing fundamentals deeply rooted.

In the physiognomy of the human being is seen the imprint of Nature. Apparently it was gradually modeled to be suitably adapted, among other things, to natural lighting.[5] Protection is afforded from powerful brightness overhead. Certainly the eyes are well adapted for the best seeing that a nimble two-eyed upright human being could accomplish. The selectivity of the visual sense for the radiant energy from the sun is about perfectly developed to utilize this energy most efficiently and still have the enjoyment and usefulness of color vision. The wavelengths of radiant energy to which the eye is maximally sensitive correspond closely to the wavelengths of maximum energy in sunlight. The infrared is unused by the visual sense, but this varies so much due to water vapor in the atmosphere it is well that it is not used. If the various wavelengths of infrared produced color sensations as they do in the visible spectrum, great changes in the color of sunlight and skylight would take place. Now we are only greeted with relatively mild and pleasing color symphonies at the beginning and end of the day.

Such details multiplied into an uncounted myriad have established the great principle of adaptation to environment and aid in establishing something of the fact and course of evolution. Singly they are interesting, but en masse they are inspiring and convincing. They encourage one to expect more and more evidence of the fact that we human beings were designed by and for Nature. They prepare us to have faith even in indirect evidence which sometimes is the only kind of data obtainable in certain studies of effects upon human beings. With the great mass of facts of adaptation it does not take courage to theorize that all of Nature's environmental factors have been impressed upon us. For example, one should not be surprised if it is revealed sometime in the future when we know more about the human being, that all wavelengths of radiant energy from the sun and sky are intricately entwined in the life and health processes of human beings.

In the foregoing we have had glimpses of natural light and lighting outdoors. As to the quantity of light at the earth's surface or the illumination in footcandles, the results of our researches of the past decade are the first to indicate that brightness-levels of the same order of magnitude are ideal for human seeing-machines in the performance of critical seeing. During most of the day the illumination at the earth's surface is generally thousands of footcandles. At noon on a very clear day it may reach 9000 footcandles and even approaches 10000 footcandles in some places. In the shade of a building or a tree it is commonly hundreds of footcandles and is often 1000 footcandles. Even near a window indoors it may be 100 or 300 footcandles on the shady side of the building. But ten feet from the windows it commonly drops to less than five footcandles. Outdoors on the streets and highways the illumination at night commonly varies from a fraction of a footcandle to nearly zero. The footcandle is defined in Chapter VIII.

The enormous change man made by greatly reducing the amount of light available and by introducing unnaturally prolonged near-vision is illustrated in Fig. 3. Certainly the prolonged severe critical visual tasks of civilization have imposed upon vision and upon human seeing-machines. Man's control of his environment in this respect has been very great. He made these alterations without knowledge. He could still see in a way and that has tended to obscure still more the possibility of unobvious consequences. Can one view this with complacency and without suspecting penalties arising therefrom? Even if we had no knowledge, faith in the principle of adaptation to environment would prevent a thoughtful person from assuming that a few footcandles are enough for critical seeing over long periods. Still this has not only been assumed but dogmatically stated for years. No researches have proved that a few footcandles are enough. On the contrary,

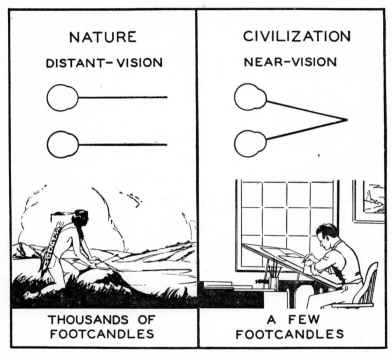

FIG. 3.—Illustrating two great differences between the natural and artificial worlds which are fundamentally important in any adequate consideration of seeing and of human seeing-machines.

our recent researches indicate that much higher footcandle-levels are desirable. Certainly there are powerful reasons for avoiding the risk of stating that a few footcandles, or any less than those hundreds and thousands of footcandles which would produce the average brightnesses of outdoor areas on average days, are enough for performing critical visual tasks over long periods.

[15]

Certainly there can be no harm in exposing the eyes to brightnesses comparable with those that are prevalent over large areas in outdoor landscapes. Naturally, common sense would exclude the unusual brightnesses of the sun itself or of its image reflected from water, or even large areas of sunlit snow. These are unusual over the year and over the area in which the human race evolved. A green leaf is about as bright under 8000 footcandles outdoors at noon as a white paper would be under 1000 footcandles indoors. On the other hand, the green leaf under 8000 footcandles is no brighter than a "black" cloth under 25000 footcandles. These are facts of brightness with which one must be familiar if he is to avoid ridiculous assumptions and statements about the magnitudes of brightness or quantities of light that human beings need or can tolerate.

Inasmuch as the brightnesses to which human beings have long been exposed outdoors are important, some average ones of the more common areas are presented in Table I. The brightnesses are expressed in millilamberts. (See Chapter VIII). Incidentally the brightness of a "white" diffusing surface having a reflection-factor of 92.9 per cent is one millilambert when it is illuminated by one footcandle. Therefore, the brightness values in Table I are also numerically equivalent to the footcandles necessary to produce the equivalent brightnesses of a socalled white diffusing surface which reflects 92.9 per cent of the incident light. Actually most socalled white surfaces have reflection-factors of 75 to 85 per cent. It is seen from these brightness values that human eyes and human beings are adapted to brightnesses far greater than commonly encountered indoors. It is ridiculous to state, as has often been done, that a normal person cannot tolerate the brightness of a printed page when it is illuminated to 10 or even 100 footcandles. Pleasing areas outdoors such as sunlit pastures and woods commonly have brightnesses during a clear summer's day equivalent to that produced by 1000 footcandle on a printed page. There may be other factors which are disturbing or unsatisfactory indoors, such as brightness-contrast and distribution. Of course, the actual performance of critical seeing may influence tolerance somewhat, but even on a dull overcast day when the illumination at the earth's surface is 1000 footcandles, the brightnesses of the earth areas are one-tenth the values given in Table I. They are still equivalent to that of a printed page of a book under 50 to 1000 footcandles.

TABLE I

Average Brightnesses in Millilamberts of the Sky as Viewed from the Earth, and of Earth Areas as Viewed from an Airplane, Near Noon on a Clear Midsummer Day. These Values also Represent the Footcandles Necessary to Produce Equivalent Brightnesses of a White Diffusing Surface Having a Reflection-Factor of 92.9 Per Cent.

Very clear sky	250
Average clear blue sky	500
Thin haze	1,000
Moderate haze	1,500
Dense haze or thin cloud	2,000
Medium cloud layer	1,000
Thickly overcast	250
Densest overcast approaches	0
Sunlit cloud approaches	10,000
Deep clear water	500
Shallow inland water	1,000
Grass and green crops	1,000
Green woods	500
Barren soil	2,000
Thick clouds, maximum	10,000
Snow, maximum	10,000
Individual green leaf	2,000

When man came indoors he had to have light in order to see. Fortunately he can see with a little light. He left a hole in the entrance of the cave or in the wall of the crude hut. This was enough light for his activities which involved casual seeing. It is enough light now for conversational purposes. Then as civilization advanced artificial light came in the form of crude flames. Later these were refined into candles and lamps. By accident all these flames were of the order of one candlepower; that is, they provided illumination of about one footcandle at a distance of one foot. But suppose they had been 1000 candlepower! Then the first practical electric lamp would have been of comparable candle-power instead of a hundredth of that. Thus, beginning with only the need for barely seeing there came by accident the artificial light-sources comparable with the ordinary candle which continued the era of barely seeing. Combine with this the fact that the science of vision reveals little more about light than that necessary for barely seeing and we readily account for the meager quantities of light in use today and also for the false and inadequate concepts which are prevalent. However, the science of seeing reveals the proper objective of easiest seeing which also generally means most speedy, safe, accurate and certain seeing. Also, the new researches in seeing point to the average brightnesses outdoors in the day-time as being of the order of magnitude which is ideal for the severe prolonged tasks of our artificial world. There are many threads in the tangled skein of seeing. To disentangle these has been a major objective of our researches over the past quarter of a century.

SEEING IN MODERN CIVILIZATION

Civilization is largely a world of seeing. Throughout its intricate pattern seeing is an intimately and universally important factor in the education, experience and performance of human beings. In obvious and unobvious ways it is a powerful and universal influence in the efficacy, efficiency, safety, comfort, behavior, health, life and happiness of human beings, individually and collectively. And year by year it is becoming more involved and important as civilization increases in complexity. Great changes take place in visual tasks and in the responsibilities of seeing due to great changes wrought by new applications of new knowledge. Contemplate such inventions as printing and the automobile and the development of many crafts. In general, those that endure and progress increase the productiveness or enjoyment of mankind. But while our more obvious burdens diminish and our partial emancipation from physical slavery and drudgery has greatly increased our leisure and enjoyment, the burdens and responsibilities of seeing have greatly increased.

Printing has contributed incalculably to the progress of mankind, but it has greatly increased the burdens of seeing. Through-out all its ramifications uncounted millions of persons are engaged many hours daily in the unnaturally close, critical and prolonged task of reading, or its equivalent, under unnatural and apparently subnormal seeing conditions. What are normal conditions? That is one of the questions which the science of seeing must answer in order to remodel the artificial world which has been built without such knowledge. Certainly, if there are great fundamental differences, normal conditions are likely to be nearer to natural than to artificial conditions. The science of seeing already has supplied

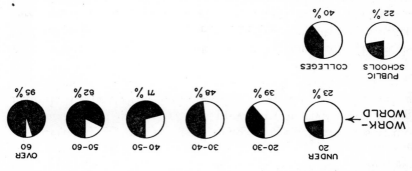

Fig. 4.—Approximate percentages of persons having defective vision in various age-groups in the work-world and also in schools and colleges.

important parts of the answer through measurements of fundamentals which influence the visibility of the task, ease of seeing, and the comfort of the reader. In the matter of light it appears that brightnesses of the order of daylight are more nearly ideal than those close to darkness, which are prevalent indoors in the daytime as well as everywhere at night.

The abnormal visual tasks of civilization which so generally have to be performed in the man-made environment of our artificial world are found on every hand. Through the development of many crafts millions of persons perform difficult critical tasks of seeing for many hours daily with eyes accommodated and converged for near-vision. Certainly prolonged close work is un-

natural. Millions of children enter school with no handicaps excepting those imposed by civilization and the artificial world which
it has created. Eye-defectiveness mounts year after year as indicated in Fig. 4. These data [2] represent an average of the results
of many surveys by various investigators using different methods.
Naturally more eye-defects will be discovered by a refined technique than by hurried examinations. Therefore, the exact rate of
increase of eye-defectiveness with age cannot be established without
first agreeing upon criteria and technique. However, Fig. 4 serves
the present purpose inasmuch as the surveys involved large groups
of school children. It is likely they do not include insignificant
defects because the most refined methods could not have been practicable in such extensive surveys.

Certainly it is not necessary to accept eye-defectiveness as unpreventable and inevitable. Its prevalence in civilization is unnatural. Certainly the costs of seeing in eye-defects and in other
ways should be reduced by whatever aids science discovers or dictates. It seems reasonable that if seeing is made easier by any
means, eyes and human beings would be benefited. There is
evidence that this is true. Certainly there is plenty of evidence
that the occupation [1] and the seeing conditions leave their mark on
eyesight as indicated in Fig. 5. One familiar with seeing can often
detect the imprint of severe visual work under poor conditions upon
the faces of human beings. The science of seeing is revealing
still more deeply hidden costs in penalties of seeing.

Millions of automobiles on the highways make life and death
a matter of split-second seeing. Quick, accurate, certain seeing
becomes essential to safety on highways and in much of the work-
world. Still how generally seeing is ignored in such considerations
and how inadequate is the general conception of it! Great progress has been made in the application of safety devices, but proper
concepts and knowledge of seeing have been absent from safety
considerations. One may see something when he knows it is there
and is doing nothing else but looking for it or at it. For example,
seeing a pedestrian or traffic aid may be readily accomplished by a
person sitting in a parked automobile. But when he is driving a

motor vehicle or is engaged in any other task requiring some of his sense capacity, it may be a far different matter. Now his efficiency as a seeing-machine is decreased, often very greatly. He

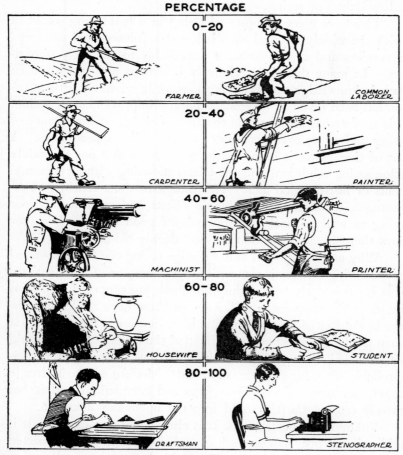

PERCENTAGE

FIG. 5.—Approximate prevalence of defective vision in percentages of persons having measurable eye-defects in various occupations.

needs factors of safety in seeing in order to see safely for himself or others. It is a function of the science of seeing to determine reasonable factors of safety for various visual situations. This is a new concept of seeing whose absence from safety considerations has caused enormous losses in life and property. The highway and work-world where dangers lurk at all times are excellent examples of the general lack of a seeing consciousness and of an understanding of seeing.

These are mere glimpses of seeing in a half-seeing world in which are widely enjoyed numberless conveniences and comforts, preventives and cures that were unavailable to anyone yestercentury. In many directions relatively enormous progress has been made in knowledge and its applications while relatively little attention has been given to understanding and improvement of seeing. This neglect has continued in the face of the great importance of seeing and of its ever-increasing burdens and responsibilities. A part of the answer is found in the assumption that one can safely judge seeing conditions and the effects of seeing without measurements or instrumental aids. This cannot be done reliably. Furthermore, there are the unobvious effects and penalties of poor seeing as well as unobvious rewards of good seeing. We now know there are such and that they are deeply hidden.

Why one should feel able to judge seeing conditions unaided by measuring devices is somewhat mysterious, or at least curious. This is particularly true if the individuals are supposed to possess the scientific viewpoint. Still, some of these have made this mistake in the face of the fact that modern science was born in earnest when thinking men came to realize that their unaided senses could not be relied upon to discover the unobvious. Even reasoning is unreliable when facts are rare or absent. Modern science is already largely an array of unobvious facts and correlations and it has scarcely crossed the threshold into the unobvious unknown.

Vitamin A is not obvious. It is elusive and, for example, it is hidden in carrots. No stomach ever discovered or even suspected its existence or its far-reaching effects. No human sense or function could do so unaided. A deficiency of vision known as night-blindness now appears to be due to a deficiency in vitamin A. Certainly no unaided eye or human being could discover this. A photometer is now used in connection with correlated knowledge to detect this deficiency in vision and in vitamin A. Certainly no human being unaided could possibly detect a connection between plenty of carrots in a diet and a motor vehicle accident on a dark highway at night. However, modern science makes these discoveries of unobvious facts and of unobvious correlations among them.

The foregoing argument and example could be paralleled in many ways for all our senses, various organs and our reasoning. Long ago modern science turned to aids which could not be deceived as the senses and reasoning can be. As a consequence we now trust only this method of approach. We make measurements. We obtain tested and testable, and therefore, incontestable knowledge. Why should we trust our vision or ourselves as seeing-machines? But many do and therein lies another part of the answer to the question, Why has there been such a neglect of seeing and of seeing conditions?

A change is rapidly taking place since the conception of seeing has been properly extended and the scope of a science of seeing has been definitely outlined. Radically new researches are discovering unobvious causes and effects. Modern science is extending its front in this realm. It can be depended upon to point the way and to lead in providing new knowledge in the many existing gaps. But more than knowledge is needed. Wherever there is ignorance there is prejudice or indifference, which are degrees of the same thing. Knowledge when widely used and understood combats these false guides or deterrents. A seeing consciousness is sorely needed throughout the highways and byways of human activity in this half-seeing world. The new science of seeing is awakening and developing such a consciousness.

It should be continually recognized that civilization is not all profits. There are losses, too. Modern sciences are reducing the losses and no science holds more promise in this direction than the science of seeing. Belated though it may be, it deals with the most universally important voluntary activity of human beings. It can safely promise much, for seeing is nearly as complex as living. As we contemplate blindness and the blind, seeing seems as important as living.

SEEING IS MORE THAN VISION

To say that seeing is the most prevalent voluntary act and activity of human beings is another way of stating that vision is our most important sense. But seeing is more than vision—very much more. Seeing is work that human beings do with eyes, muscles, nerves, energy, heart and mind. It requires such tools as light and vision, but also human effort and intelligence. It involves muscular activity, the nervous system, expenditure of energy, mental functions, but also human reactions, rewards and penalties. Seeing is an activity of the human body and mind. Its end-products are human behavior in its full sense. Thus, seeing involves a complex chain of events beginning with the external physical world which affects visibility and comfort, passing through the visual sense, eventually entering a complex realm of unobvious physiological and psychological effects and finally ending in an accomplishment of some kind. But at what cost? Some ultimate rewards and some penalties are obvious. By suspecting that many are not, we were led into the development of new concepts and new researches. Already the results of the latter have justified the concepts and are verifying the suspicions.

In Fig. 6 is shown a simple diagrammatic view of approaches to knowledge of seeing and realms encompassed by the science of seeing. The chain of events from the physical variables of the external world extends through various realms including dioptrical aspects of the eyes, retinal sensitivity and other factors, nerve impulses and activity, mental processes, and finally into human behavior. This approach is through complex highways with many confusing byways. It encounters gaps in knowledge which must be spanned by theory and reasoning, which alone do not guarantee safety or certain arrival at the objective. Another approach is to begin with the controllable physical variables of the external world and detour around the complex incomplete chain of phenomena. This leads directly to the end-products of human behavior—human costs, values and accomplishments. This detour begins at the stimulus and the factors which affect visibility and comfort. It passes through the realm of sensation into the human activity of seeing and determines the results of seeing. Both approaches are independent as a matter of technique. Obviously they are the same fundamentally, but a good deal of speculation is avoided by the detour. As knowledge increases due to either approach, the hidden functions, phenomena and events along the entire course may become better understood. However, growth of the more inclusive science of seeing can take place without corresponding

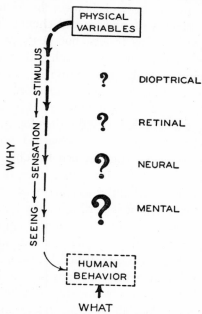

FIG. 6.—Illustrating how researches may detour the complex realms which are not fully understood. They may deal with controllable variables of the external physical world and be satisfied with *what* happens, instead of being primarily concerned with *why* it happens.

growths in the included sciences. This reveals the practicability of the detour. A civilization in which the responsibilities of seeing have been so suddenly and greatly increased and so radically altered is sorely in need of knowledge pertaining to *what* happens. Knowledge of *why* it happens is fundamentally just as desirable, but is not so urgently needed.

In viewing the diagram in Fig. 6, it is seen that the question mark becomes greater as the chain extends from the physical variables of the external world toward the ultimate end-product which is human behavior. This is readily explained by a glimpse of the development of the sciences. The dioptrical realm is one largely founded upon the physical science of optics. Physical science developed before other sciences which deal with human beings because its difficulties are small in comparison with such sciences as physiology, biology and psychology. Likewise, the science of physiology has the physical sciences of physics and chemistry to build upon. It is concerned with living things, but deals primarily with the processes, activities and phenomena incidental to and characteristic of life or of living organisms. Naturally, it developed before neurology and psychology because it had more of a base to build upon and objective methods are more readily applicable. By a similar reasoning it is revealed why the development of psychology as a science necessarily lagged somewhat behind neurology. In fact, it has barely emerged from the usual preliminary struggles to become a science. Psychology for a long time dealt with the soul or something as indefinite and therefore was little more than a branch of philosophy. But it is finding its field in behaviorism and in other avenues in which the experimental approach of modern science can be applied. Thus, by analysis facts are unearthed and by synthesis correlations are established. These are the structural materials and coordinations of which any science is made.

The foregoing indicates something of the reasons why we know less about man than about distant stars and hidden atoms. It also provides a further glimpse of the complexity of seeing and why knowledge of eyes and vision was developed first. A science of vision has been developing for many decades and some other aspects of seeing have been invaded by research during those decades. However, a correlation of scattered parts of the incomplete picture into a science of seeing could not precede some development of the other sciences. It is a natural offspring of the evolution of new concepts and the expansion of the relatively narrow concept of vision into one which adequately and properly encompasses seeing.

Many years ago in the natural course of our researches we were forced to evolve new concepts and to extend old ones, if we were not to be stranded upon the threshold of knowledge of seeing by the restricted knowledge of thresholds which limits the science of vision. The latter establishes the limitations and abilities of the visual sense as a tool. It reveals conditions of *barely seeing*. The concept of easy seeing or of easiest seeing did not clearly exist. It could not exist in a conception largely limited to vision as a tool. It could only be born when the human being became involved and was recognized in a primary role. The idea of *easy* or of *easiest seeing* was born of the same thought and analysis which clarified seeing as an activity of the entire human being. This is also largely true of such ideas as *certainty of seeing* and of *factors of safety* in seeing. Thus, the old word—seeing—with its vague, inadequate meanings was revitalized and promoted to its proper sphere. Thus, the idea of the *human seeing-machine* came into existence. Thus, the *science of seeing* became clearly defined and greatly enlarged to proper and adequate proportions. For these reasons it is really *new.* [6]

These points and distinctions are purposely emphasized, for we have found that the difference between vision and seeing cannot be clearly and adequately grasped without such emphasis and definitions. Many years of intimate experience with this matter reveal that the greatest obstacle toward understanding the significance of seeing conditions and of the factors influencing them is the belief that vision *is* seeing. The distinction is not merely a matter of definition. Vision and the science of vision are very definite. Seeing and the science of seeing encompass these and much more. The distinction is that between an essential tool and an activity of a human being in which this and other tools are necessary or present. A micrometer is an essential tool for a skilled machinist. As a worker he uses this tool; possibly damages it. At least the tool is subjected to wear. The machinist's activity is best described as making something, not in using a micrometer and other things.

In describing this activity with adequate completeness one would not completely describe the micrometer and how and why it works. It may also aid to consider biology, a subject or science of enormous compass. It contains many branches which are actually sciences of more restricted viewpoint and compass. Still, there is an overall science which can be handled in a practical manner by avoiding details of the included sciences, or at least by considering chiefly their end-products. The same may be said of the science of seeing. Vision, physiological optics and some other branches of science remain undisturbed, excepting as the new concepts and knowledge of seeing reveal inadequacies, additions, or modifications. Naturally some of these are being revealed as will be seen throughout these chapters. Seeing must eventually include consideration of all the many factors which influence the ability to see, the responsibilities of seeing, obvious and unobvious psychophysiological effects of seeing upon the human seeing-machine, and the ultimate results of this human activity.

Already the revitalized word—seeing—is beginning to gain something of its proper place in everyday language. But it has a long way to go before it receives its rightful attention and usage in a world in which vision has been emphasized and seeing has been ignored or taken for granted. Already the science of seeing has inspired powerful movements which have swept around the world. However, it is just at the beginning of a service which can scarcely be excelled by any other science in contributions to the efficiency, welfare and happiness of human beings. It touches all human beings in innumerable ways—excepting those unfortunates who are blind. If it is necessary to prove or to emphasize the absence of a science of seeing and of a seeing consciousness in this civilized world in which seeing is almost synonymous to living, one scarcely needs to do more than ask, Where are the seeing specialists? There are none; although since the advent of the science of seeing with its clarified concepts and new knowledge, their evolution has begun in the eyesight profession and to a slight extent in the practice of lighting. Opportunities and responsibilities await them everywhere in the replacement of guesswork and indifference by analysis and specific knowledge dictated by science, just as medical diagnosis and practice are dictated by supporting sciences.

Specialists have been serving eyes and eyesight very well in a limited capacity for many years. They provide glasses and treatment for correcting or reducing defects in this tool—vision. But the new concepts and complex knowledge have a long way to go in this direction before service of the eyesight specialist will be adequately revised and extended to that of a full-fledged seeing specialist. A patient visits the eyesight specialist because he wants to improve his ability to see. A skilled refractionist will supply him with suitable glasses and perhaps will propose or give treatments which may aid in overcoming certain defects. This is a worthy but incomplete service, for the patient returns to his world of seeing with its deficiencies. The eyesight specialist has sharpened the visual tool of the patient, but in so doing, has done little or nothing toward improving the conditions under which it is used. He has served the human seeing-machine well within the narrow limits of refraction or ophthalmology. The seeing specialist will do more than this. He will serve the patient and the community out in the world of seeing. Many progressive eyesight specialists are already striving to serve in the greater capacity. On every hand are visual tasks and seeing conditions which need analysis and improvement in order to reduce the waste of human resources and to improve the efficiency and welfare of human beings.

There are other aids to seeing which a seeing specialist would also emphasize and even prescribe. Among these light is the other primary essential whose importance is equal to that of vision. The aid which light and lighting may render to seeing depends upon the particular task. Before the science of seeing appeared with its broader concepts and knowledge, eyesight specialists very generally ignored light even as a factor in their own practice. Fortunately, their technique was of such a nature and limitation that no serious consequences generally resulted as far as their service and prescriptions applied. Nevertheless, this emphasizes in another way the dominance of the narrow concept of vision and the absence of an adequate concept of seeing.

Some very common conditions which reduce visual efficiency and cause eyestrain and resulting effects are indicated in Fig. 7. These are negative factors, just as optical defects of the eyes are. Faulty lighting and undue glare of light-sources, glossy paper or polished surfaces cause eyestrain and tend to reduce the size of the pupil. The brightness of a visual object or task has much to do with the visibility. Actually it is the brightness of the retinal image that is important. Just as in the case of a camera, the brightness of the image decreases with the size of the diaphragm or pupil. It is well known that the size of the pupil of the eye

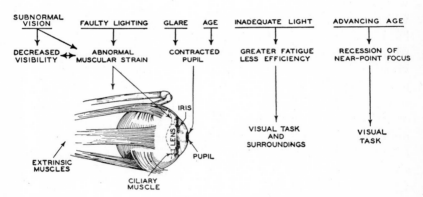

FIG. 7.—Illustrating some of the negative factors in seeing. These hindrances can often be reduced or counteracted in some manner.

decreases with age and more light is necessary to compensate for this. Inadequate light, which is so prevalent, causes eyestrain, fatigue, decreased visual efficiency, and in other ways increases the costs of seeing. None of these negative factors is reduced or eliminated by the eyesight specialist in supplying glasses. With advancing age the near-point recedes and farsightedness results. This is compensated by means of plus lenses. It can also be compensated somewhat by means of more light. These are only a few of the commonplace negative factors that a seeing specialist would take into account. He would consider all the aids towards easier seeing.

Lighting practice has not been based upon seeing, notwithstanding the fact that light is made, sold and bought for the purpose of seeing. But light and lighting have not been prescribed on this basis because there was little or no knowledge available for such prescriptions. As a consequence, attention was confined to the means towards the end instead of being directed to the end itself, which is seeing. Attention was given to the physical things, such as light-sources, fixtures and footcandles. In the absence of knowledge pertaining to the contributions of light and lighting to seeing, specifications were empirical and very largely a matter of guesswork, or what could be sold. With little or no knowledge of the value of more light or better lighting available, there is little wonder that a lighting consciousness did not develop. It is now developing along with a seeing consciousness.

The science of seeing is evolving the empirical crude art of lighting into a science.[7] This is moving slowly not only because such knowledge is difficult to obtain and interpret, but also because the attitude of lighting practitioners must be elevated to one which is searching and scientific. They must travel a course similar to that over which the medical profession traveled. The physician was once ridiculed and eventually tolerated. With the development of the sciences which dictate drugs and treatment, the public eventually began to desire the physician. Now his aid is demanded. The lighting specialist will progress similarly as his prescriptions become founded upon science. No other course can establish his prestige and a profession of lighting. He must be an ambassador of science as the physician is.

In the same manner many other specific fields could be discussed. However, at this point only sufficient glimpses are presented to indicate a widespread need for the science of seeing. Certainly on every hand there is a lack of a seeing consciousness, there is a need for knowledge of seeing, and there are countless opportunities for the application of aids to seeing. On every hand human beings and civilization itself are suffering from misconceptions and lack of knowledge of this universal activity of human beings. And this suffering is not always obvious nor is it always moderate. It may be a mild or slow waste in eyesight, energy and health which is easily ignored. At the other extreme are real handicaps to living a full life, and real tragedies in suffering and death. A world built largely upon seeing and primarily involving human seeing-machines, sorely needs the development, understanding and applications of the science of seeing.

CHAPTER II

The Human Seeing-Machine

It has been necessary to invent a term of adequate compass, such as the *human seeing-machine*,[8] to include all of the human being that is involved in the performance of the visual task and in the entire activity of seeing. Certain results of this performance are the physiological and psychological effects of seeing upon the human being. The ultimate end-products of seeing and of associated activities are the behavior of the human being or the quality and the quantity of his achievements. The entire complexity from external task to ultimate achievements can be divided into four realms such as:

1. The external visual objects and tasks and the external factors affecting seeing.
2. The eyes and visual sense.
3. Internal physiological and psychological effects of seeing.
4. Ultimate human behavior and achievement.

The chain of events begins with the physical object in the external world and the stimulus which is light, or more accurately, radiant energy, sent by the object to the eyes. The cross-section of this flow of radiant energy toward the eyes eventually reveals the form and other details of the object or objects. Next is the sense-organ which converts the energy into sensation. It has certain abilities and limitations due to functions and peculiarities of the eyes and retinae. The nerve stimulation in the retinae and elsewhere is followed by nerve activity which reaches the brain-centers, and perception or recognition of the object is achieved. Various interpretations, in addition to mere seeing, arise in a similar manner. But this is not the end. It is more nearly the beginning from the viewpoint of human beings. From here on the chain of events branches extensively into the important realm of the human being. These effects which accompany the eventual accomplishments are not included in scientific studies and practical applications of vision. They arise from the activity of seeing. They are not obvious or obviously connected with seeing. They are far removed from the region of the eyes or are hidden through-

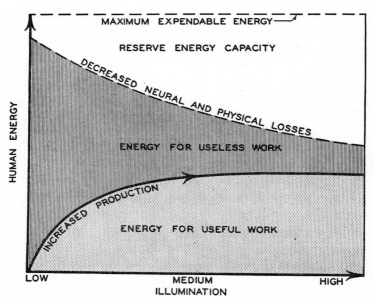

FIG. 8.—This is part of a diagrammatic view of seeing and of the human seeing-machine. Any other controllable factor can be used instead of illumination. Energy is expended for useful and useless work but as seeing becomes easier, the total expended energy decreases.

out the human body and human reactions. The ultimate end-products are human efficiency, behavior and welfare. Knowledge of these and the ability to prophesy results of specific conditions are major objectives and obligations of a science of seeing.

It may aid further in developing this concept of the human seeing-machine to refer to Fig. 8. This is a diagrammatic view of the expenditure of energy by a human being engaged in the performance of a visual task. Seeing results in other effects upon a human being besides the use or waste of energy, but Fig. 8 emphasizes the fact that seeing is work for the human seeing-machine.[1] This diagram was drawn years ago in theorizing our way to a broader and adequate concept of seeing and of its effects and other end-products. It conceives the human seeing-machine performing the work of seeing and as a result accomplishing useful work, which is usually measurable in quantity and quality. It originates the more important conception of useless internal work and expands it to include preventable and unpreventable waste of energy and of other human resources such as eyesight, health and even life. Of the many factors which influence seeing, we choose light or illumination, which produces brightness, because it is universally essential for seeing and is controllable and readily describable and measurable. Also we have much accurate data pertaining to the relation of footcandles or brightness-level to useful work performed by a worker and to other aspects of achievement through seeing. Many other factors are controllable by someone, but usually not by the person who must do the seeing.

The general form of the production curve [5] of a worker performing a visual task, as influenced by the illumination or brightness of the task is shown in the diagram. The rate of work done usually rapidly increases as the amount of light is increased from zero or a very low value. Any other controllable factor which influences seeing may be substituted for footcandles. Eventually the curve tends to flatten out, but it continues to rise slowly as the illumination is increased, as is revealed by many careful and extensive tests. Any point on this curve is commonly considered to represent the efficiency of the worker as determined in the narrow sense of useful output. Inasmuch as the production of workers engaged in the usual manual tasks that require the guidance of seeing generally ceases to increase appreciably when a level of 20 or 30 footcandles is reached, it had been narrowly assumed that no more benefit would be obtained by further increases in brightness-level or footcandle-level. For various reasons we could not accept this assumption nor could we accept this as a proper definition of the efficiency of a worker or human seeing-machine.

The efficiency of any physical machine is the ratio of the useful output or work done to the total input or work done. The efficiency of an electric motor, for example, is measured by the ratio of the energy output to the energy input.

From a broad and human viewpoint the efficiency of the human seeing-machine or human worker is not adequately measured by the amount of useful work done per hour or per dollar. It is better represented by the ratio of the energy expended in useful work to the total energy expended in useful plus useless work. It is emphasized that useless work means all the obvious or unobvious useless work done by the human seeing-machine, whether measurable or not. Upon this reasoning we constructed the upper portion of the diagram in Fig. 8. The upper curve indicates that with increasing footcandles (or improvement of any other factor which influences seeing) the task of seeing becomes easier and easier even though production of useful work ceases to increase appreciably. In other words, the internal and other useless work of the human seeing-machine decreases as seeing becomes easier. Above the upper curve is indicated the reserve energy that could be expended by the worker but is not. In a sense it may represent that percentage of the worker that is at rest or not working.

Admittedly the reasoning at the time was supported only by some qualitative data and experience and, therefore, Fig. 8 was largely theoretical. However, theories are essential for probing the unknown. They are temporary lines of communication between the known and the unknown. We had a variety of evidence that the rate of performance of useful work through seeing was not a true measure of the burden upon the human seeing-machine. Since the development of this diagram and theory, researches inspired by them have yielded impressive quantitative proof over a range from 1 to 100 footcandles at least, that seeing does become easier and easier even for a visual task that can be performed, apparently with ease, under a fraction of a footcandle. Similar results have been obtained with other factors which influence seeing. Thus, Fig. 8 has become more than a mere diagram. It represents a new viewpoint of seeing. It is a specimen diagram of the human seeing-machine in which other factors besides light or brightness can be substituted. It provides a glimpse of a new conception which is demanded by various facts and experiences and which indicates and emphasizes the proper goal-optimum conditions for seeing. It reveals the limitations of the viewpoint of vision and the neglect by modern science and civilization of the important universal activity of seeing. The human seeing-machine has been burdened with responsibilities without adequate knowledge and consideration of this human activity.

V I S I B I L I T Y   A N D   H U M A N   B E I N G S

The visibility of an object or task is a basic aspect of seeing. It is a logical place to begin the unraveling of the complexity of seeing. However, visibility is meaningless apart from the human being. If human beings were identical in characteristics and endowments, and if they did not possess any other senses and abilities besides the visual sense and the ability to see, the complexity of seeing would be greatly simplified. But this is not true, and, therefore, a complete consideration of visibility must include many other factors. Characteristics of the visual task, environment, eyes, visual sense, human being and eventual achievement influence visibility and considerations of it. The obvious scientific approach is to standardize these other factors in fundamental studies of visibility. In other words, a representative group of socalled normal persons with socalled normal vision are used as observers or subjects. Variables are eliminated from the surrounding visual field and from the entire environment. The requirements of performance of the chosen visual task are also specified. Then the basic relationships of the fundamental visibility factors pertaining to the visual object or task can be obtained.

Such data apply only to controlled laboratory conditions and adequate allowances or factors of safety must be applied in the everyday world of seeing. However, this is not impractical. It can be accomplished by common consent based upon further research upon this aspect and upon practical experience just as factors of safety have been standardized for engineering practices, such as the specification of steel members of a bridge. Given the load and span, the bridge designer computes the threshold steel requirements and multiplies these by a large factor of safety to cover emergencies and uncertainties. The science of seeing must first provide the basic threshold data and then recommend adequate factors of safety. The latter will be determined by knowledge of quick, accurate and certain seeing under average or even the worst conditions of surroundings and environment and for human beings reasonably subnormal in eyesight and in other human endowments or resources. In other words, correlations between visibility and the effects of seeing upon the human being and also the ultimate achievements in the performance of the visual task will determine factors of safety and the degree of ease of seeing. Progress toward this end is revealed in other chapters.

Fig. 9 may aid in visualizing the part of the chain of variables which affects visibility.[9] At the left-hand of the diagram is the human being with many characteristics which are merely indicated as physiological, psychological and possibly pathological factors. Purely physical parts of the eyes are not indicated although defects of the eyes and of binocular vision are common. All these influence visibility appreciably and sometimes very much. For the present they may be considered to be included in the three realms indicated at the left of the diagram. Certainly they are included in the characteristics of the observer considered as a human seeing-machine.

The parameters of visibility, as viewed largely apart from the human being, are size, brightness, brightness- (and color-) contrast, and time available or necessary for seeing to perform the given task. These are usually associated with the object. Often time is not important, but it is commonly a hidden factor in the performance of a visual task. It is usually very important where safety is involved as on the highway and in the work-world. Next a group of modifying factors is indicated. Some of these, such as the method of lighting and the spectral quality of light, are directly associated with the visual object or task. Others, such as surroundings and afterimages, directly affect the sensitivity of

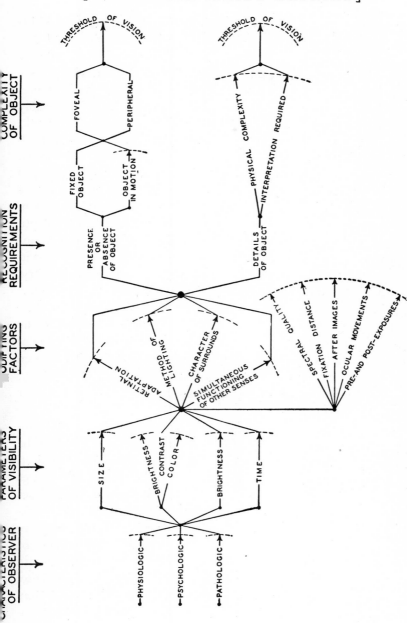

COMPLEXITY OF OBJECT →

RECOGNITION REQUIREMENTS →

MODIFYING FACTORS →

PARAMETERS OF VISIBILITY →

CHARACTERISTICS OF OBSERVER →

FIG. 9.—Illustrating the major variables which influence visibility. The human seeing-machine, located at the left, encompasses various human factors which are discussed later.

the visual sense. Still others, such as the environment to which other human senses respond, directly affect the ability of the human being. For example, noise and other distractions may affect the quality and quantity of performance of a visual task. Of course, all these mutually affect visibility and performance.

Visibility and the human seeing-machine are inseparably related, but the efficiency and welfare of the human being should be of primary and ultimate importance. Therefore, our considerations of visibility have the human being very much in mind. Our analyses and measurements of visibility are a means to an end and that end is easy, quick, accurate and certain seeing. Visibility is fundamentally determined by threshold measurements, and methods must be devised for bridging the span between these and optimum conditions for the desired degree of ease of seeing. A major objective of the science of seeing has been the development of suitable methods. Sometimes a degree of arbitrariness is necessary, but this is common throughout science and practice. All measuring units and scales are arbitrary and their value lies in their general acceptance. We have incorporated such a method in the Luckeish-Moss Visibility Meter and have originated a rational unit and scale of visibility. In other phases of seeing it has been necessary to attempt to develop new units and scales involving effects of seeing conditions upon human beings and their behavior and achievement.

Again referring to Fig. 9 the requirements of the performance of seeing are represented in their simplest form. It may be necessary to distinguish only the *presence* or *absence* of an object, as is often the case on the highway at night and in other cases where safety is the primary requirement of seeing. Sometimes this is all that is necessary in inspection of materials in the work-world. Generally throughout seeing it is necessary to *recognize the object*. This requires discrimination and interpretation of characteristic or distinguishing details. Involved in all this are characteristics of the observer such as intelligence, experience, reaction-time, concentration, vision, and fatigue. All these factors are still more important in the usual visual tasks whose performance involves much more than recognition of an object. Such factors as criticalness, severity, continuity and duration of the task of seeing are common characteristics or requirements of performance. Certainly threshold conditions determined by momentary measurements of visibility under ideal conditions cannot possibly be adequate or even approximately so. Certainly large allowances or factors of safety must be provided even for the bare requirements of seeing under practical conditions. Besides these, other allowances or factors of safety are necessary for arriving at optimum conditions which make the task of seeing as easy as possible for the human seeing-machine.

As indicated in Fig. 9, the visual object or task may be in motion relative to the observer. Accurate discrimination of details is accomplished best by direct or foveal vision; that is, when the observer is looking directly at or toward the object. Averted or peripheral vision is far more effective in detecting movement than in discriminating details. Movement in seeing means a change in the brightness pattern as the brightness of the object eclipses or is replaced by other brightnesses when it moves with respect to the observer. The capable functioning of peripheral vision in detecting movement is an important factor in seeing. It plays a prominent part in safety on the highway and elsewhere. Generally we ignore common unobtrusive brightnesses in the peripheral visual field, but a sudden change in brightness, which signifies motion is conspicuous to us.

All the foregoing factors and others are so intricately involved that seeing is indeed a complexity. The combined result of the physical and human variables determines visibility in the full and practical sense. These and the requirements of performance of the task show the need for specifying the latter. For example, reading is a visual task which varies so enormously that to make a task such as proofreading fine print on paper of poor quality comparable with that of leisurely reading a well-printed book with large type, a great many times more light is necessary. The folly of any dogmatic recommendation of light (footcandles) as being enough for reading should be obvious. Also it should be apparent that the vast complexity of visibility and seeing is not comprehended by anyone making such a sweeping statement.

Many of the factors which influence visibility and ease of reading can be controlled by someone. Others can be reduced to insignificance. In everyday seeing we are interested chiefly in those aids to seeing which can be directly controlled by us or by others not too remote. Among these there is no doubt that light is the most universally controllable necessity. This is why the science of seeing deals with it so prominently and extensively. Also, this is why a heightened consciousness of seeing developed by the recent new concepts and knowledge has extensively aroused a lighting consciousness. The determination of the influence and application of all aids to quick, accurate and certain seeing is a primary objective of measurements of visibility and of their correlations with the effects and results of seeing.

At this point let us summarize briefly the major factors which influence visibility. This is done with the understanding that many subdivisions can be made and that all occur in countless combinations in everyday tasks and situations of seeing.[10]

1. *Size* of the object or of critical details is not merely a matter of physical dimensions. From the viewpoint of seeing, visual size is also a matter of distance.

2. *Visual size* is the visual angle subtended by the object or critical dimension of details at the eye. It is conveniently expressed in minutes. A given object decreases in visual size approximately inversely with the distance from the observer.

3. *Brightness* is the result of illumination (footcandles) and reflection-factor of diffusing surfaces. For polished surfaces it is the more or less perfectly mirrored image of the brightness of another object or area.

4. *Brightness-contrast* is the ratio of the brightness-difference (between object and its background) to the brightness of the background and is conveniently expressed in per cent. Perfectly black print against a perfectly white paper would represent 100 per cent contrast.

5. *Color-contrast* cannot be expressed in simple numerical terms. Brightness-contrast is very generally present along with it.

6. *Time* is necessary for seeing.

7. *Normal vision* has definite abilities and limitations.

8. *Subnormal vision* is a commonplace factor.

9. *Transient phenomena* of the visual sense such as pupil-size and retinal adaptation.

10. *Characteristics of the visual task* such as severity, critical-ness, continuity, duration, novelty, and unexpectedness.

11. *Surroundings* seen in the visual field with its color, brightness and pattern.

12. *Lighting* (distribution of light) affects the appearance of objects and the distribution of brightness in the surroundings.

13. *Environment* provides distractions for the visual sense such as glare and motion, and distractions through other senses such as noise and simultaneous performance of other work than seeing.

14. *Ability of the human being* depends upon such factors as intelligence, experience, reaction-time, concentration, stimulation, and fatigue.

VARIOUS THRESHOLDS OF SEEING

Quantitative measurements and formulated knowledge in the various parts of the chain of complexities involved in seeing vary from the precise and absolute data of the physical realm to the variable and relative data of the psychophysiological realms. For this reason the former are more plentiful and have been given more attention than the latter. In view of this it is not to be expected that the effects and results of seeing may be stated in simple empirical terms for various visual conditions and tasks. As knowledge of the effects of seeing accumulates, valuable correlations are made as in other complexities. As a consequence, measurements of the external factors and of visibility which can be readily made will become a sound basis for predicting the unobvious internal effects and the ultimate results of seeing and for specifying various aids to seeing.

A diagrammatical view of the kinds, limitations, and possibilities of measurements [8] is presented in Fig. 10. The left-hand edge of the diagram may represent inadequacy of any factor of seeing. For example, the size of an object may be too small to

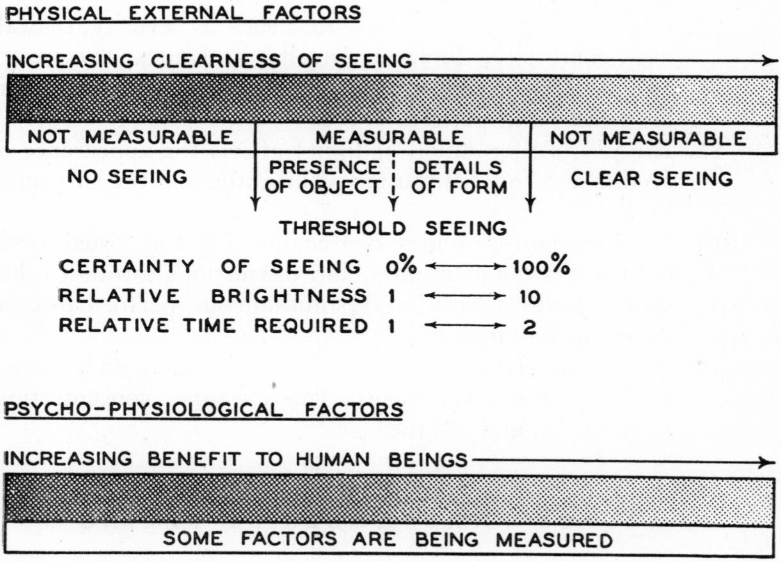

PHYSICAL EXTERNAL FACTORS

INCREASING CLEARNESS OF SEEING ——————————————→

NOT MEASURABLE	MEASURABLE	NOT MEASURABLE
NO SEEING	PRESENCE OF OBJECT ¦ DETAILS OF FORM	CLEAR SEEING

THRESHOLD SEEING

CERTAINTY OF SEEING   0% ←——→ 100%
RELATIVE BRIGHTNESS   1 ←——→ 10
RELATIVE TIME REQUIRED   1 ←——→ 2

PSYCHO-PHYSIOLOGICAL FACTORS

INCREASING BENEFIT TO HUMAN BEINGS ————————————→

SOME FACTORS ARE BEING MEASURED

FIG. 10.—Illustrating two kinds of measurements pertaining to seeing. Above are illustrated the physical external factors which determine the condition of barely seeing. Measurements of psychophysiological effects will determine the conditions of easy or easiest seeing.

be visible. This is equally true of contrast, of brightness or of time available or necessary for seeing. The right-hand edge represents adequacy of the factors or conditions of seeing. The upper portion of the diagram is confined to the socalled external factors which are commonly measured in physical units. It will be noted that visibility measurements are possible only in a limited region. Usually they have been considered to be possible at one point which is termed the threshold. However, upon more careful analysis it is found that there are different kinds of thresholds depending upon the requirements of seeing.

For the purpose of demonstrating the diagram shown in Fig. 10, let us consider the visibility factor, brightness. For surfaces which diffusely reflect light the brightness depends upon the reflection-factor as well as upon the illumination in footcandles. Everyone has had many experiences of not being able to see an object under a dim light and of being able to see it when it is held near a lamp or window. Beginning at the left-hand end of the upper portion of the diagram, let us assume that there is no light. Seeing a given object or the performance of a visual task is impossible. Obviously no measurements can be made until there is sufficient light to see the object. More and more light is provided until the *presence* of the object can be distinguished.[9] This is one kind of threshold of illumination or brightness. At this point visibility in its crudest form is measured. As the illumination (footcandles) is increased, eventually the brightness is sufficient for the object to be *recognized* because characteristic distinguishing details can now be seen. This is the second kind of threshold of illumination or brightness.

So far our attention has been devoted entirely to the external factors although, of course, the visual sense and the human seeing-machine have been in operation. Now the human being enters more prominently along with the important neglected factor of certainty of seeing. When the amount of light is barely enough for recognition of the object, this condition may be described as zero certainty of seeing. This is the third kind of threshold condition. It is determined in actual research by finding the condition under which the observer sees the object only half the times it is presented for observation. By extensive researches it has been found that the illumination or brightness must be increased ten times, or the time available must be doubled, in order to obtain the condition of 100 per cent certainty of seeing. This is a fourth kind of threshold condition.

As the illumination or brightness is still further increased no more measurements of visibility can be made. When attention is confined entirely to visibility, or to the limitations and abilities of the visual sense, it is natural that other possibilities are not considered. We could not believe that, for example, still more light would not be beneficial in some manner. When we extended our viewpoint from visibility and vision to seeing and the human seeing-machine, such conceptions as ease of seeing were born. Owing to adaptation to Nature's light and brightness and to various experiences, it seemed reasonable that eyes, the visual sense and human beings would be benefited by still more light than that necessary for threshold seeing. One diagram of this kind of theorizing is indicated in Fig. 8. We then turned our attention to possible physiological and psychological factors and effects. These are represented diagrammatically in the lower portion of Fig. 10. Beginning with no light and gradually increasing it as in the preceding consideration of visibility, it seemed reasonable to believe that the internal effects of seeing upon the human being could be measured throughout the entire span from the poorest conditions to the best conditions for seeing. This has proved to be true with all the effects we have so far studied. Furthermore, the benefits have been found to continue for conditions far above threshold. It is in this realm that knowledge of optimum conditions is being established. Briefly, this is a view of our escape from the shackles of knowledge of threshold seeing into the realm of ideal optimum conditions for easiest seeing. Maximum ease of seeing is actually another kind of threshold condition, and it is the most difficult one to define and to determine.

Now it should be obvious that there are various kinds of threshold conditions for seeing and that the level of any specific one is influenced by any factor which influences visibility and is determined by the combined effect of all the factors—physical or human. The actual order of all the possible thresholds can be determined for any given task of seeing provided the requirements of performance are specified in each case. The following is a brief summary of major threshold conditions ending with the simplest or lowliest threshold which is appropriately placed at the bottom of the list:

Maximum ease of seeing or minimum cost of seeing to the human seeing-machine.

Maximum performance of useful work regardless of cost to the human seeing-machine.

Maximum certainty of recognition of critical details.

Minimum certainty of recognition of critical details.

Maximum certainty of distinguishing presence of object.

Minimum certainty of distinguishing presence of object.

Many intermediate thresholds could be listed by defining specific cases and factors involved. However, the main purpose here is to emphasize the two outstanding thresholds—barely seeing and easiest seeing. Much is known of the former, but the latter can only be established by knowledge of the effects of seeing upon the human being or seeing-machine. Actually the threshold of maximum ease is the optimum condition for seeing.

OPTIMUM CONDITIONS FOR SEEING

No one is satisfied with a condition in which it is impossible to see to perform a necessary visual task. One or more visibility factors will be altered until the task can be performed. However, beyond this there is no tendency to proceed. Of course, size and other factors are often above the threshold. Some of this practice may be due to a vague idea that seeing may be easier; that eyes may be less fatigued; or that eyesight may be conserved. But nearly everyone and even the practices which can contribute much toward better or easier seeing are dominated by the idea of threshold rather than optimum conditions for seeing. Our development of new concepts and knowledge of seeing was born of a realization of this narrow and often erroneous viewpoint. This was really the beginning of a science of adequate scope to encompass the entire complexity of seeing. As a result attention is beginning to be directed toward optimum conditions for performing the critical visual tasks imposed by civilization.

In theorizing along the lines illustrated in Figs. 8 and 10 we assumed that, seeing being an activity of the human being, certain physiological and psychological effects should be detectable by measurement. Considerations revolved around the ideas of ease and certainty of seeing. If seeing is work done by the human being, a measurable decrease in the effects of such work should result, if the task were made less difficult by applying any of the various aids to seeing. The research problem appeared to be one of investigating the human seeing-machine piecemeal. In planning and prosecuting a research attack many matters have been considered such as comfort, discomfort, waste of energy, muscular and bodily fatigue, heart reactions, nervous muscular tension, and mental and motor efficiency. It seemed reasonable to expect that the limitations and abilities of the human seeing-machine would also be measurably affected through the doorway of the eyes by such factors as ability to concentrate, the degree of stimulation and even attitude. Such effects determine the costs and values of seeing to the human being. They are not the ultimate objectives of the performance of seeing, but being incident to the processes of seeing they provide the important basis for determining optimum conditions and factors of safety for seeing. The elimination or reduction of undesirable effects and the creation or augmentation of desirable effects is a major objective of the science of seeing.

At this point it appears desirable to present some summarized results of extensive researches in the realm indicated by the upper part of Fig. 8 and by the lower part of Fig. 10. These [7] are seen in Fig. 11. Visual acuity, or the ability to distinguish fine details, was accurately measured for simple black details on a white background for illuminations of the latter of 1, 10, and 100 footcandles. Contrast sensitivity increases in a similar manner. From many years of research and other experience we have learned that brightness generally varies in approximate geometric ratio for changes in effects in arithmetic ratio. Therefore, in studying the effects of brightness we choose levels separated by equal distances on a logarithmic scale. It is seen that visual acuity increases about as much for the step from 10 to 100 footcandles as for a similar geometric step from 1 to 10 footcandles. Visual acuity being a basic factor in reading, it is appropriately included with the results of performing the task of reading summarized from four extensive

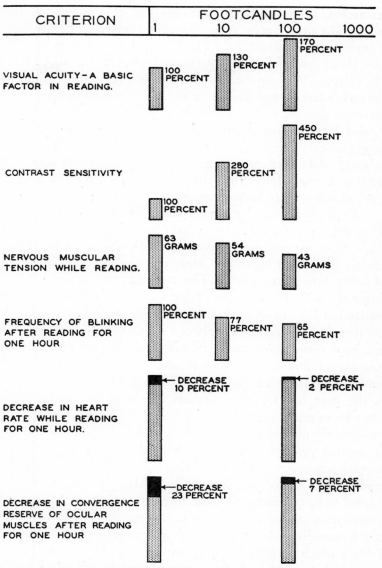

FIG. 11.—A summary of results of extensive researches which reveal the influence of illumination upon important aspects of visual efficiency and upon even more important effects of seeing. Researches dealing with these and other effects are revolutionizing the viewpoint from barely seeing to easy seeing. (See Chap. VI.)

researches. The reading task consisted of well-printed books of 10-point and 12-point type. Actually they could be read under a fraction of a footcandle. Therefore, they represent relatively easy visual tasks involving contrast and size very far above threshold values. We reasoned that if we obtained measurable effects for such a task, it was likely that the effects would be even greater for more difficult tasks. Certainly it is far more difficult to read 6-point type of poor printing than excellent printing with much larger types. Furthermore, the visibility of the essential objects in many tasks such as sewing, inspection, engraving and proof-reading, is much lower than that of large black type of high contrast with the white background.

Four physiological effects of seeing are illustrated in Fig. 11. They are merely touched upon here but are discussed in Chapter VI. Nervous muscular tension or tenseness is an undesirable effect. Actually it indicates a waste of human energy and perhaps of other human resources. The tenseness was measured at the finger tips without the readers being aware of it. The results summarized in Fig. 11 show that this tenseness markedly decreased as the illumination increased. Sixteen subjects individually read for one hour many times under each footcandle-level and otherwise constant conditions. A million measurements of nervous muscular tension were recorded. Also, a million heart-beats are summarized in the next test for nine subjects involving an hour's reading many times under each footcandle-level. The heart-rate remained more nearly normal when there were 100 footcandles on the book. In another research it was found that the fatigue of certain eye-muscles was much less after reading for an hour under 100 footcandles than under one footcandle. Also the rate of blinking seemed to be consistent with the foregoing results. The levels of illumination outdoors [5] on gloomy days are commonly more than 100 footcandles. In this connection it is interesting to refer to Table I which presents brightnesses of common areas outdoors on a sunny day. Although our researches on the effects of reading deal with brightnesses produced on the white paper of the printed page under illuminations as high as 100 footcandles, this maximum brightness is well below brightnesses encountered outdoors which are well within the limits of tolerance. There is strong indication that the effects briefly summarized in Fig. 11 would continue to decrease for brightnesses or footcandle-levels still higher than the maximum used. However, it should be pointed out that a brightness which is quite tolerable when critical seeing is not being done may become intolerable when one is engaged in critical seeing. However, this limiting brightness of the visual task has not been established; it appears to be well above the brightness produced by 100 footcandles on a diffusely reflecting white paper. This means it is well above 100 millilamberts or footlamberts.

CORRELATIONS

As has been emphasized many times, studies of the external physical factors have almost invariably dealt with threshold conditions. For example, the size of an object is reduced until it can be barely seen under the combined conditions resulting from association with other factors. This is also true of measurements of the effects upon visibility of the other major physical factors—brightness, contrast and exposure-time. These threshold data are very valuable as basic measurements and knowledge. However, one of the outstanding demands of the human seeing-machine is that threshold data and conditions cease to hold the center of the scientific stage and that attention be given to the study of optimum conditions. Everyday seeing is generally done above the threshold. In fact, that is one demand that a human being will make. He insists upon seeing even though it is barely seeing. The human seeing-machine unaided cannot make any satisfactory estimates of the degree of ease of seeing or of the factors of safety above threshold conditions. A human being is a marvelous seeing-machine but a very poor seeing-meter.

Controlled laboratory researches must develop the correlations between readily obtainable data pertaining to threshold visibility and the psychophysiological effects of seeing and even the ultimate characteristics of performance and accomplishment. In doing this, complex researches must be performed to ascertain the effects of various visibility factors upon the human seeing-machine and the ultimate accomplishments. Laboratory researches are arranged to investigate certain characteristics common to a large number of visual situations but not necessarily involving all the factors of an individual case. Hence, experimental results inherently require interpretive treatment in order to be applicable to practice and to fit the results into the ever-growing structure of knowledge of seeing. For this reason, even the most specific and precise research data may seldom be isolated from the restrictions necessarily imposed by the research technique.

The difficulty of interpreting such data naturally varies with the directness with which the experimental criteria appraise the specific case. Usually two or more interpretive steps are required in order to apply measurements of seeing to common seeing conditions. As has been emphasized, threshold visibility measurements are readily made and, therefore, means must be found to interpret these into the usual or ideal conditions of seeing. The usual conditions are above threshold and distractions, for example, exist. In the laboratory these are minimized. The ideal conditions are determined by tedious measurements of internal physiological effects, for example. Correlations between these and threshold measurements are established by determining the effects in each case of a controllable physical factor.

It is more practicable to make measurements for brief test-periods. These "momentary" data must be correlated with the effects of extended periods of visual effort and seeing. The latter data are obtainable only through tedious researches involving a great deal of time of the subjects. Such tests can actually be conducted in the work-world if proper controls can be established. However, the best fundamental data of this sort are generally obtained in the laboratory. The need for an interpretive step or a correlation connecting the data from brief test-periods to extended periods is often not recognized. In many cases investigators naively extend "momentary" data to cover all kinds of practical situations. This is entirely unwarranted until some kind of correlation is established. Sometimes the momentary appraisal may be actually reversed by an appraisal made after experience with the situation over a long period. This is common when novelty is an influential factor initially. When this wears off the appraisal may be reversed. The difference between the results of initial short-period measurements or appraisals and extended-period ones must be taken into account. This point cannot be over-emphasized throughout the complexity of seeing conditions, both in the laboratory and in the everyday world.

Obviously in such a complexity as seeing with its many factors combined in countless ways, specific criteria must be chosen for test-purposes. The ultimate human interest lies in the effects upon the entire human seeing-machine. Enough correlations must be established in order to utilize the former as criteria for predicting and even measuring the latter. As in all cases of effects upon the human being, correlations at first may be vague or approximate. But even these must serve until the correlations are perfected. For example, the effects summarized in Fig. 11 are at least approximate for the controllable variable (footcandles or brightness) which was studied. Certainly the relationships between this variable and visual acuity and visibility are well established. A direct correlation is thereby established between the readily measurable factors which require only a brief period for measurement and the deep-seated effects of extended periods of seeing which must be determined by extensive researches over long periods.

All basic data must first be established by socalled normal human beings possessing socalled normal vision. However, subnormal vision is common and many persons are subnormal seeing-machines for other reasons. Certainly it is important to establish correlations between the normal and the subnormal for all important controllable seeing factors.

The process of interpretation and correlation is greatly facilitated by a ready familiarity with the reservoir of fundamental or backgound knowledge of the science of seeing. Even though the latter is far from complete, it provides the only means of spanning the wide gap between the data usually available or obtainable and the actual practical conditions of seeing. Significant correlations, in some instances, have been found to exist between the results obtained by the use of widely varying experimental techniques. Objective measurements can be correlated with subjective judgments. For example, measurements of visibility as influenced by glare can be correlated with the judgments of comfort or discomfort. The appraisals by specific criteria can be correlated with those by more inclusive criteria. For example, speed of reading can be correlated with nervous muscular tension developed incidental to reading. Another example which has been emphasized is the correlation between threshold visibility and ease of seeing. This correlation is presented graphically in Fig. 36. It will be noted that threshold visibility and tenseness are similarly related to level of illumination.

In controlled tests the subject may or may not expect an object to be presented to view. However, complete unexpectedness is difficult to achieve in actual research. At least the subject is usually looking in the general direction of the object which is to appear or not appear. Our researches on certainty of seeing were designed to meet this problem partially at least. Obviously, a correlation must be established between seeing expected and unexpected visual objects or tasks in order to meet many practical situations or conditions of seeing.

These are glimpses of a phase of the science of seeing which is of major importance. Such correlations often permit general conclusions to be drawn from restricted researches that would be impossible if the latter were analyzed independently. By conducting a research attack in the two realms, visibility and effects of seeing, the necessary correlations can be established. Already much progress has been made toward appraising ease of seeing for any specific visual task performed for long periods by simple momentary measurements of the visibility of the task. One of the major objectives of the science of seeing is to discover and establish correlations between the simple and the complex and between the obvious and the unobvious. Naturally such correlations between visibility and ease of seeing were not conceivable until an adequate concept of seeing was created and comprehended.

CONTROLLABLE FACTORS IN SEEING

In order to aid the human seeing-machine, it is necessary to direct attention to the universally important factors which can be controlled.[11] In fact, these are the factors which are deliberately made the variables in researches in seeing. Obviously, the external factors are directly controllable by someone but not always by the person confronted with the visual object or task. Instead of listing all the controllable factors and tediously describing them at this point, let us view them in connection with a few of the common visual tasks with which everyone is familiar. These controllable variables are adequately treated in later chapters in relation to their influence upon visibility and upon the ability of the human seeing-machine.

Reading as a seeing task is so important that it is treated in detail in later chapters, but it is such a common task that it is used here to illustrate controllable aids to seeing. Certainly reading involves many factors which affect visibility and the ability to perform the task of seeing. The size and design of the type are prominent factors whose influence upon visibility can be directly measured as is shown elsewhere. These factors have been given far more consideration in the past than others of comparable importance. This is due in part to the fact that size is readily comprehended and that it has been emphasized and used to the almost entire exclusion of other visibility factors by the eyesight specialist, in researches in vision and in appraisals of practical conditions. However, as we have shown, contrast affects visibility greatly and usually surprisingly because reductions in contrast which are not conspicuous may reduce visibility markedly. Such knowledge can only be obtained by measurements which could not be made conveniently or with very definite meaning until recently.

Contrast in brightness, in the case of printed matter, is that between the ink and the paper. Therefore, the quality of the ink, the paper, and the printing affects this important visibility factor. In well-printed books the contrast may be 97 per cent, but it is commonly as low as 80 per cent in newspapers and telephone directories. The brightness factor or footcandles must be increased several times to compensate for the lower contrast.

In addition to the foregoing factors, the spacing of letters, which may be a matter of type-setting or type-design, affects visibility. The spacing and length of lines affect readability and produce strain and fatigue of the eye-muscles and other physiological effects more deeply hidden. In fact, this is true of the factors which contribute solely to visibility. We do not see while the eyes are in motion. Therefore, in scanning a line the eyes make a number of stops. The number of stops per line depends upon such factors as visibility, readability, familiarity, intelligence, purpose of the reader, etc.

These factors involved in reading printed matter are not under the control of the reader, but many of them can be controlled by the designer of type and by the printer and publisher. However, other factors now enter which can be controlled by others and often by the reader. The brightness of the printed page is the result of the reflection-factor of the paper (and ink) and the illumination which is measured in footcandles. In places where the location of the work and the position of the reader are fixed, this factor is under the control of those responsible for the lighting system. In many cases the person performing the task of reading can, by altering his position or location, greatly alter the amount of light upon the page. The distribution of the light may affect visibility very greatly if the paper is glossy, and control over it may be exercised by the same persons who can control the footcandles.

Now the environment enters. Dark surroundings decrease the visibility of the reading matter and contribute to discomfort and fatigue. The contrast in brightness between the printed page and the immediate surroundings should not be too high. If obvious glare is present, visibility is reduced and discomfort and certain unobvious physiological and psychological effects are produced. The brightness of the general surroundings may also affect visibility by affecting retinal sensitivity and by altering the size of the pupil. The latter determines the brightness of the retinal image which is the brightness of ultimate importance. All these factors have some influence upon the efficacy and efficiency of the visual sense and of the human seeing-machine. Other factors in the environment, such as noise, cause distractions which reduce visibility and the efficiency of the reader as a human seeing-machine. Obviously, there are still other factors which affect the alertness and general well-being and, therefore, the performance of the human seeing-machine. A discussion of these would lead far afield; however, they must be taken into account in scientific studies of the human seeing-machine.

The characteristics and requirements of the performance of the task influence the ease of seeing. Severity, criticalness, continuity, and duration of the task must be taken into account in the application of aids to seeing. Casual, leisurely reading for pleasure is a far different task from proofreading and other reading tasks which require accuracy and close application over long periods. The introduction of responsibility affects ease of seeing. Unexpectedness and novelty are factors affecting visibility and the ability to see. All these factors produce physiological effects within the human seeing-machine. In connection with these effects, the human being is not ordinarily considered with adequate emphasis. All play their part in the cost of seeing to the human seeing-machine. In addition to these, psychological effects arise from such factors in a complexity which can be superficially described but which is not completely understood. The difficulty of the task, the responsibility of performance, the brightness and color of the surroundings, and even esthetic factors of the decorative scheme and furnishings influence the attitude and feelings of the reader to some degree. Human seeing-machines, being human, are susceptible to all such influences.

In this brief survey of the task of reading printed matter, it is obvious that the external factors can be directly controlled by someone quite generally. In this manner, indirect control can be exercised to some extent over the visual sense, and to a great extent over the internal effects and the ultimate results of performance. Certainly even this condensed sketch of the task of reading matter and its performance reveals a conception of seeing and the human seeing-machine which is appropriate and which aims to be adequate eventually. It should be obvious why we have emphasized the advantage, whenever possible, of developing researches which would detour much of the complex chain as emphasized in Fig. 6, but which would provide knowledge pertaining to the realm indicated in the upper part of Fig. 8. We have made much progress by proceeding as directly as possible from controllable factors of the visual task to the end-products of human effects and behavior.

The foregoing brief sketch of reading as a task for the human seeing-machine provides an opportunity for viewing many of the factors of seeing. However, in other tasks certain factors are allied in different ways and even new factors enter. Manual work is insignificant in reading. The material may be held in the hands and pages may be turned. In much other work physical activity is prominent. The skilled mechanic working with his hands and applying skill gained from long experience is the same sort of seeing-machine, but actual physical activity or degree of skill may influence the ability to see and, therefore, the ultimate quality and quantity of work done. Seeing may be difficult or easy without this difference being detectable in the quality and quantity of useful work. Great differences in ease of seeing may be entirely submerged by other factors as shown in later chapters.

The engraver cutting fine lines on metal has little control over the important factor of size. By this we mean that he must cut fine lines, not large ones. He cannot increase size as an aid to seeing as the printer or publisher can. He must call on other aids. Perhaps a magnifying glass is practicable. Certainly light and lighting are very important in such a case in promoting visibility and ease of seeing. The same is true of many types of inspection where small defects or fine scratches are to be detected. By manipulating the lighting and making measurements of visibility one can ascertain the kind of lighting which is most desirable. This is true of all three-dimensional objects. They are modeled by highlights and shadows and, therefore, the lighting greatly affects their visibility.

Such studies will reveal that lighting or distribution of light is a very important factor. When the surfaces are dull or diffusing the lighting is largely a matter of distribution of light. However, when specular reflection is present, as in the case of polished surfaces, the brightnesses of the light-source and surroundings are reflected from the polished surfaces. In other words, one sees the perfect or imperfect images of these brightnesses. This entire matter of lighting now becomes one of quality of lighting as well as of quantity of light. In special cases quality or spectral character of light may also become an important factor. No mere empirical method of distributing light more or less uniformly over an interior can possibly provide these essential aids to seeing in the best manner excepting by accident. Measurements of visibility can serve admirably and adequately in this direction, particularly when the visual task involves the discrimination of three-dimensional objects.

When a person is driving an automobile [11] great responsibility is vested in seeing. The time element or speed of seeing also assumes a prominent role. Split-seconds may be very important. The driver is engaged in various tasks which utilize some of his sense capacity so that all of his ability is not available for seeing. These are unobvious distractions, just as noise or conversation are obvious distractions. All encroach upon the availability of human resources to the human seeing-machine for performing the very important task of seeing. There is always the possibility of unexpectedness being introduced into the complexity of seeing. These factors emphasize the need for adequate factors of safety in seeing. Even in the daytime minimum conditions of effective visibility sometimes prevail. All hazards on the highway or aids to seeing may be plainly visible to the person who knows they are there. But the unexpected is always a possibility. When the human seeing-machine is doing nothing else but seeing he can "do all that his eyes can do". This is not true when that human being is doing, or must be prepared to do, the many other things involved in operating an automobile and in seeing on streets and highways.

When there is no factor of safety we have a low threshold

condition for seeing. This can be attained not only by inadequacy of physical factors directly involved in the visibility of the hazard or aid. Threshold conditions for seeing can be attained through human vagaries, limitations and abilities. In other words, by drawing upon the abilities of the human being or his sense capacity for other purposes, threshold and even sub-threshold conditions of seeing are attained. The consequences are to be seen in the wreckage of automobiles, property and lives along the highways. It is a statistical fact that accidents are more severe and are just as numerous at night as in the daytime notwithstanding the fact that traffic is greatly reduced. If threshold and sub-threshold conditions of seeing are found in the daytime, it is obvious that they are far more prevalent at night.

What are the controllable factors of seeing on the highway? Certainly the visibility of hazards and aids cannot be fundamentally controlled by the driver of an automobile. He can drive slowly enough so that he can see safely. At night he can have proper headlamps properly adjusted. He can eliminate carelessness. But after these contributions to his ability to see safely, he can do little more. It remains for others to understand seeing and the human seeing-machine. The highways must be stripped by the proper authorities of the obstructions and inadequate aids to seeing. These are found in the daytime in great plenty. At night darkness is an obstruction and hazard almost everywhere, but it is controllable by the controllable factors of light and lighting which in turn control the brightness of pavement and objects.

These are a few highlights of common tasks and conditions of seeing which should aid in developing an adequate conception of visibility and a proper understanding of the part the human seeing-machine plays in the important activity of seeing. They have been introduced here even though they are emphasized and elaborated upon in other chapters. Repetition is perhaps justified by the importance of establishing a fairly complete background for the more specific and extensive treatments later.

CHAPTER III

Visual Sensory Processes

When the eye is opened, countless retinal-cortical connections transmit pulsating electrical currents to the brain centers and arouse visual sensation. The latter is a conscious sensory process which is correlated with a physiological process. Then numerous efferent activities are inaugurated and through these innervations leading from the brain, the various elements of the visual mechanism are made operative in adapting the eye to the stimulus. Thus the eyes are oriented, converged and focused upon a definite visual object or task; and the sensitivity of the retinal receptors as well as the aperture of the iris are adjusted to the intensity of the stimulus. An eventual result of these events is seeing. In general, the present discussion is confined to phenomena over which some control may be exercised for the betterment of human vision. Certain morphological and histological characteristics of the visual mechanism are briefly presented when such data are helpful in understanding the physiological functions of vision. However, throughout this book the discussion of physiological optics as such is minimized as much as possible in developing the concepts and knowledge of seeing. Since the realms of many sciences must be invaded, it follows that the present discussion will be restricted to glimpses which are considered to be representative from the viewpoint of the science of seeing. Thus we are more concerned with the activities of certain elements of the visual mechanism than with the anatomical characteristics of these elements. In brief, our attention is focused upon the attainment of optimum conditions for seeing rather than upon theoretical aspects of physiological optics. For obvious reasons, pathological factors are not discussed although it is recognized that these are of considerable importance in the science of seeing.

RETINAL FUNCTIONS

The stimulus. Radiant energy within a certain range of wavelengths or frequencies (Fig. 12) is capable of arousing a chain of events in the visual sense which enables one to see. For convenience this may be termed *light*. Therefore, we may say that light is the adequate (*i.e.*, appropriate) stimulus which actuates the visual mechanism and inaugurates a series of psychophysio-

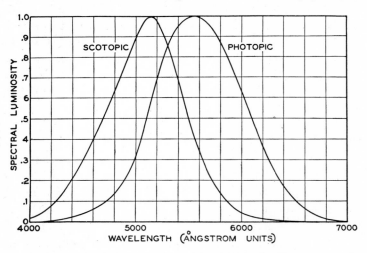

FIG. 12.—The relative luminosities of equal intensities of radiant energy of various wavelengths for ordinary brightness-levels and for brightness-levels less than 0.1 millilambert. These illustrate the Purkinje effect or difference in the spectral sensitivity of the visual sense due to rod vision or scotopic (dark) adaptation and to cone vision or photopic (light) adaptation.

logical events which ultimately result in sensation and in seeing. Furthermore, light *per se* possesses but one inherent or fundamental characteristic—spectral quality. (See Chapter XI.) However, as a visual stimulus, it may be varied in both intensity and in duration; and the retinal image may be altered in size, in configuration, and in complexity with respect to all of these variables. Furthermore, the light may be directed to different regions of the retina which possess unique characteristics as receptors for the visual stimulus. Even though the physical, and even retinal, characteristics of the stimulus remain constant, the effectiveness of the latter may be altered by the simultaneous functioning of other senses,[12] by physiological factors such as fatigue, and by innumerable psychological factors [13] such as the emotional state of the individual. Thus the study of any one variable of the stimulus, such as intensity, for example, is important in the science of seeing

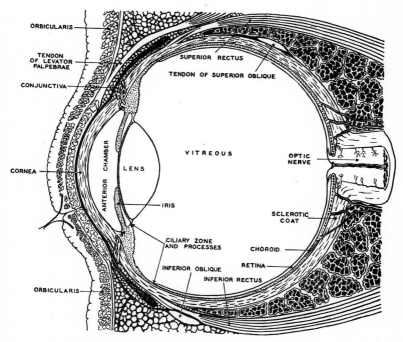

FIG. 13.—Vertical anterior-posterior section of the eye 15 degrees oblique in order to show the optic nerve. (After Parent.)

largely to the extent to which the experimental conditions are representative of seeing conditions in practice. For this reason, data characteristic of the science of seeing are usually significant in a relative rather than in an absolute sense.

Visual receptors. The retina, which constitutes the innermost of the three layers of the globular structure of the eye (Fig. 13), may be likened to a fine mosaic of minute light-sensitive cells

[63]

which are connected, through an enormously complex system of nerves, to the higher brain centers. In fact, the retina itself may be considered as a part of the central nervous system since it is formed in the embryo by a protrusion of the fore-brain. A micro-

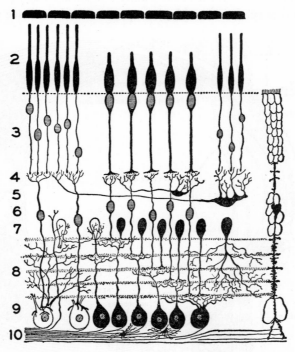

FIG. 14.—The structure of the human retina (Greeff): 1, pigment layer; 2, rod and cone layer; 3, outer nuclear layer; 4, external plexiform layer; 5, layer of horizontal cells; 6, inner nuclear layer; 7, layer of amacrinal cells; 8, inner plexiform layer; 9, ganglion cell layer; and 10, nerve fiber layer. The latter is adjacent to the vitreous humor.

scopic examination of a section of the retina reveals that there are two types of receptors. These have been designated as rods and cones in conformity with their respective shapes. These receptors, lying in the second from the outside layer of the ten layers of the retina, are clearly shown in the sectional view of the retina in Fig. 14.

The rods are 0.04 to 0.06 millimeter in length and about 0.002 millimeter in diameter, and it is estimated that there are 130,000,000 in the human retina. These receptors are functional at low levels of illumination or brightness and under such conditions neither fine details nor color may be discriminated. This situation is described as twilight or scotopic vision. They are supposed to be entirely absent in the small central area of the retina (fovea centralis) devoted to acute vision. They are about equal in number with the cones in the rest of the yellow spot (macula lutea) and are far more numerous than the cones in the peripheral or parafoveal regions of the retina. Usually a number of rods are connected to the same nerve fiber and in addition, the various portions of each retina are so interconnected with fibers that a stimulation of one area also affects other areas not directly stimulated. A distinguishing characteristic of the rods is that the apparent brightness of a fixed stimulus increases greatly as the level of general illumination is lowered.

The cones vary from 0.022 to 0.085 millimeter in length and 0.0025 to 0.0075 millimeter in diameter, and it is estimated that there are some 7,000,000 in the human retina. In general, it is reasonably accurate to state that a single cone occupies an area of the retina equivalent to a solid angle of about one square minute. Hence this anatomical fact indicates a definite limitation in the ultimate resolving power of the eye. The latter is of importance in many practical problems concerning the discrimination of fine detail. The cones are responsible for both color vision and the recognition of fine details. The latter are the characteristics of daylight or photopic vision. The visual receptors in the fovea centralis comprise only cones and each of these is connected to the higher centers by single fibers, thus explaining, at least in part, the greater visual acuity in this region. Obviously a helpful association for the memory is cones—color—central retina. The highest brightness at which the cones cease to function, or at least at which the rods begin to function noticeably, is of the order of 0.1 millilambert.

Visual fields. The extent of the monocular visual field varies not only with the prominence of the eye in its orbit, but also with the physical characteristics of the test-objects used in mapping it. The central region of the visual field about the point of fixation is seen in minute detail and in color with these characteristics diminishing toward the periphery. Traquair has described the visual field topographically as a hill of vision surrounded by a sea of blindness. The visual fields have been mapped for white and colored lights and these "maps" are often of considerable value in diagnosing pathological conditions. In general, the extent of the typical monocular field, as described by Hartridge, is presented in Table II.

TABLE II

Angular Extent of Typical Monocular Visual Field

	Nasal	Degrees from Point of Fixation Temporal	Above	Below
White	60	100	50	70
Blue	42	52	32	58
Red	35	56	28	43
Green	20	23	22	20

Retinal adaptation. The phenomena of retinal adaptation involve a set of processes, which occur after a change of exposure from light to dark or *vice versa,* whereby the eye is better fitted to receive stimuli under the new conditions. It includes (1) dark adaptation in which the brightness of a fixed stimulus is increased due to a decrease of the general illumination, (2) light adaptation in which the brightness of a fixed stimulus is decreased due to an increase in the general illumination and also (3) color adaptation in which the hue or saturation (or both) of the stimulus is altered due to pre-exposure to light of certain other wavelengths. In general, the third of these three characteristics of retinal sensibility is of the least importance in the performance of most visual tasks. However, it may be quite important in a particular situation and particularly in appraising fine differences in color.

It has been stated that the eyes are functional, to various degrees, over a range in stimulus energy of about ten billion to

one.[14]   The investigations of Cobb, for example, indicate that
brightnesses as low as a few millionths of a millilambert are
recognizable by the completely dark-adapted eye. If the eyes
are light-adapted, one may look at an ordinary 100-watt frosted
lamp without significant discomfort although the brightness of the
bulb is about 38,000 millilamberts. The brightness of the sun is
of the order of 500,000,000 millilamberts! When Nagel prevented light from entering one of his eyes for 16 hours, he found
his sensitivity to brightness increased 270,000 times. Although the
visual mechanism which makes possible such changes in the sensitivity of the eye is extremely complex, it is important in this discussion to consider some of the changes which are known to occur
when the retina is exposed to light.   In general, at least four different effects may be demonstrated: (1) the retina becomes slightly
acid in reaction; (2) there occurs a migratory movement of the
rods and cones as well as a forward displacement of the dark pigment of the retinal layer (epithelial) adjacent to the rods and
cones; (3) a bleaching of the visual purple (rhodopsin) found in
the rods; and (4) electrical currents flow in the retina and optic
nerve.   Of these four phenomena, it is certain that the first three
are involved in the process of retinal adaptation.

When the retina is exposed to light, the inner limbs of the
cones contract, thus withdrawing their free ends from the region
of the epithelial layer. Concomitantly, the rods increase in length
although it is believed by some physiologists that this change is a
passive one which results from a movement of the cones. Furthermore, the epithelial cells with their granules dip down between the
individual rods and cones, and when the retina is stimulated with
light, these cells prolong their projections. Thus as far as the
rods are involved, both of these mechanical changes tend to shield
them from stimulation due to the absorption of light by the dark
pigment. However, this explanation of the effects on vision of
these mechanical changes is not universally accepted.[15]

Both the rods and cones contain visual pigments which absorb radiation of certain wavelengths with the result that certain
photochemical effects are produced. The objective change due to

[67]

stimulation by light is that of bleaching the visual pigment and the subjective change that of decreased sensation. The analyses of Hecht show a striking similarity between the bleaching of the visual purple of the rods by light of different wavelengths and the luminosity curve of the dark-adapted eye. Hence there can be little doubt that the visual purple is the sensitizing component of the rod visual processes. In this connection, it is of interest to note that the concentrations of visual purple in the retinae of night-prowling animals is generally much greater than it is in animals whose activities are usually confined to the daytime.

Since the stimulation of one retina will produce some of these changes in the unexposed retina, it follows that these retinal changes are also under nervous control. For example, Hartman has shown that visual acuity of one eye is increased through illumination of the other.[16] Similarly, light entering one eye adds its pupillomotor influence to that entering the other eye. For *a priori* reasons, it may be assumed that the complete process of retinal adaptation is not describable by a series of photochemical reactions and mechanical changes in the retina. However, the end-product effects of adaptation have been carefully measured and these data are available for appraising certain visual situations encountered in seeing. Certainly no other controllable phase of visual function is as important in seeing.

Recent investigations have shown quite conclusively that significant correlations exist between vitamin A, visual purple and night-blindness (nyctalopia).[17] This deficiency of vision involves diminished powers of dark adaptation, reduction or absence of the Purkinje phenomena, and blue-weakness, and not infrequently is caused by a dietary deficiency of vitamin A or its precursors. Thus the efficiency of the mechanism of adaptation may be controlled, as other visual functions are controllable, by indirect and unobvious methods. The latter constitute a very definite part of the science of seeing. Other examples of more or less indirect control of visual functions are cited elsewhere in this discussion.

The temporal course of adaptation. It has been stated by Hecht [18] that the decrease in the intensity of the threshold stimulus shown by the eye during dark-adaptation proceeds in two steps. The first is rapid, short in duration, and small in extent. The second is slow, prolonged, and large. Hence it may be surmised that the first is probably due to cone function and the second to rod function. The data of Hecht, whose researches in this field of physiological optics have become classic, indicate that the dark adaptation of the foveal region proceeds at a very

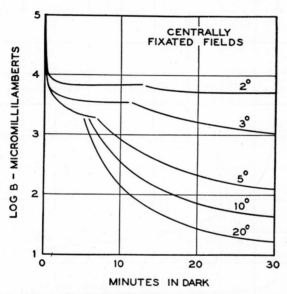

FIG. 15.—The threshold of brightness perception during dark adaptation for centrally fixated areas of different size. (After Hecht.)

precipitous rate during the first 30 seconds, and that the process practically ceases after 10 minutes. In general, it may be stated that the retina as a whole attains its maximum sensitivity after being in the dark for 45 minutes or an hour. These temporal relationships are shown in detail in Fig. 15. It will be noted from these data that the course of dark adaptation depends upon the size of the test-field. According to Hecht, the behavior in dark adaptation of centrally located fields of different size is determined, in the main, not by the area as area, but by the fact that

[69]

the retina gradually changes in sensitivity from the center to the periphery. Therefore, the larger the field the farther it reaches into the regions of permanently greater sensitivity.

At times the eyes are required to change their adaptation from a dark to a bright environment. In such cases it is of interest

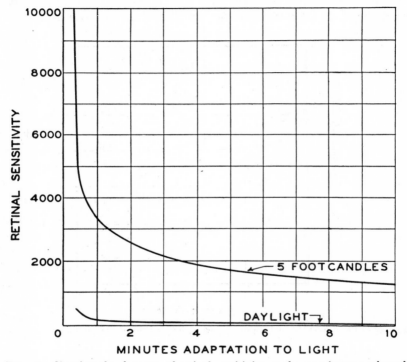

Fig. 16.—Showing the decrease of retinal sensitivity as the eyes become adapted to light. A comparison of the two curves indicates the influence of level of illumination upon the time required by the eyes to reach a constant state of adaptation.

to know the duration of the period required for the functioning of the adaptive processes. The decrease in retinal sensitivity to brightness during the course of light adaptation is shown in Fig. 16 for two radically different levels of illumination. The daylight level was several thousand footcandles. The starting point of the experimental procedure was a state of dark adaptation produced by being in the dark for 45 minutes. Therefore, it may be assumed that the eyes were completely dark-adapted from the practical viewpoint. The subject then looked at a white surface illuminated to 5 footcandles and the decrease in brightness sensitivity was measured at intervals. In a similar experiment the adaptation was made under daylight levels of illumination. It will be noted that the decrease in retinal sensitivity takes place rapidly, as might be supposed from teleological considerations, during the first minute and then more slowly. Even in the case of daylight, the lowering of sensitivity can be traced for ten minutes. It is also evident that moderate levels of illumination are slow in nullifying the effect of dark adaptation. In general, it may be stated that the temporal characteristics of retinal adaptation from dark to light, and *vice versa*, are qualitatively similar to those of the pupillary light reflex; that is, rapid from the dark to light condition and far slower for the reverse condition.

The flame of a match is intensely glaring to the completely dark-adapted eye although it may be scarcely noticeable in bright sunlight. Thus the sensation of glare may be considered as an entoptic phenomenon rather than as a characteristic attribute of light-sources. Obviously, the intensity of the glare-sensation is a function of the state of retinal adaptation, as well as of the absolute brightness of the light-source, and thus the data presented in Figs. 15 and 16 have great significance in lighting practice. For example, the lighting of the foyers of motion-picture theaters might well be designed in accordance with the changes in retinal sensibility which occur as the patron passes from the light exterior to a dark interior.

Intermittent stimulation by light. The phenomena associated with flicker are highly important in seeing both from a technical sense, as in color photometry, and in everyday seeing, as in viewing a motion-picture. A fundamental characteristic of flicker phenomena is expressed by the Talbot-Plateau law. This states that intermittent light-stimuli of any sort, when presented at a frequency sufficiently high to eliminate flicker, have an effect

on the organ of vision indistinguishable from that due to the
same total light flux continuously and uniformly applied. Furthermore, Porter's law states that the frequency of intermittence
of a visual stimulus just necessary to abolish flicker, increases by
equal amounts for equal increases in the logarithm of the brightness of the stimulus, and is independent of its wavelength composition or color.

The data of Fig. 17 may be regarded as typical of those
obtained by empirical methods. In general, it will be noted that

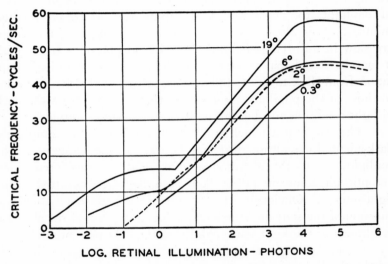

FIG. 17.—The influence of brightness and area of the stimulus upon the critical
frequency of flicker. (After Hecht.)

these data [19] are in agreement with Porter's law over a wide but
nevertheless restricted range in brightness. It is also obvious that
this law, while valid for rod vision or for cone vision, is not valid
for brightness ranges which involve a transition from rod to cone
vision. Since these data are expressed in terms of photons, the
relationships of Fig. 17 may be regarded as characteristic of the
retinal processes. The photon is a unit of visual stimulation and
is defined as that illumination upon the retina which results when

a surface brightness of one candle per square meter (0.3141 milli-lambert) is seen through a pupil of one square millimeter area. The relationships between the critical frequency of flicker and brightness are also available and have been summarized by Lythgoe and Tansley.[20]

Brightness discrimination and adaptation. The intensity range in cone adaptation has been estimated as 100 to 1 while the

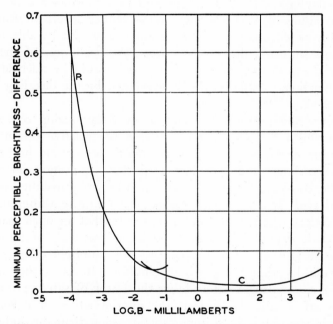

FIG. 18.—The relationship between field brightness and minimum perceptible brightness-difference for the rods, curve *R;* and cones, curve *C.* (After Hecht.)

range in rod adaptation is probably of the order of 10,000 to 1. Hence it follows that changes in retinal sensitivity are far more advantageous in scotopic than in photopic vision. This fact is obvious from the data of Fig. 18. It will be noted from these data that there is no appreciable change in retinal sensitivity, as measured by minimum perceptible brightness-difference for the range in brightnesses usually encountered in the work-world. This

[73]

fact is in agreement with Weber's Law which states that the just perceptible difference in sensation occurs when the stimulus is increased (or decreased) by a certain proportion of itself, that proportion being constant for any given sense over limited ranges. Obviously, Weber's "constant" is not a constant for the lower ranges of brightness. If it were strictly true for the lowest brightnesses, we should be able to see as well under moonlight as under daylight. Retinal fatigue and other factors are involved in the failure of Weber's law for the higher levels of illumination, for as Zoethout has pointed out, we should be able to see sun-spots since the difference between the brightness of the sun-spot and the general surface of the sun would be adequate for discrimination. Actually, this is prevented by the dazzling glare from the sun.

Since the practical problem in everyday seeing consists in recognizing and discriminating between the relative brightnesses of various areas, the values of minimum perceptible brightness-difference shown in Fig. 18 are particularly important since they may be considered to represent the ultimate capability of the normal eye. It is to be emphasized that brightness-differences of these orders will not insure, for example, that an open manhole on a dark street will be seen. Distractions, lack of attention, fatigue, brightness of surroundings, and countless other factors may radically alter the actual threshold. However, the data of Fig. 18 are useful in determining the factor of safety present in the actual situation. In fact, the discrimination of differences in brightness is far more important in seeing than the judgment of absolute brightness; and the eye is quite accurate in appraising brightness-difference while it is notoriously inaccurate in judging brightness-level.

The sense of brightness-interval, termed *value* in certain arts such as painting and decoration, is important in many human activities. A scale of ten values is commonly used by the artist for encompassing the range of reflectances or reflection-factors of surfaces from socalled black to white. Actually these are relative brightnesses and for everyday practical purposes are independent

of the level of illumination.[21] Munsell [22] using six subjects determined their estimates of ten equal brightness-intervals or values
between 0 and 100 per cent reflectance of diffusely reflecting surfaces. The subjects were light-adapted. The illumination was
22.8 footcandles and the surrounding field had a reflectance of
19.1 per cent. The estimates of the six observers did not differ
markedly from one another. The experimental data are presented in Table III. It will be noted that the brightness-steps are
not constant percentages, but gradually decrease from lower to
higher values.

TABLE III

Reflectances of Diffusely Reflecting Surfaces for Ten Equal "Values" or
Brightness-Intervals as Determined by Munsell for Six Subjects

Value	1	2	3	4	5	6	7	8	9	10
Observer				Per Cent Reflectance						
A	1.25	3.1	6.5	12.1	19.6	29.2	40.7	55.7	74.2	100
B	1.3	2.5	4.6	9.2	15.7	24.0	35.0	49.5	69.1	100
C	1.0	2.9	6.4	12.3	20.2	31.0	43.3	57.7	75.5	100
D	1.2	3.1	6.4	11.4	17.5	25.7	36.5	50.5	70.5	100
E	1.2	3.9	8.0	13.3	20.0	29.0	40.0	55.0	75.0	100
F	0.75	1.9	3.8	8.0	15.0	25.0	37.9	53.4	72.6	100
Average	1.12	2.90	5.95	11.05	18.0	27.3	38.9	53.6	72.8	100

Retinal basis of visual acuity. Hecht [23] has advanced the
theory that the variation in visual acuity with illumination is due
to the functional characteristics of the retinal receptors. Obviously
the fineness of detail which the retina can register depends
upon the number of retinal elements present per unit area. Since
this number is fixed anatomically, it must be assumed that the
number of elements involved in a given image is variable functionally. Furthermore, it seems reasonable to assume that the
normal curve of distribution is representative of the functional
thresholds of both the rod and cone populations, as it is for other
populations. If this assumption is correct, it follows that the
experimentally-determined curve relating visual acuity and illumination (or brightness) should be identical with that obtained by

combining the integral curves of the statistical distributions of sensitivity of the rods and cones. The analyses of Hecht indicate that the two curves can be brought in agreement by assuming a somewhat "skewed" form of distribution of the thresholds of the retinal receptors. It is quite possible that the distribution of sensitivity of the rods and cones is actually a normal one, and that the observed relationship between acuity and illumination is distorted from its theoretical form by anomalies of the refractive system of the eye. For example, it is obvious that the effect of aberrations upon visual acuity is greater under the higher illuminations than under the lower, because of the smaller threshold image under the former conditions. Hecht also rationalizes his theory with the all-or-none law of nerve response and with certain characteristics of color-vision and color-blindness.

As the density of the cone population decreases from the fovea towards the peripheral regions of the retina, it follows that visual acuity should decrease correspondingly. The data of Aubert and Foerster in Table IV show this relationship and emphasize the relative acuteness of vision in the foveal region.

TABLE IV

Relative Visual Acuity at Different Distances from the Fovea or Retinal Region of Most Acute Vision

Distance from Fovea $0.0°$	Visual Acuity
0.0°	1.00
2.9	.20
3.6	.15
5.8	.10
12.	.05
30.	.01

Since the average size of the fovea is about 70 minutes in diameter, it will be apparent that rather exact fixation is required in order to obtain maximal visual acuity. For example, the foveal area can contain only six 8-point letters when the latter are viewed from the average reading-distance of 14 inches. It may be assumed, from the teleological viewpoint, that the restricted retinal area of high sensibility has been developed to assist in concentrating upon small critical details in the visual field.

Notwithstanding the fact that vision is far less acute in the peripheral than in the foveal regions, we notice a bright object in the peripheral field and the eyes tend to fixate it. This strife between the chief object of attention or fixation and the secondary one is annoying and perhaps is a major cause of tenseness and fatigue due to glare. Likewise, an object in motion in the peripheral field is quite noticeable and this characteristic is very useful to man. It is possible that it has been of some importance in the survival of man. In addition to the assistance this function provides in avoiding accidents, it may also be the cause of useless expenditure of human energy in many work-world situations. For example, if a glare-source is present in the visual field, the inherent tendency is to direct our fixation upon it thus distracting our attention from the critical details of the task at hand. Obviously, we may suppress this inherited tendency, but it is not unlikely that in doing so we add to the strain and effort of performing work-world tasks. Hence, a glare-source, even though it is so mild that discomfort is not experienced when looking directly at it, may serve as a distraction whose influence is significant. Even great expanses of bright ceiling may be distracting if the brightness of the primary visual task is not considerably greater in order to enhance its attention value. This principle has been generally ignored in lighting practice.

Retinal fatigue. When the retinal receptors are sufficiently stimulated socalled afterimages [24] are formed when the stimulus is removed. As such, these images represent a prolongation or renewal of a sensory experience after the external stimulus has ceased to operate. Although the term implies a central origin of the phenomena, they are usually considered to be of peripheral origin. It can be demonstrated with ease that two different types of afterimages, designated as negative or positive, may be elicited. The negative afterimage is definable as an experience which follows another and is dependent upon prior stimulation, but which is of a quality antagonistic or complementary to the preceding experience. For example, a visual afterimage in which black and white relations are reversed, or in which the colors are approximately complementary to those of the original sensation, would be designated as a negative one.

A positive afterimage is defined as an experience which follows another in the absence of direct stimulation, and reproduces the qualities of the first experience. This type of afterimage may be seen by fixating a small white object on a black background and then covering the eyes with the hands without exerting any pressure upon them. After vision has thus been occluded for one or two minutes, uncover the eyes for a fraction of a second, and after some little time, a clear image of the white object will be seen entoptically. Afterimages continually play a part in seeing and very generally reduce the ability to see. Sometimes this reduction is so great that adequate seeing is impossible for a few moments. Many accidents are due to this temporary reduction in the adequacy of seeing. Liability cases involving this factor are becoming more numerous.

NEURAL PATHWAYS AND ACTIVITIES

The stimulus and the refractive characteristics of the eyes are generally controllable variables in seeing. A consideration of the nervous mechanisms involved in the perception of the stimulus is of value in correlating retinal and oculomotor phenomena which serve as criteria for determining optimum conditions for clear and easy seeing. In general, the concept of the reflex arc or circuit is sufficient for an appreciation of the nervous mechanism of vision from the practical viewpoint of the science of seeing. It consists of (1) the visual receptors to which the stimulus is applied, (2) the afferent or sensory-nerve fibers which lead to the brain, and (3) the efferent or motor-nerve fibers which come from the brain and end in muscle fibers.

The connections between the retina and the brain are shown in Fig. 19. The optic nerve, as described by Starling,[25] contains four different sets of nerve fibers: (1) those which convey visual impressions to the brain; (2) those going to the pupillomotor centers; (3) those which come down from the brain to the retinae; and (4) those which connect one retina to the other through the crossing at the chiasm. These neural circuits, as diagramed by Adler,[26] are shown in Fig. 19. It will be noted that the fibers from each retina meet at a junction point, the

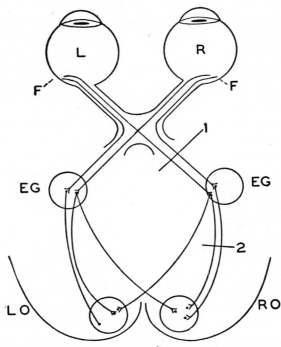

FIG. 19.—The arrangement of the fibers from the fovea, showing the double-crossing at the chiasm and back of the external geniculate body. (After Adler.)

L	Left eye	EG	External geniculate body
R	Right eye	LO	Left occipital cortex
F	Fovea	RO	Right occipital cortex

chiasm, from which they diverge again and pass to the respective cerebral hemispheres. Thus each retina is connected to both hemispheres. These paths are described by Starling [25] as follows: (a) Those from the right halves of the periphery of both retinae, which join at the chiasm and travel to the brain *via* the right optic tracts; (b) those from the right halves of both foveae which

travel *via* the right tracts; (c) those from the left halves of both
foveae which travel *via* the left tracts; and (d) those from the
left halves of the periphery of the retinae, which also travel *via*
the left tracts. The right optic tract thus contains all the visual
fibers from the right sides of both retinae and thus transmits all
the impulses belonging to the left half of the field of view. The
left tract travels to the brain in a similar manner. Hence an
injury to the optic tract (fibers between chiasm and brain centers)

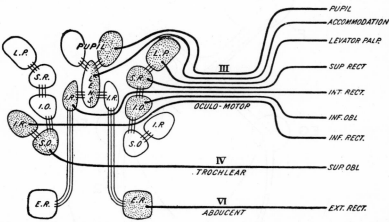

Fɪɢ. 20.—Illustrating the relationship of different parts of the third nerve nuclei,
the fourth and the sixth nuclei, and the connections between them. (After
Starling.)

will produce blindness for the halves of both retinae on the same
side as the injury.

The central origins of the motor or efferent nerves are shown
in Fig. 20, and their peripheral terminations in the involuntary
(intrinsic) ocular muscles are shown in Fig. 21. The connections
to the voluntary (extrinsic) muscles will be evident from the
names of the muscles. These neural pathways are of particular
interest since (1) the efficiency of the eyes depends largely upon
the speed and accuracy with which the muscular activities are accomplished; and (2) by reason of the fact that unobvious effects
of strain and fatigue in seeing may be revealed by the move-

ments of the eyes, changes in pupil size and by the opening and closing of the eyelids. There are numerous cross-connections between the various nuclei in order that all muscular elements may work in harmony. For example, when the superior rectus muscle rotates the eye upward, the muscle of the upper lid (levator palpebrae) raises the lid and thus prevents any restriction of vision. In other cases, the cross-connections between various nuclei permit the relaxation of one muscle when an antagonistic one is contracted. For example, when the internal rectus is con-

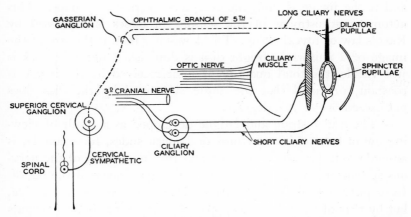

FIG. 21.—Showing the pathways of the oculo-motor nerves and their connections to the intrinsic muscles of the eye. (Modified from Howell.)

tracted, the external rectus relaxes because of the reciprocal innervation. Since these cross-connections exist, it is reasonable to expect that the fatigue induced by prolonged reading, for example, might be revealed by a change in the rate of blinking or in the size of the pupil. Such changes have in fact been noted and are discussed in Chapter VI.

Since the nerves to the ciliary muscles and iris belong to the involuntary (parasympathetic) system which supplies the inhibitory (vagal) innervation of the heart, it is to be expected that overstimulation of these ocular nerves would be associated with a slowing of the heart beat.   An experimental confirmation of this effect is presented in Chapter VI.

According to Houston [27] the retina should not be considered as a mosaic of receptors leading by independent pathways to the different fibers of the optic nerve.   Undoubtedly, there is a closer connection to one particular fiber, but the same fiber is open to the spread of excitation from other parts of the synaptic layer.   Apparently the visual mechanism adjusts itself automatically to the best way of registering the image.   For example, if the image is bright and contains much detail, the receptors function independently; and if the image is dim, the receptors operate in groups.   This automatic adjustment of the sensory processes is expressed by Ricco's law of foveal vision.   This law states that, if the size of the image of a uniformly bright disk is diminished until the disk is just visible, the total quantity of light received on the image is constant, provided that the angle subtended by the disk does not exceed one or two degrees.

The ocular strain and fatigue developed as a result of viewing out-of-focus motion-pictures or lantern slides, for example, is an end-product result which indicates the functioning of the nervous system of vision.   In this case the retinal image of the out-of-focus picture is blurred, not by the refractive system of the eye, but by that of the projection apparatus.   Since the brain demands clear vision, the innervation of the ciliary muscle which controls the lens is continually altered in the effort to obtain better accommodation.   Obviously, there can be no muscular solution to this problem.   However, the interchange of nervous stimuli over the communication system between the brain and the muscle continues notwithstanding the fact that the muscle becomes fatigued and that no *improvement* in seeing is accomplished by the efforts of accommodation.

This characteristic of the visual mechanism may be demonstrated by a simple experiment.   If the pattern of parallel-diagonal lines of Fig. 22 is viewed steadily, it will be noted that the eyes rapidly tire.   Due to the uniformity of the pattern and to transient eye-movements,[28] it is quite difficult for the eyes to remain fixated upon a definite part of the pattern. But it may be assumed that the brain insists upon a steady clear image and that the extrinsic muscles are innervated for this purpose. However, the task of holding steady fixation is apparently too difficult and

FIG. 22.—Illustrating one of the patterns of the Luckiesh-Moss Visual Test. This test-object is formed by breaks in dark gray parallel diagonal lines. On this particular pattern is the letter "T." For this illustration the visibility of the test-object has been increased by the use of a white background instead of a gray one of 16 per cent reflection-factor as used in the actual printed test.[1]

the point of fixation shifts continually and rapidly. As a result, the normal eye-movements are greatly accelerated and the eyes become fatigued. This oculomotor activity, however, is *non-vo-litional*—a characteristic which the authors have used to advantage in devising a visual test [29] in which the effort expended by the subject was not under voluntary control. In this test, letters made by breaks in the lines, such as the letter T in Fig. 22, were used as test-objects to be recognized one after another.

Electrical potentials in the brain. Very recently Adrian,[30] Berger, Loomis and others have definitely established the existence of recordable electrical potentials arising in the cerebral cortex of man. Although this phase of physiology is extraneous, at the present time, to the practical objectives of this discussion, these phenomena are of interest from a scientific viewpoint. The present results, as they pertain to sensory phenomena, indicate that flickering lights give rise to brain potentials in some persons that exactly follow the flicker frequency.[31] Furthermore, it has been observed that the spontaneous electrical activity, known as the Berger rhythm, ceases when the subject attempts to see. Certainly these fascinating experiments emphasize the fallacy of considering the visual mechanism of man in the light of mere optical equipment or that vision adequately encompasses seeing.

PUPILLARY PHENOMENA

Researches pertaining to pupillary phenomena often may have a dual role in visual science. They not only indicate the influence of the pupil in controlling retinal illumination or brightness of the retinal image, but also may be an objective means for revealing the effects of complex psychophysiological factors which otherwise might escape or defy appraisal. For example, it has been shown (1) that elderly people require a higher intensity of illumination than young people do in order to obtain retinal images of equal brightness due to the gradual constriction of the pupil with age; and (2) that there is usually a significant dilation of the pupil following several hours of exacting visual work, which may be interpreted, at least relatively, as an indication of general fatigue. These transient and permanent changes in pupil size are often extremely important in seeing as a universal human activity.

In the performance of visual work, the size of the pupil varies with the intensity of photic stimulation, with the associated movements of accommodation and convergence, and to a lesser extent with such factors as the emotional state and degree of bodily fatigue. Slight rhythmical changes may also be observed, under proper experimental conditions, which are caused by the emptying and filling of the iridic blood vessels. The pupils are also constricted rather than dilated in sleep. This fact indicates the complex nature of the innervation of the iridic muscles which control the iris.

The pupillary light reflex. If the size of the pupil is measured after fifteen minutes' exposure to a white surface illuminated

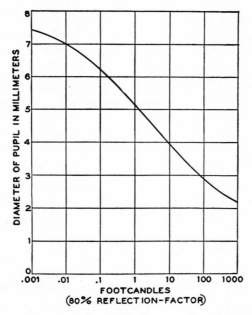

FIG. 23.—Showing the size of the pupil after 15 minutes' exposure to various levels of illumination or brightnesses of a "white" surface of 80 per cent reflection-factor. (After Reeves.)

to various brightnesses, it will be found that its diameter, for the average eye, varies from about two millimeters to nearly eight millimeters for brightness-levels of approximately 1000 millilamberts and 0.001 millilambert, respectively. The data of Reeves,[32] Fig. 23, show the relationship between pupil size and illumination in detail. It will be noted that the pupillary area and, therefore, the percentage of light incident on the cornea admitted to the retina is variable in the ratio of 1 to 16 for these two brightness-levels. Obviously, this ratio may be larger or smaller in the individual case involving different eyes, exposure-times, and numerous other factors. In Fig. 23 the brightnesses have been given in terms of footcandles on a white surface having a reflec-

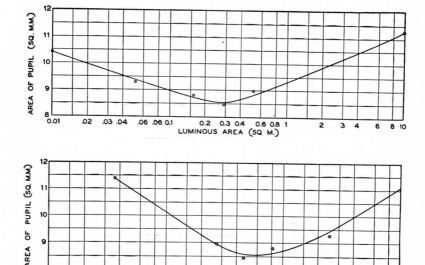

FIG. 24.—Showing the area of the pupil of the eye for various combinations of area and brightness of a circular test-field seen amid comparatively dark surroundings. The illumination at the eye due to the luminous test-area was always 10 footcandles. The test-field was located at a distance of 2 meters from the eye.

tion-factor of 80 per cent. This is a convenient way of visualizing the brightnesses due to various footcandle-levels.

If the eyes are fixated upon an illuminated area within the visual field, it is obvious that the size of the pupil would be influenced by the extent as well as the brightness of the illuminated area.[33] The relationship between these variables and pupil size, for certain environmental conditions, is shown in Fig. 24. A conspicuous characteristic of these data is that a minimum in pupil size is obtained for a definite combination of area and brightness. If the population of the pupillomotor nerves were of uniform density throughout the retina, it appears that the relationship between pupil size and the variables of area and brightness should be represented by a straight horizontal line in Fig. 24, since, as these data were obtained, a reciprocity relationship existed between the two variables. Therefore, it may be concluded from these data that the density of the pupillary reactors is not uniform and that it varies in a rather complex manner. From the practical viewpoint, these data indicate that small areas of relatively high brightness and large areas of relatively low brightness, respectively, are most effective in admitting light to the retina. This is an important matter in lighting practice if light is to be used most effectively.

Although the response of the pupil to light is often considered as a means provided by Nature for protecting the retina from excessive stimulation by light, this viewpoint is inadequate in many respects. For example, since one is dazzled by the brightness of snow in direct sunlight, it is obvious that the pupil does not provide adequate protection. As the range in brightnesses found in Nature is of the order of several billions to one, it follows that a device with a maximal operating range of about 20 to 1 could not possibly compensate all changes in brightness. Furthermore, it is easy to demonstrate that the pupil remains practically constant in size for changes in the brightness of the visual field as high as 200 to 1 if the increase in brightness is accomplished by gradual and almost imperceptible changes. However, there is a rapid alteration in pupil size when the same change in brightness is made abruptly.

It is contended by some physiologists that the pupil ultimately reaches a definite or "physiological" size even under a wide variety of lighting conditions. This socalled physiological size is that corresponding to the size of the pupil after an exposure of a few minutes to a field-brightness of approximately ten millilamberts. However, this fact, regardless of its significance in physiological optics, is of little practical importance. The eyes are continually

[87]

and usually rapidly fixating upon objects of different brightnesses and at different distances and these influences prevent the pupil from attaining and maintaining any particular size.

It is probable that the most useful function of the pupil, as a device for controlling retinal illumination, is that of admitting considerably more light when the transition is from a field of relatively low brightness to one of much lower brightness, and where the objects to be seen are not far above threshold visibility. For example, if one moves from an ordinarily well-lighted room to the outdoors under moonlight conditions, the data of Reeves indicate that the pupil dilates some 400 per cent in area. Hence, objects of borderline visibility before dilation may be considerably above borderline visibility after dilation. In other words, a four-fold increase in the amount of light admitted to the retina may be highly effective as an aid to seeing when there is barely enough, or even less than sufficient, light to enable objects to be seen. In fact, anthropologists often credit this characteristic of the visual mechanism as a factor in the survival of man. In general, the changes in pupil size may be of temporary and partial assistance while retinal adaptation is taking place.

The rate of response of the pupillary reflex to changes in the lighting environment is a characteristic of primary importance in appraising the influence of pupillary phenomena in seeing. In general, it may be said that the pupil contracts to a given degree in about as many seconds as it takes minutes to dilate between the same limits in size. This is illustrated in Fig. 25. During the first second of exposure to a bright stimulus, the contraction of the pupil is precipitous. Thereafter the rate of constriction progressively decreases until a point of equilibrium is attained after an exposure of about four seconds.

These temporal relationships between changes in photic stimulation and time of response have a direct bearing upon many lighting problems. For example, the question often arises regarding the effectivenesses of the pupil in compensating for the rather sudden changes in brightness as one passes from one brightness-level to another. In view of the data presented in Fig. 25, it is obvious that the pupil cannot effectively compensate for many of the brightness changes commonly encountered. For example, a motorist traveling at a relatively rapid rate past automobile head-lamps and other isolated light-sources does not obtain the advantage of a wider pupil, after leaving a lighted area, in discerning objects of near-threshold visibility until he has traveled a considerable distance. However, the protection of the state of adap-

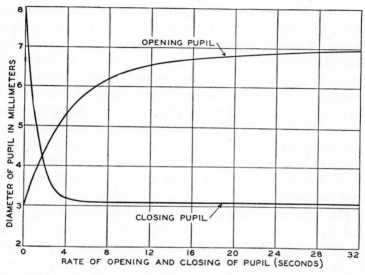

Fig. 25.—Showing the rate of opening of the pupil after a brightness of 100 ml. has been replaced by darkness; also the rate of closing after darkness has been replaced by a stimulus of 100 ml. Obviously the pupil closes much more rapidly than it opens.

tation may be quite important. On the other hand, the protective characteristic of the pupillary light reflex operates with maximum effectiveness for the pedestrian because he moves at a much lower speed. These practical examples of the role of the pupillary light reflex in seeing are merely illustrative of the cases where this phenomenon may well be considered.

It may be assumed that the involuntary alterations in the size of the pupil due to changes in photic stimulation are not detrimental, *per se,* to the well-being of the pupillary mechanism since Nature has evolved this function. However, it is quite possible that this function may be over-taxed under certain conditions. For example, a bright light-source within the field of view may constrict the pupil to its minimum size without significant consequences, but such a constriction may be quite detrimental if long continued. In such a case, the contracted sphincter muscles of the iris are in a state of maximum tension and the situation may be likened to mechanical devices operating under maximum loads. Usually, this is undesirable from considerations of well-being and efficiency. The rate of the heart-beat may be cited as an analogy. In this case, the rate may rise from about 75 beats per minute while standing to about 150 beats per minute while climbing stairs. Obviously, no one would suppose that the latter rate could be maintained without deleterious effects. Yet lighting conditions are commonly found in offices which, due to excessive brightnesses within the visual field, have resulted in a prolonged contraction of the pupil to its minimum size. That a stenographer may complain of headaches under such conditions does not seem to be an unrelated fact.

The intimate relationship between physiological and psychological factors involved in the visual sensory processes is indicated by the intriguing fact that it is not necessary to be able to "see" in order to elicit pupillary responses. It has been shown that the pupils of the eyes of the blind tend to contract when they think of a brilliant sunny day. This phenomenon and others which might be cited illustrate the difficulty of presenting visual effects in socalled practical terms, graphs or equations. Also, they continually emphasize the generally ignored fact that seeing is a human activity which is affected by uncounted unobvious factors. Too often extensive conclusions are drawn from the restricted knowledge and influences of vision and physiological optics without consideration of the human factors.

Pupil size and oculomotor functions. A marked contraction of the pupil occurs when the point of visual fixation is brought nearer the eyes. This response, which is of anatomical origin rather than of a reflex nature, is due to the fact that the sphincter pupillae, ciliary, and the internal recti muscles are innervated by the same nerve. Thus by bringing a book closer to the eyes, the pupil contracts and this contraction may serve to mask errors in the refractive system of the eye. It is obvious that such an expedient for attaining better vision is undesirable from the basis of ocular hygiene. However, such practices are not infrequently substituted for eyeglasses.

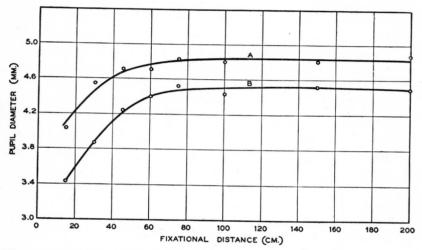

FIG. 26.—The relationship between pupil size and fixational distance for a bright-ness-level of o.1 millilambert. The results shown by curves *A* and *B* are for monocular and binocular observation, respectively. The data shown by curve *A* were obtained with the visual field of the right eye obscured by the pupillometer.

The curves of Fig. 26 show the quantitative relationship between pupil size and fixational distance.[33] It will be noted that similar relationships between these variables are obtained for both monocular and binocular vision. These data also indicate that the size of the pupil is not altered significantly even by large increases in fixational distance when the latter is approximately 60 centimeters or greater. In considering these phenomena, it is of interest to note that light entering one eye adds its pupillomotor influence to that entering the other eye. This relationship, indicated by the difference in pupil size for monocular and binocular vision, is another indication of the complex interneural connections of the visual organs.

Pupil size and visual acuity. The highly controlled investigations of Cobb [34] established the fact that visual acuity improves as the diameter of an artificial pupil is increased from a minimum to a diameter of about two millimeters; and that beyond two millimeters, visual acuity remains practically constant although it reaches an optimum value. This may be attributed to the predominance of optical defects of the eye in the case of the larger pupil and the diffraction effect in the case of the smaller pupil. The eye in this respect behaves like other optical devices. As the pupil increases in size, the resolving power increases and the definition of the image decreases. Cobb proved that over a range in pupil size from about two to five millimeters the greater resolving power of the larger pupil is quite counterbalanced by a decrease in the sharpness of the retinal image. His results were obtained for a constant brightness of the test-object and also for a constant brightness of the retinal image.

Pupillary changes with age. Statistical methods have shown that the pupils gradually and permanently become smaller as the individual grows older. The pupillary changes accompanying age as determined by Nitsche and Gunther [35] are shown in Table V.

TABLE V

Age	Diameter of the Pupil in Millimeters		
	In Daylight	At Night	Difference
20	4.7	8.0	3.3
30	4.3	7.0	2.7
40	3.9	6.0	2.1
50	3.5	5.0	1.5
60	3.1	4.1	1.0
70	2.7	3.2	0.5
80	2.3	2.5	0.2

It follows from these data that the pupils at the age of 50 years admit, for the average case, only about one-half as much

light as they do at the age of 20 years. It is also of interest to note
that the magnitude of the pupillary changes between daylight-
vision (photopic) and night-vision (scotopic) gradually diminishes
with age. Thus the elderly person is largely deprived of the
advantages of pupillary adjustments and is particularly handicapped at low levels of illumination. He is also handicapped by
the loss of the power of accommodation and by the decrease in
retinal sensibility.

Pupil size and fatigue. In Tables XL and XLI are presented the pupil sizes of nine subjects determined under constant
conditions of brightness before and after the day's work in offices.
It is seen that the size is greater at the end of the day than before
beginning the day's work. Also, the size gradually increased as
the week progressed and diminished over the weekend.[36]

THE EYELIDS

The movements of the eyelids serve the obvious purposes of
protecting the eye from injury, shielding the retina from too intense stimulation, moistening the surface of the eyeball and re-
moving foreign paricles from the surface. In addition, it is
also believed that the movements of the lids are related to the
mental tension of the individual and that they may constitute a
kind of relief mechanism. When the lids are opened, the lower
naturally drops and the upper is raised by the muscle known as
levator palpebrae superioris. The latter is innervated by the third
nerve as are certain other ocular muscles. The lids are voluntarily
or reflexly closed through the action of a sphincter muscle known
as orbicularis palpebrarum which is innervated by the seventh or
facial nerve. These muscles are shown in Fig. 13. In general,
the movements of the eyelids involve the actual opening and
closing of the lids and fine fibrillary movements. The latter are
not present during true sleep. The duration of these movements
in voluntary blinking has been determined by Weiss [37] and the
data are summarized in Table VI.

TABLE VI

Time Intervals in Voluntary Blinking

Total duration .... 0.197 second
Falling of lid .... 0.060 second
Duration of closure .... 0.031 second
Elevation of lid .... 0.111 second

These anatomical considerations have been presented in this discussion due to (1) the fact that the movements of the eyelids can be readily studied and (2) that these movements may be correlated with fatigue or the expenditure of human energy in seeing. Such correlations are presented in Chapter VI.

Although a consideration of eyelid movements in pathological cases is beyond the purposes of this discussion, it may be stated that the closing of the lids in photophobia is due to inflammatory conditions in the eye, and particularly in the iris. Thus, as Zoethout states, the intolerance of light in such cases may exist in certain forms of transient blindness in which no objective changes are demonstrable.

ORIENTATION AND CONVERGENCE

The extrinsic or extra-ocular muscles consist of three pairs for each eye: the internal rectus and external rectus, which rotate the eyeball inward and outward, respectively; the superior rectus and inferior rectus, which rotate the eyeball upward and downward, respectively, and also inward; and the superior oblique and inferior oblique, which rotate the eyeball downward and upward, respectively, and also outward. These are the muscles which permit the orientation and convergence upon a particular point in the visual field—a faculty which is usually not fully acquired before the age of six years. Recent investigations by Grimm indicate that convergence, as far as it generally acts, determines the position of the fixation-point in space. Apparently accommodation does not play a leading part. The extrinsic muscles and their direction of pull are shown in Fig. 27.

The response of the extrinsic muscles to visual stimulation is of such an order of automaticity that "visual acuity" can be measured by means of the movements of the eyes even in cases involving cortical blindness. In the latter, images are transmitted to the thalamus but they are not recognized in consciousness. However, the muscular elements respond as though the objects were recognized by the subject. The automatism of the muscular system is also clearly indicated, in the normal case, by the fact that the eyes often adjust themselves to a bright peripheral object notwith-

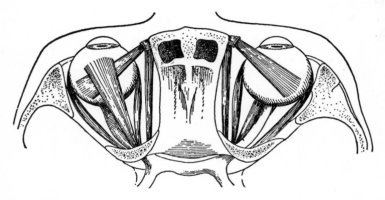

FIG. 27.—The origin and insertion of the external ocular muscles and their direction of pull. (After Adler.)

standing the fact that the attention is directed elsewhere. Thus it would seem that these two phenomena are closely related.

Maddox has divided convergence into three functional classifications. *Tonic convergence* is exerted to fixate an object at infinity. It may be positive, negative or nil depending upon the characteristics of muscle balance for distance-vision. *Accommodative convergence* is always positive. *Fusional convergence* is exerted to obtain single binocular vision. It has been assumed that, for any given near-point, the reserve power of convergence should be twice as great as that required for binocular vision at that point. Hence the loss in convergence reserve, as a result of prolonged visual effort of a critical nature, is correspondingly important as a criterion for appraising the severity of the visual task. We have applied this criterion of ocular hygiene to the task of reading under various physical conditions as discussed in Chapter VI.

A highly important characteristic of oculomotor function is summarized by Donder's law which states that every position of the lines of regard in relation to the head corresponds to a definite and invariable torsion of the eyes, regardless of the path by which that position has been reached. For example, a vertical line invariably appears as a vertical line even though the head is tilted in various directions. The confusion which would be encountered in interpreting our visual experiences in the absence of this correlation between the movements of the head and eyes can be imagined better than described! These movements of the eyes are further defined by Listing's law which states that when the line of fixation passes from its primary to any other position, the angle of torsion of the eye in this second position is the same as if the eye had arrived at this position by turning about a fixed axis perpendicular to the first and second positions of the line of fixation.

The eyes are continually in motion even when apparently fixated upon a small object. Their movements through the action of the extrinsic muscles have been shown to consist of rapid sweeps, long or short, with brief pauses.[38] During very rapid sweeps it is impossible for details of objects to make a sufficient impression, since at these times the image is rushing across the retina at a corresponding rate. In addition to this, there may be other reasons why we do not see blurred images, at least when the eyes are roving over the external field. It is only during the fixational-pauses in the eye-movements, when the image is practically at rest upon the retina, that an adequate impression is made. Actually the image is seldom, if ever, stationary upon the retina due to continual fluctuations in the point of fixation of the order of magnitude of 30 seconds of visual angle. In general, very few fixational-pauses are as short as 0.05 second and few as long as 0.3 second. It has also been shown that the distribution of separate measurements of fixational-pause is not far from normal. Furthermore, it may be assumed that the duration of these pauses is controlled by the central nervous system since it has been shown that the fixational-time [39] is a function of the perceptual difficulty of the object or objects of regard. For example, the pauses are longer in studying algebra than they are in reading fiction.

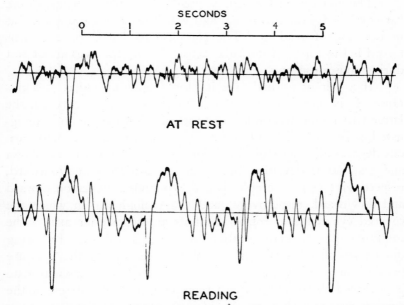

FIG. 28.—Electromyograms showing the activity of the ocular muscles as indicated by the minute electric currents while the open eyes were at "rest" in a darkened room (upper curve) and while reading (lower curve). The electrodes were placed directly above the right eye and at the right temple, respectively. See Chapter XII.

We have studied the activities of the ocular muscles by recording the action currents developed while the subject performed various visual tasks. The electromyograms, reproduced in Fig. 28, were obtained by placing electrodes at the center of the forehead and at the right temple, respectively, thus confining the record of the eye-movements largely to those of the right eye. In obtaining these records an amplification of about two million was required.

[97]

The record during reading clearly reveals, by the fairly regular waves of high amplitude, the muscular activity involved when the fixation sweeps from the end of one line to the beginning of the next. The smaller changes between these larger ones may be attributed to the various fixational movements (usually involuntary) occurring during the reading of a single line.

The upper record in Fig. 28 was obtained while the eyes were "at rest" in a darkened room, and with the same amplification as in the case of reading. The conspicuous characteristic of this record is the apparent muscular activity while the eyes are at rest during consciousness.

If a pair of normal eyes is fixated upon an object at a distance of six meters or more and if one eye is then covered, the latter will retain its position of fixation. This condition is designated as orthophoria. However, it is not infrequent to find various degrees and types of muscle imbalance, such as (1) esophoria and exophoria, deviation of covered eye inward and outward, respectively; (2) hyperophoria and hypophoria, deviation upward and downward, respectively; and (3) cyclophoria, in which the covered eye tends to rotate about its anteroposterior axis. The condition of orthophoria will be assumed in this and following discussions of visual functions. When the axes of the eyes are parallel, or nearly so, under normal conditions the muscular state is described as orthophoria and represents the state of rest of the eyes, as near as such a state is obtained during consciousness.

In reading at the socalled normal distance of ⅓ meter, a convergence of three meter angles is required. If the eyes are normal, this convergence is readily accomplished, but it is to be emphasized that the muscles of the eyes probably were not particularly developed through evolutionary processes to maintain this state without strain and fatigue for long periods of time, as is demanded in schools, offices and elsewhere in the modern workworld.[40] In fact some authorities maintain that the use of the eyes in close work is a predominant cause of myopia. The eyeball in childhood is yielding and continued convergence with its accompanying tension of the motor muscles on the globe may tend to lengthen it in the region of the posterior pole and thus to develop myopia. Since the fixation-distance is controllable by the individual, the latter may also exercise some control over the functioning of the extrinsic muscles and avoid or minimize the penalties of abnormal use of the eyes. Periodic relaxation of the eye-muscles by looking at more distant objects and actual eye exercises are doubtless worth while. In addition, proper use of various aids to seeing is likely to be helpful.

BINOCULAR VISION

When normal eyes are in their primary positions; that is, with the head erect and the eyes fixated upon an infinitely distant point, the retinal impressions are transmitted to the brain and fused as a single image. In this case, a point in space is imaged upon corresponding points [41] in the two retinae and the two stimuli are received by the brain as one. If the image is focused upon non-corresponding portions of the retinae, the brain is unable to fuse them and hence two separate impressions (diplopia) are perceived. Furthermore, the two images must be similar, or nearly so, for fusion. If they are appreciably dissimilar, first the one and then the other will be presented in sensation and rivalry between the two ensues. It is very easy to demonstrate this rivalry by placing a red filter over one eye and a green one over the other. First one and then the other color is the predominant sensation. They do not mix into a yellow as two such lights would if the mixture were presented to both eyes. In its highest state of development, binocular vision results in stereopsis or the perception of depth. However, it is possible to possess single binocular vision without the faculty of depth-perception.

The urge for single binocular vision is one of the strongest inherent characteristics of the human visual processes. In addition to providing for the perception of solidity and depth, it serves to increase visual efficiency through the integration of color and brightness, to increase the extent of the visual field, and to mask optical defects in one eye. These advantages may be more than offset in cases involving muscular anomalies. Due to the tightness of the nervous bonding between accommodation and convergence, slight imbalances in oculomotor functions often result in severe strain and fatigue.

Binocular visual functions. An extensive research by Cobb [42] quantitatively established the relationship between binocular and monocular visual acuities. For subjects possessing normal or near-normal vision (20/15 to 20/30) Cobb found that

$$V = 0.75V_1 + 0.16V_2 + 0.18$$

where V represents the binocular visual acuity, and V_1 and V_2 the monocular visual acuity of the better and poorer eye, respectively. These data were obtained with the Snellen Chart. It will be noted from these results that binocular visual acuity depends to a major degree upon the vision of the better eye. However, it is not to be assumed that the better eye is necessarily the dominant eye. This conclusion is supported by the recent data of Schoen and Wallace which indicate that retinal asymmetry is not responsible for ocular dominance.

There seems to be no doubt but that binocular vision is superior to monocular vision in lowering the brightness-thresholds under low levels of illumination. For example, Shaad [43] found that the stimulus brightness for binocular thresholds is approximately 30 per cent lower than that for monocular thresholds. Lowry [44] concluded that at brightnesses below 50 millilamberts there is a marked difference in brightness sensitivity between monocular vision and binocular vision. On the other hand, Piper, McDougall and others report a failure to find evidences of binocular summation for relatively high brightnesses under higher levels of illumination.

Since the perception of depth is a function of the angular separation of the eyes, it is to be expected that this faculty decreases with increases in the distance of the object of regard. Actually, the limit of binocular depth perception is reached at distances of about one hundred meters. This is due to the fact that the maximum possible angular disparity between this point and infinity is less than the threshold value which is between five and ten seconds of arc.

ACCOMMODATION

Accommodation is defined as the change in shape and, concomitantly, in refractive power of the eye-lens as the eyes are focused for a different distance. In an eye which is normally perfect in its refractive system, the image of an object at infinity is accurately focused upon the retina. However, in practice it is customary to regard a distance of six meters or 20 feet as "optical infinity". If an object is fixated at less than this distance, the convexity of the crystalline lens is automatically or involuntarily increased in order to provide the additional refracting power required. For example, the refractive power of the eye must be increased by one diopter when the point of fixation is moved from infinity to a distance of one meter since the measure of a lens in diopters is the reciprocal of its focal length in meters, *plus* for convex and *minus* for concave lenses.

A single lens of 58 diopters placed at the posterior nodal point would be equivalent to the entire dioptric system of the average eye. Actually, the cornea contributes about 40 to 47 diopters of the total refracting power.[45] Although the crystalline lens, in its position in the eye, may have a refracting power of some 15 or 16 diopters, seldom more than three diopters of adjustment are required in seeing near and distant objects. When this relatively low refracting power cannot be supplied with comfort by the visual mechanism, additional power may be added with convex lenses. In addition, refractive errors due to distortion of the cornea or the eyeball may also be corrected with lenses. Usually such corrections are not greater than a few diopters and often are less than one diopter. In fact, small *uncorrected* errors may cause greater eyestrain (asthenopia) than much larger ones since the former may be corrected through excessive innervation. When the refractive error is unusually large, the human seeing-machine generally finds it more desirable to accept the low degree of resulting visibility rather than to expend much effort in attempting to correct it by muscular effort. However, it is certain that mere ability to compensate for refractive errors is not a satisfactory excuse for neglecting to correct them with eyeglasses.

The changes in curvature of the lens during accommodation are illustrated in Fig. 29. These changes are accomplished as a result of the innervation of the ciliary muscle or body through the third nerve. The ciliary muscles consist of an annular mass of unstriped muscle fibers (Fig. 13) (activated by the autonomic

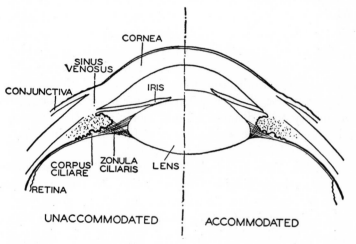

CORNEA

SINUS VENOSUS

CONJUNCTIVA

IRIS

CORPUS CILIARE   ZONULA CILIARIS   LENS

RETINA

UNACCOMMODATED   ACCOMMODATED

FIG. 29.—Showing the changes in curvature of the lens during accommodation. (After Adler.)

nervous system) which surrounds the eye-lens and regulates its curvature, thereby accommodating or focusing the eye for vision at various distances. Although numerous theories of accommodation have been advanced, those of Helmholtz and Tscherning are given chief consideration. Of these, the relaxation theory of Helmholtz is the more generally accepted. The latter theory, as summarized by Starling,[25] supposes that the lens when removed from the eye is strongly convex and is accommodated for near vision. However, when in the eye it is caused to become flatter through the traction of the suspensory ligaments of the eyes on its capsule, and is therefore focused for distance. When the ciliary muscle contracts it removes the tension on the zonula which permits the lens to return by its elasticity to its more spherical form.

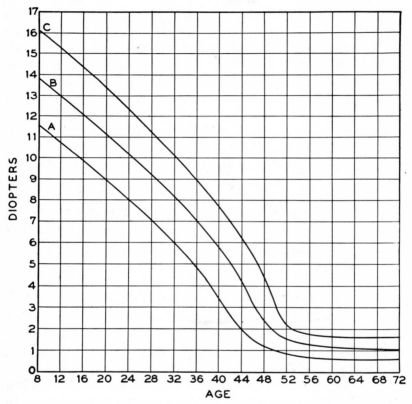

FIG. 30.—The decrease in the amplitude of accommodation with age. Curve *B* represents the average amplitude of accommodation; and curves *A* and *C* indicate minimum and maximum amplitudes, respectively.

Obviously, an understanding of the mechanism of accommodation is essential to an adequate appreciation of the effects of such factors as age, fixation-distance, duration of visual effort, physical well-being and others upon the functioning of this highly important element of the visual apparatus.

Accommodation versus age. In youth the amplitude of possible accommodation is high. It is believed that this is due to the elasticity of the crystalline lens. A child of eight years may accurately accommodate an object situated at a distance of three inches or less. Obviously, mere ability to accommodate objects at such short distances is not an indication that temporary fatigue and eventual harm does not result from such practices. For this and other reasons, it is safer not to hold objects such as toys near the eyes of infants and not to permit children to read or perform other visual tasks at distances appreciably nearer to the eyes than twelve or thirteen inches. As the eyes grow older, the lens gradually hardens and loses some of its power of accommodation. This gradual decrease in amplitude of accommodation is shown in Fig. 30. These biological data are so reliable that it is usually possible to determine the age of an individual quite accurately by measuring the amplitude of accommodation. The onset of the socalled "bifocal age" near the age of forty-five will be obvious from these data. In general, it is considered advisable that about one-third of the total power of accommodation be kept in reserve.

Presbyopia designates loss of accommodation with the result that distant objects may be focused clearly but nearby objects may not be. Although it is an unavoidable deficiency which develops with advancing age, it may be corrected with bifocal glasses. Furthermore, the investigations of Ferree and Rand [46] indicate that higher levels of illumination can be used to defer the use of "reading glasses" in many cases when the failure of accommodation is slow, and also in the earlier stages of presbyopia to lessen the need for frequent changes in the strength of the glasses. In Fig. 31 is shown the relationship between the apparent amplitude of accommodation and intensity of illumination for three subjects of different ages. It will be noted that the presbyope was greatly aided by the use of the higher levels of illumination. It is seen that the youngest person with normal vision (emmetrope) had more than 10 diopters of accommodation which increased somewhat as the level of illumination was increased. The other subject, whose nearsightedness (myopia) was corrected with glasses, was also aided in accommodation reserve appreciably up to 20 foot-candles which is very much more light than is commonly available throughout the artificial world.

Accommodation and visual efficiency. It has been shown [47] that the efficiency of the eye, as appraised by the criterion of visual

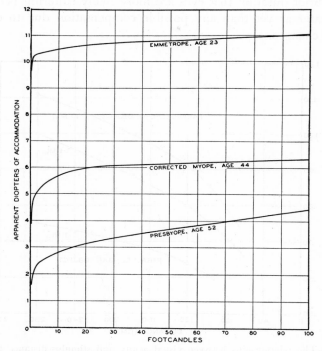

FIG. 31.—The relationship between level of illumination and apparent amplitude of accommodation for an emmetrope, a corrected myope and a presbyope. (After Ferree and Rand.)

acuity, gradually decreases as the accommodation in force is increased. This relationship is shown in Fig. 32. The experimental conditions under which these data were obtained were such that the data are interpretable from practical viewpoints since they apply to (1) everyday seeing conditions, (2) binocular vision and (3) to radically different test-objects. The fact that the eyes are more efficient for distant-vision than for near-vision might be considered as teleological evidence that human eyes were developed for distant-vision. Furthermore, it is conceivable that through evolutionary processes the eyes may gradually become more efficient for near-vision, as this form of seeing becomes more prevalent and predominant. However, it is likely that civilization has been of such a brief duration that eyes are more likely suffering penalties far greater as yet than any possible compensation due to evolutionary changes.

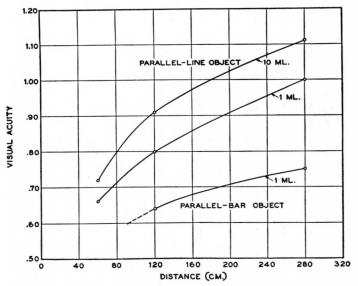

FIG. 32.—The relationships between visual acuity and stimulus-distance for two different test-objects.

Speed of accommodation. The speed with which the eyes may focus alternately for near- and distant-vision is of practical importance in many situations. For example, the driver of an automobile frequently glances back and forth from the road to the instrument panel and, obviously, the time required to focus his eyes for vision at these distances is very directly related to his safety. This is also true of many work-world operations. Actually this and other factors make themselves felt in the efficiency and production of the worker as well as in safety. Innumerable situations involve the alternate fixation of near and distant objects.

The data of Fig. 33 show the time required for accommodation by various groups of individuals as determined by two different investigators.[48] It will be noted from these data that the average time required for accommodation is approximately 1.5 seconds. Different individuals required from one second to nearly

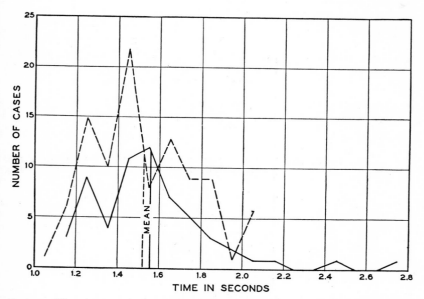

FIG. 33.—The time required to accommodate the eye from near to far vision as determined by two investigators.

three seconds to make the adjustment in accommodation. In general, the speed of accommodation is lowered by age, heterophoria, astigmia, ametropia, low visual acuity, and other visual anomalies. It also has been shown[49] that ocular fatigue induced by prolonged close work increases the time required to focus the eyes for clear vision. Since visual acuity is a function of such physical factors as the size and brightness of the object of regard, it is reasonable to assume that the speed of accommodation is also a function of these variables and may be controlled to some extent by various aids to seeing.

A paradox of accommodation. When an observer looks at a two-dimensional picture of a three-dimensional scene, such as a landscape, changes in accommodation not infrequently take place as different parts of the picture are viewed, notwithstanding the fact that all parts of the picture would be in focus for the same accommodation. This paradox of accommodation again emphasizes the complex psychophysiological nature of the visual processes

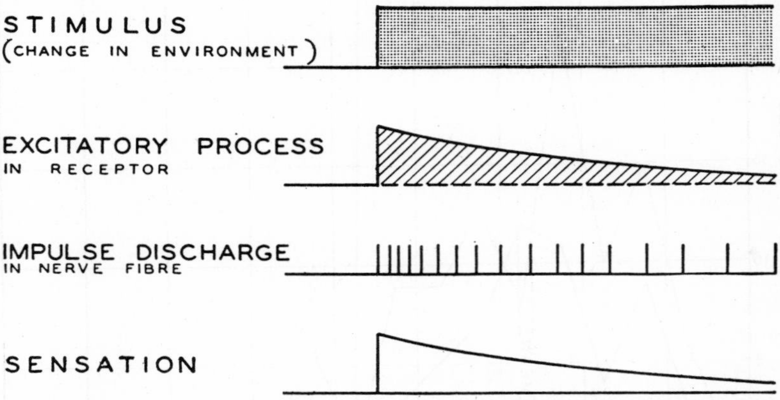

STIMULUS
(CHANGE IN ENVIRONMENT)

EXCITATORY PROCESS
IN RECEPTOR

IMPULSE DISCHARGE
IN NERVE FIBRE

SENSATION

FIG. 34.—The relation between stimulus, sensory message and sensation. (After Adrian.)

and particularly that seeing is a human activity involving many human factors which have been commonly ignored.

SENSATION

Troland [24] has so defined sensation as to involve the relationships between experience on one hand, and the visual stimulus, ocular and optic nerve processes on the other hand. The sequence of events between the stimulus and the mind has been diagramed by Adrian [50] as shown in Fig. 34. It will be noted that the change in the visual environment (the stimulus) produces an excitatory process in the retinal receptors which gradually declines. As it declines, the frequency of the neural currents is decreased accordingly and so is the intensity of the sensation. These neural impulses possess but one unique characteristic—that of frequency which is alone responsible for the character of the visual sensation. High frequency results in high intensity of sensation. The impulses travel at the rate of approximately 220 miles per hour in the human nerve.

It has also been shown that conduction in a nerve fiber obeys an "all-or-none" law. According to this principle, the intensity evoked by a stimulus in a nerve or muscle cell is always maximal or zero, dependent only on the condition of the cell at that moment and not upon the intensity of the stimulus. Thus a stimulus of the highest intensity can cause no greater response (in magnitude) than can one of threshold intensity. Apparently such subjective phenomena as brightness, hue and saturation of color depend upon or involve this common characteristic of nerve response. Furthermore, according to Müller's law of specific irritability, a sensory nerve can give rise to only one form of sensation. This cursory consideration of subjective visual phenomena is included in this discussion due to the fact that complete control over the stimulus which arouses sensation may be exercised. From the practical viewpoint of seeing, the law of Merkel pertaining to sensation is both concise and applicable to practice. According to this theoretical principle, equal differences between sensations correspond to equal differences between stimuli. Merkel's law and Weber's law, however, do not conflict. The former is based upon the maintenance of adaptation and the latter upon adaptation proportional to the stimuli.

Growth and decay of visual sensations. A sensation of brightness or color does not grow immediately to its full or final value the instant the image is incident upon the retina, and it does not immediately decrease to zero when the stimulus disappears. This characteristic is of primary importance in many familiar visual situations, as in viewing motion-pictures and in the measurement of brightness with the flicker photometer. The temporal characteristics of this visual phenomenon have been investigated by Broca and Sulzer [51] whose data are summarized in Fig. 35. In obtaining these data, the brightness of a white screen illuminated by light of short duration was compared with that due to a standard steady

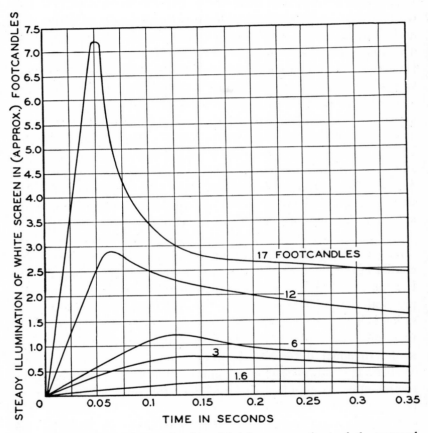

FIG. 35.—Illustrating the overshooting of brightness sensation and the temporal characteristics of retinal adaptation.

light. A conspicuous characteristic of these results is the "overshooting" of the final luminous sensation. It will also be noted that the growth and decay of visual sensation [52] is a function of the illumination. The overshooting of color sensations depends upon the color and brightness. [53]

[110]

Induction.   The indirect arousal of visual effects [54] as a result of mutual, spatial, and temporal induction, are of a too varied and complex nature to be abstracted here.   However, some of these phenomena are not only of academic interest but also of practical importance.   For example, a reflectance gauge has been devised by one of the authors in which the point of photometric balance, along a slot bordered by two strips similarly graduated in reflectance, between the gradient and the sample to be measured, is indicated by induction phenomena.   Thus the sample appears darker than it actually is at the lighter end of the gradient and lighter than it is at the darker end of the gradient.   As a result, the reflectance of the sample is determined by the rather sharply defined transition.   Differences in color between the gradient and the sample are also unimportant because one merely notes the point of transition of the induced brightness and darkness.   This device is illustrated, somewhat diagrammatically, in Fig. 97 in its simplest form, which is also used as the basis of a colorimeter.

Irradiation is an effect of an apparent increase in size of a visual stimulus of relatively high intensity and is believed to be due to the spreading of excitation to adjacent retinal elements. For example, a white object upon a black background or a glowing filament of an incandescent lamp appears to be larger than it actually is.   In practice, the fusion of adjacent bright areas of an electric sign may be either a desirable or an objectionable result of irradiation phenomena.

When a bright light-source is viewed it is usually seen as surrounded by a halo.   It is believed that these socalled physiological halos are a result of diffraction at the corneal endothelium and the lens epithelium.[45]   The angular diameter of the outer ring of the halo is commonly seven or eight degrees in size when produced by white light.   In a darkened room the source of light is seen surrounded by a dark ring, and beyond this a colored ring is observed in which the various spectral colors appear with the violet ring nearest the source of light.   Obviously, these halos are very effective in reducing the visibility of objects located at less than five degrees from a bright light-source.

[111]

Visual illusions. In addition to the complexities of sensation which have been indicated, there are superposed the complexities of sensory illusions. Important classifications of the latter are (1) geometric-optical illusions, (2) physical distortions, (3) physiological phenomena, (4) illusions of motion, and (5) illusions of distances. These subjective phenomena influence the behavior of the human mechanism in countless ways and cannot be regarded merely as phenomena of academic interest. They are always present in seeing and often contribute in a major role to a complete analysis of a seeing condition or result. The reader is referred elsewhere for detailed discussions of visual illusions.[55]

PERCEPTION

Visual projection. This phenomenon of vision may be defined as the total process by which activities within restricted portions of the nervous apparatus of the visual organs of the observer may, in conscious experience, be correspondingly localized in space. Thus projection is not a faculty of the retina but is a mental act. Although projection is a congenital faculty, it is perfected in childhood by the discovery of the real positions of objects by other senses. In brief, we see objects as they are and not as pictures upon the "retinal screen." This is one of the most refined perfections of a potential endowment of the human being's development into a human seeing-machine.

As the course of the sensory processes leads from sensation towards perception, which includes the cognition or apprehension occasioned by the presence of the sensation in the consciousness, it is to be followed by the psychologist [56] rather than the seeing specialist. Hence this discussion will be redirected toward the more obvious, known, and controllable phases of seeing.

COLOR VISION

Since frequency is the only inherent characteristic of nerve response, it follows that the various phenomena of color-vision should be expressible as functions of this variable. There are many visual phenomena which must be explainable by any acceptable theory of color vision.[53]   Among these for which quantitative data are available are spectral luminosity, complementary colors, hue discrimination, color-mixture and hue saturation.[57] Although the course of this discussion is continually intersected by interesting byways which must be ignored, it appears desirable to summarize two of the well-known theories of color vision from which many others have evolved.   A third one is included because it embodies something of both with admirable originality and ingenuity.

Young-Helmholtz theory.   This theory arose chiefly out of the knowledge that three primary colors—red, green and blue—when mixed in various proportions can match any and all colors. It approaches the matter chiefly from a physical viewpoint.   It involves the assumption of three independent mechanisms in the retina or its attached nervous systems.   These mechanisms when aroused are assumed to give rise to the sensations of red, green and blue, respectively.   All other sensations of color are supposed to be due to combinations of these three primary sensations.   It satisfactorily explains many phenomena of color, but does not fully satisfy some requirements.

Hering theory.   This theory approaches the matter chiefly from the psychological viewpoint.   It starts with the assumption that there are only six "pure" sensations—black and white, red and green, yellow and blue.   In gray one can "see" both black and white.   In orange one can see both red and yellow.   Likewise in all other colors than red, yellow, green and blue more than one of these is supposed to be seen.   Hering assumed that visual sensations are due to three pairs of antagonistic processes, one member of each pair being catabolic and the other anabolic. The pairs are assumed to yield, respectively, the sensations of white and black, red and green, yellow and blue, in different proportions so as to account for all chromatic and achromatic sensations.   This theory fits many facts, but the controversy which began among the Teutonic originators of these two theories still continues, although in a much milder manner.

Ladd-Franklin theory. This theory assumes that in the retinal nerve-endings the respective light-stimuli red-, green-, and blue-stimulating substances form a complex photosensitive molecule. Of these, red and green, when present, unite to form a yellow-stimulating substance, which may in turn unite with blue to form a white-stimulating substance.

It may be said that histological evidence is not available to support the various assumptions which are involved in these theories of color vision. Much attention has been given to the quantitative correlation [57] of the various characteristics of color vision, which have been determined experimentally with considerable exactness. However, regardless of theories the facts are important and unaltered.

Spectral luminosity. Although human eyes differ in their sensitivity to various spectral qualities of light, the data of Table VII may be regarded as typical of the approximate wavelengths, in Ångström units, corresponding to various spectral regions. The data [58] were compiled by the U. S. Bureau of Standards.

TABLE VII

The Wavelengths in Ångström Units Corresponding to Red, Orange, Yellow, Green, Blue, and Violet, and Their Intermediates

Violet	λ 4120
Blue-violet	4390
Blue	4730
Green-blue	4980
Green	5150
Yellow-green	5680
Yellow	5770
Orange-yellow	5920
Orange	6000
Red-orange	6310
Red	6730

These spectral components of white light cannot be distinguished by the eye in a manner analogous to the detection of the several tones of a chord by the human ear. The visual sense synthesizes the individual sensations and we see, for example, a yellow made by mixing red and green lights in which there may be no yellow light. There is no simple relation between the physical stimuli and the resulting sensation. Hence for general purposes, the data of Table VIII may be regarded as typical of the approximate wavelength limits of various spectral regions.

TABLE VIII

Approximate Wavelength Limits, in Ångström Units, of Various Spectral Regions

Violet	....	λ 3900–4300
Blue	....	4300–4900
Green	....	4900–5500
Yellow	....	5500–5900
Orange	....	5900–6200
Red	....	6200–7700

Complementary colors. These are defined as any pair of chromatic colors whose stimuli, when mixed additively, give rise to the sensation of gray or white. The data of Sinden,[59] Table IX, show these relationships as well as the relative luminosities required to produce the sensation of white. The sum of these values is equal to 75 photons.

TABLE IX

Relative Luminosities of Spectral Complementaries

Complementaries		Luminosities	
λ_1	λ_2	L_1	L_2
6500	4960	31.6	43.4
6090	4935	39.3	35.7
5910	4900	50.3	24.7
5860	4875	55.4	19.6
5800	4825	62.0	13.0
5785	4805	64.2	10.8
5765	4775	65.8	9.2
5755	4745	67.7	7.3
5740	4720	69.0	6.0
5730	4665	70.6	4.4
5720	4590	72.1	2.9
5705	4430	73.2	1.8

Hue discrimination. About 160 different hues can be distinguished by persons with normal color vision. This number may appear large in view of the fact that only a few different color-names are generally applied to the spectral colors. In fact, red, yellow, green and blue are the markedly different hues. To these are usually added violet and orange; but there is little excuse for not including blue-green if these two are added. Newton used indigo as his seventh color-name and did not include blue-green. Hue sensitivity varies in an irregular manner throughout the spectrum. There are prominent maxima at about λ 4900 and λ 5800 where the visual sense is able to distinguish hue differences corresponding to about 140 Ångström units. There is a prominent minimum of hue sensitivity at about λ 5350 where the minimum perceptible hue difference corresponds to about 290 Ångström units.

Saturation discrimination. The minimum perceptible difference in saturation of color varies considerably with the color. In general, it is of the order of one to two per cent. This is comparable with the minimum perceptible brightness-difference for daylight brightness-levels. The discrimination of differences in saturation is important only in relatively rare cases.

Color-blindness. This visual defect, which is usually congenital, is marked by a reduction in the number of hues which may be discriminated. In some cases (achromatism) all color vision is absent, whereas in others the visual sense is partially color-blind. In the latter type (dichromatism) the hues retained are usually blue and yellow and more rarely red and green. In general, it is commonly stated that about four or five per cent of the population is color-blind. However, this is very misleading. In everyday seeing a very much smaller percentage is actually handicapped. For example, it is not likely that more than five or possibly ten persons in a million cannot distinguish between red and green traffic signals. Even though these signals may not be recognized as "red" or "green," they may appear enough different in color and brightness to be distinguished from each other. Among the various tests for color-blindness, that devised by Ishihara is probably the most critical and reliable for practical purposes.

Statistics indicate that color-blindness is about ten times as prevalent in men as in women. In view of this fact, Horner's law of the inheritance of color-blindness is of interest. This law states that the common type of color-blindness is transmitted from males to males through females who have normal vision unless they have inherited the characteristic of color-blindness from both parents.

Visual Thresholds

A direct comparison of the areal, photometrical and temporal characteristics of many usual visual tasks with the corresponding characteristics of threshold stimuli, reveals a surprisingly large number of situations in which the visual demands of the task are only slightly exceeded by the ability of the eyes to meet them. For example, in reading the fine print of telephone directories, the critical details of the letters and numerals are only slightly larger than those which may be resolved under otherwise favorable conditions for seeing. Also, on the highways at night the degrees of contrasts between obstacles and the road surface are often of a near-threshold order. Thus if the limitations of the visual functions are known, these data are useful in appraising the relative difficulty of visual tasks.[9] However, a far more important use of threshold data is in the determination of the effectiveness of various aids to seeing in raising the visibility of the object of regard above the level of barely seeing. In physiological optics the characteristics of threshold stimuli are important in understanding visual phenomena, while in the science of seeing these functions serve as criteria for the development of superior conditions for seeing. They serve as a foundation upon which to erect factors of safety in seeing, just as the conditions of failure of a steel beam are the basis for establishing factors of safety in strength.

SIGNIFICANCE OF THRESHOLD FUNCTIONS IN SEEING

When an object is seen with certainty a further augmentation of factors favorable for seeing obviously increases the degree of visibility, although the magnitude of the latter is not directly measurable. But the introspective method of appraising seeing is far from reliable even from a qualitative viewpoint. For example, a number of subjects were asked to report upon the certainty with which they "saw" an object of near-threshold visibility.[60] The results of this introspective experiment are given in Table X. In general, when the subjects were "certain" that their responses were correct, they were in error in about 30 per cent of the cases; and when they were "almost certain," the error was about 40 per cent. These data were obtained with untrained subjects. When the same test was given to trained introspectionists, the results were as unreliable as those shown in the table. These data again emphasize the well-established fact that the individual is a rather poor estimator of his ability to see. In other words, unaided human beings are poor seeing-meters. Hence, behavioristic methods of appraisal should be used in preference to introspective methods wherever possible.

TABLE X

Question	Response	Cases	Per Cent Error in Response
Letter read correctly?	Certain	66	27
	Almost certain	438	43
Letter read incorrectly?	Certain	21	33
	Almost certain	251	41

It is axiomatic that a higher degree of visibility makes the task easier and, as a result, fatigue is decreased and human resources are conserved. The latter effects are measurable although the techniques involved are often complex and tedious. Thus, if correlations [8] can be established between threshold measurements of visual function and psychophysiological effects of seeing under supra-threshold conditions, the value of threshold measurements is enormously enhanced from the practical viewpoint since these are quite readily obtained. An example of one of the many correlations which have been established by extensive researches is presented herewith.

The data of Fig 36 are typical of researches involving the relationships between level of illumination and (1) the physical

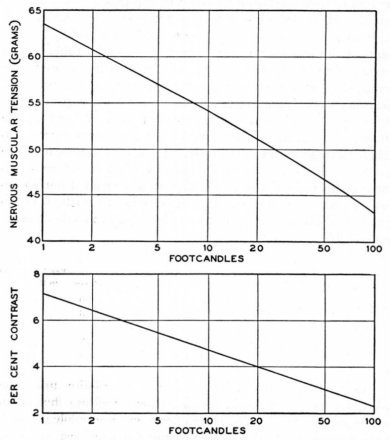

Fig. 36.—The upper plot shows the relationship between level of illumination and indicated nervous muscular tension induced by reading. The lower plot shows the relationship between level of illumination and the minimum contrast required for threshold visibility of an object equivalent in size to the book-type used in the tenseness investigation. Both relationships are generally logarithmic in character.

characteristics of the threshold stimulus (as indicated by the factor of contrast), and (2) the expenditure of human energy (as indicated by nervous muscular tension) in the performance of a task

[120]

under supra-threshold conditions. It will be noted that *both* of these relationships may be represented approximately by straight lines when the illumination values are plotted on a logarithmic scale. Thus quantity of light, as an aid to seeing, influences these diverse visual phenomena in a similar manner; and it follows that the relative effectiveness of any aid to seeing may be determined, at least as a first approximation, for supra-threshold conditions through threshold measurements of visual function. Other correlations leading to the same conclusion are presented elsewhere and particularly in Chapter VI.

The foregoing analysis is not to be construed as implying that objects of equal threshold visibility are necessarily of equal visibility for supra-threshold conditions obtained, for example, by increasing the illumination on each by the same factor. Such an interpretation would involve the assumption of a technique for measuring supra-threshold visibility. However, the *margins of safety*, in terms of the controlled variable, are identical for the supra-threshold conditions. Thus a basis is provided for establishing factors of safety in seeing as in other activities.

CHARACTERISTICS OF VISUAL THRESHOLDS

If the size of a distant and invisible object is gradually increased, it follows that the object will be seen eventually if other conditions are favorable for seeing. However, if the experiment is repeated immediately and under identical physical conditions, it is not likely that the same threshold of size will be indicated. Furthermore, if the object of regard is gradually decreased in size until it becomes invisible, a still different threshold size is usually obtained. Thus it is evident that the characteristics of the threshold stimulus must be determined by statistical methods, and that these data will correspond to the transition from invisibility to visibility, or *vice versa*, in a series of sensations or judgments. Although the magnitude of a particular threshold datum may be obtained with some exactness from the statistical viewpoint, the individual measurements are often quite variable among themselves. However, it is reasonable to assume that the individual observations may represent rather accurate appraisals of visual function under the biological conditions which prevail at the moment of measurement. Physiological fluctuations in the visual mechanism and psychological fluctuations in attention [61] alter the efficiency of the sensory mechanism and introduce uncertainty in the quantitative determination of visual thresholds.

It will be obvious from a consideration of Fig 9 that the "absolute" values of various visual thresholds are functions of almost innumerable modifying factors. Hence it may be assumed that such data as may be obtained in the laboratory possess but little significance in the specific visual situation in everyday life. However, it will be shown that these data may be applied in a relative sense to a wide variety of visual conditions, objects and visual tasks. They supply the absolute foundation upon which to erect our analyses and specifications of seeing.

PARAMETERS OF THE VISUAL THRESHOLD

Since vision as required in ordinary work is but the seeing of many details simultaneously and successively, a study of vision in which it is required to discriminate a single detail will yield results which can, without unwarranted assumption, be extended to visual tasks of greater complexity. If a simple detail is to be seen, it will appear that several important factors, by which the recognition of the object is possible, must be above certain limiting values.

To make this more clear, let us suppose a visual object consisting of a letter which is (1) of large size, (2) printed on a white card in very black ink and (3) seen under an illumination of 100 footcandles with (4) leisurely observation on the part of the observer. There are at least four ways in which this object may be made invisible to that observer, provided we have suitable control to bring about the required changes in the object.

(1) The letter might be shrunk uniformly in all its dimensions.

(2) The ink might be gradually bleached to a white like the card on which it is printed; or the white card might be gradually dyed to a black like the ink.

(3) The illumination might be reduced with the result that the brightness of card and ink would be similarly reduced sufficiently.

(4) Instead of permitting leisurely observation, the time for observation might be shortened sufficiently.

In all four of these cases, we start with the identical object, seen under identical conditions, but at the conclusion of each of the four experiments the observer is looking at one of four very different things. But these four have one thing in common. They are all on the border between visibility and invisibility. Nevertheless, each differs from the others in one fundamental factor such as size, contrast with background, brightness or duration. Thus the four fundamental variables in a visual object are:

(1) The size of its critical detail, conveniently expressed as "minutes visual angle" subtended at the eye by the detail.

(2) The contrast between the object and its background, which may be defined as the ratio of the brightness-difference to the brightness of the background, and for simplicity designated as "per cent contrast."

(3) The brightness-level to which the object is illuminated.

(4) The time during which the image of the object is allowed to rest upon the retina of the eye.

If an object is visible, it is by reason of the fact that each of these variables of the stimulus is either equal to or greater than a certain liminal or threshold value. The magnitudes of these liminal values depend upon (1) the biological characteristics of the observer, (2) the characteristics of the external physical environment, and (3) upon the character of visual recognition demanded. The latter may involve, in order of increasing visual difficulty, the mere recognition of the presence or absence of an object, the recognition of form, and the resolution of space-intervals in the discrimination of form. The complexity of color, as a variable of the visual threshold, is not discussed here for reasons which have already been presented. Some of the major variables are presented diagrammatically in Fig. 9.

The complementary relationships which exist between the fundamental variables of the visual stimulus are demonstrated, in a qualitative manner, in the performance of our usual visual tasks. For example, in examining the pattern of a suit of clothes, it is customary to stand close to a window, thus compensating to some extent for low contrasts by an augmentation of the light. However, the quantitative determination of these relationships is a more difficult problem, if distortions due to factors unique to the method of observation are to be avoided. For example, it will be shown that the relative importance of such factors as size and contrast varies with the characteristics of the test-object used for investigating these factors. This fact has led to serious errors in appraising the relative effectiveness of various aids to seeing.

Data on each of these fundamental variables are available [62] from numerous isolated investigations. If, however, an attempt is made to formulate these scattered data in a complete statement of their influence on vision, great difficulty is encountered, since the data are derived from an assortment of non-comparable visual tasks and experimental methods, and very often cover altogether too restricted ranges of the variables involved.

INTERRELATIONSHIPS BETWEEN FUNDAMENTAL VARIABLES

We have studied these fundamental variables of the visual threshold over wide ranges and by a uniform experimental technique throughout extensive and carefully controlled investigations.[63] The results, therefore, represent relationships between the variables which can, for purposes of comparison, be regarded as rigid. In general, an achromatic test-object of simple geometric design was so arranged that it could be presented to the subjects in (1) all grades of contrast from the deepest black on white to the point of zero difference, (2) in various sizes from the smallest visible to the largest which could be encompassed by foveal vision,

(3) under various illuminations producing brightnesses from 1 to 100 millilamberts, and (4) from various exposure-times from the shortest to the longest times during which the eyes pause under ordinary conditions. The test-object, Fig. 49, consisted of two parallel black bars upon a white background (or *vice versa*) made by eliminating the middle third of a square. Thus it involved discrimination of the two bars. Size is expressed in visual angle of

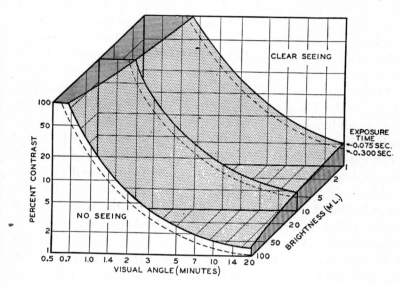

Fig. 37.—The curved surface, indicated by the dotted area, represents the relationship between combinations of size, contrast and brightness for threshold visibility for a constant time of exposure. The effect of various exposure-times may be illustrated by raising or lowering this curved surface.

the space between the two bars. A detailed description of the experimental technique is available elsewhere.

If the data thus obtained are plotted upon three-dimensional coordinates, the locus of all points will describe a curved surface, as in Fig. 37, representing the threshold of vision with respect to three of the four fundamental variables under the ideal laboratory conditions. Similar curved surfaces may be generated for other values of the fourth variable. These plots may be considered as topographical maps of human vision. If the physical characteristics of the object are represented by a point below the curved surface, the object will be invisible. Similarly, a point on the surface represents threshold visibility and a point above the surface assures visibility of the object to observers possessing average normal vision.

The dotted curved surface of Fig. 37 may be considered to represent an infinite number of combinations of the variables of size, contrast and brightness which produce threshold visibility for a constant exposure-time of 0.075 second. Similarly, the curved surface defined by and including the broken-line curves relating size and contrast at different brightness-levels would represent the borderline between visibility and invisibility for an exposure-time of 0.3 second. These temporal values represent approximately the shortest and longest fixation-pauses, respectively, which are usually involved in critical seeing.[38] By thinking of this curved surface as varying between these two levels, we have a representation of the complete relationship between the four fundamental variables in vision—size, contrast, brightness and exposure-time for the ranges indicated. Furthermore, this survey of the boundaries of normal vision involved over two hundred thousand separate measurements. As a result, the probable errors of these data are of the order of one-half of one per cent. It is emphasized that these threshold data were obtained under the ideal conditions of the laboratory. In everyday seeing in which many factors are not controlled, subdued or eliminated, the threshold values are generally increased and ofttimes very greatly.

Thresholds by resolution criteria. The relationship between the background brightness and the size of the threshold object is shown in Fig. 38 for various degrees of contrast between the object and its background. In this case, the actual test-object consisted of two parallel black (or gray) bars on an extended white background and separated by a distance equal to the width of the bars, as illustrated in Fig. 49. Recognition of the object required resolution of the two bars; therefore, the width of the bars or the distance between them is the nominal dimension of the object and is the areal characteristic of the object. The length of the bars is three times the width of each and the entire pattern may be described as a black (or gray) square from which a strip constituting its middle third has been removed. Thus the recognition of this object involves the resolution of a space-interval and hence the data are applicable to a wide variety of visual tasks which

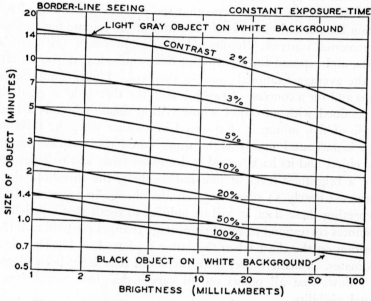

Fig. 38.—The relationship between size and brightness for threshold visibility of our standard parallel-bar test-object of various contrasts. The exposure-time was 0.17 second.

involve critical seeing. Furthermore, the presentation of this test-object was immediately preceded and followed by other patterns in such a manner that the threshold measurements required the recognition of *one* of a series of successive patterns. Obviously, the latter requirement is a characteristic of seeing since the eyes are continually in motion and various images are rushing across the retina at a corresponding rate. Thus these data may be described as "dynamic thresholds of resolution." In general, the

[127]

magnitudes of such threshold data are significantly different from those which would be obtained in the absence of pre- and post-exposure patterns.[64]

It will be noted from Fig. 38 that the threshold size varies approximately as the logarithm of the brightness over a range in brightness from 1 to 100 millilamberts, although a departure from this relationship is indicated for the lower values of brightness-contrast. These data indicate that the dynamic threshold of resolution for normal vision is of the order of 0.6 minute for an object of maximal contrast, illuminated to a brightness of 100 millilamberts, and exposed for a period of time equivalent to the duration of the average fixational-pause of the eyes. Under similar conditions and for a contrast of two per cent, the threshold of resolution is obtained with an object whose critical detail subtends a visual angle of five minutes. Expressed in another way, the threshold size is increased nearly eight times when the contrast between the object and its background is decreased from 100 to 2 per cent. For a brightness-level of one millilambert, the threshold size is increased nearly 14 times for a similar change in contrast. In interpreting these data, it will be helpful to recall that equal linear distances correspond to equal percentage changes regardless of their position on the chart when the latter is plotted on logarithmic coordinates. Furthermore, since threshold data have been plotted, it follows that all points on all curves designate test-objects of equal visibility.

These data are also plotted in different ways in Figs. 39 and 40 in order to facilitate their interpretation. For example, it will be noted from Fig. 39 that the relationship between brightness and contrast, for a given size, is likewise logarithmic in character, excepting for extremely large objects. It will also be noted, for example, that the minimum perceptible brightness-difference is approximately 1.1 per cent for an object subtending an angle of 16 minutes and for a brightness-level of 100 millilamberts and an exposure-time of 0.17 second.

The numerical values of the threshold of size and contrast may be determined with exactness, for specific experimental condi-

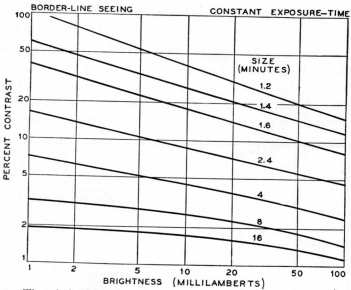

FIG. 39.—The relationship between contrast and brightness for threshold visibility.

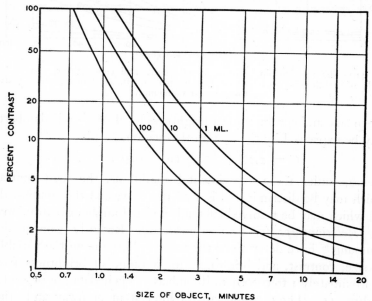

FIG. 40.—The relationship between contrast and size for threshold visibility.

tions, from the relationship between these two variables. This relationship may be expressed mathematically by the equation,

$$C = a + b\,(S - d)^{-m}$$

in which C is the contrast in per cent; S, the size of the critical detail of the object in minutes; a and d, the asymptotic values of contrast and size, respectively; and b and m, constants which depend upon the experimental procedure. Thus the relationship be-

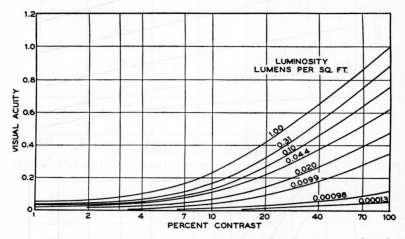

FIG. 41.—The relationship between visual acuity and contrast for various low levels of brightness expressed in lumens per sq. ft. or footlamberts. (After Conner and Ganoung.)

tween size and contrast, for a brightness-level of 20 millilamberts, may be expressed by the empirical equation,

$$C = 1.28 + 13.97\,(S - 0.56)^{-1.4}.$$

Hence, under these experimental conditions, the least contrast which may be discriminated is 1.28 per cent; and the smallest detail which may be resolved subtends a visual angle of 0.56 minute.

Relationships for low brightnesses. Recently Conner and Ganoung [65] have determined the relationships among the variables of size, contrast, and brightness for a range of brightness from approximately 1 to 0.0001 millilambert. Their data are presented in Fig. 41. These results are of interest in highway and other

[130]

forms of outdoor lighting. However, the data would be more applicable to these problems if the criterion of "recognition of presence" rather than the "resolution of space-interval" had been emphasized.

Certainty of seeing. Since the sensitivity of the visual sense varies from moment to moment, it is obvious that a liminal stimulus at one time may represent either a subliminal or a supra-liminal one at another time. If, for example, in a series of ten consecutive observations, the presence of the stimulus is reported correctly in but five instances, it follows that the certainty of vision is zero. In other words, a similar "score" would be obtained by chance since there are but two possible reports to be made by the subject. However, it is possible to increase the effectiveness of the stimulus (or visibility of the object) to such a degree that seeing is practically certain in all trials. The results of an extensive investigation indicated that the illumination must be increased ten-fold in order to raise the certainty of seeing from zero to approximately 100 per cent. The same result may also be accomplished by doubling the time of exposure, as will be noted from the data of Figs. 10 and 52.

INTERPRETATION OF THRESHOLD DATA

Size versus contrast. It is obvious that the refractive condition of the eye is a factor of much greater importance in the recognition of a very small object than it is for a relatively large object. The identical amount of blurring of the retinal image will be a major factor in the one case, and an insignificant one in the other. On the other hand, with large objects of low contrast, the interaction of the retinal receptors (Ricco's law of foveal vision) becomes an important factor. Thus it appears that for small objects, the limit of resolving power depends largely upon the actual physical intermixture of the rays of light corresponding to the images of the separate elements of the object. For the larger objects and lower contrasts, this intermixture is insignificant and the limit of contrast discrimination depends in main upon the behavior of the end-organs of the retina and of their neural connections.

The gradual transition from size to contrast, as the major variable of the visual threshold, is revealed by plotting the relationship between these variables on linear coordinates, as in Fig. 42.

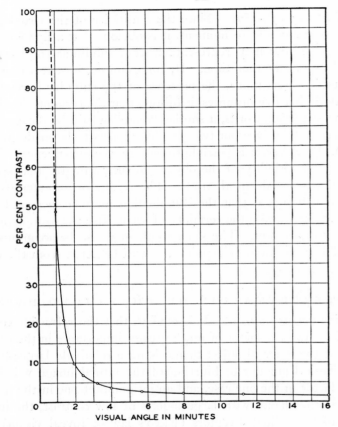

FIG. 42.—The relationship between contrast and size for threshold visibility of our standard parallel-bar test-object under a brightness-level of 20 millilamberts. This plot clearly reveals the transition from size to contrast, as the primarily important characteristic of the visual threshold, as the size is increased with concomitant decreases in contrast required to produce threshold conditions.

It will be noted from this curve that the transition-point occurs when the critical detail of the threshold object subtends an angle slightly less than two minutes. The data of Fig. 46 indicate that the transition-points correspond to sizes of objects from about 1.5 to 2.5 minutes for brightness-levels from 1 to 100 millilamberts, respectively.   Usually, human eyes are not required to resolve ob-

THE VISIBILITY SCALE (RELATIVE)		INFLUENCE OF FOOTCANDLES AND CONTRAST UPON VISIBILITY EXPRESSED AS A PERCENTAGE OF NORMAL VISION						
VISUAL OBJECTS	PER CENT NORMAL VISION	FOOTCANDLES	PER CENT CONTRAST					
			100 ★	50	20	10	5	2
E	10	1	77	57	36	25	16	5.5
		1.5	81	60	39	27	17	5.8
F P	20	2	84	62	41	29	18	6.0
T O Z	30	3	88	66	44	31	20	6.3
L P E D	40	5	93	71	47	33	21	6.8
		7.5	97	75	51	36	23	7.3
P E C F D	50	10	100	78	54	38	24	7.8
E D F C Z P	60	15	107	82	57	41	26	8.4
F E L O P Z D	80	20	109	86	60	43	28	9.0
D E F P O T E C	100	30	116	91	65	46	30	10.
L E F O D P C T	120	50	123	97	70	51	32	11.
F D P L T C E O	150	75	130	103	75	54	35	14.
		100	135	108	79	57	38	17.

FIG. 43.—Human vision is rated by eye specialists as a percentage of "normal" vision. The influence of footcandles and contrast upon the visibility of objects is interpreted in a similar manner in the right-hand portion of the table. The standard condition for comparison purposes is as follows: vision is normal or 100 per cent; the object is perfect black on perfect white or 100 per cent contrast; and the object and its background are illuminated to a level of 10 footcandles. It is seen that both contrast and footcandles exert a powerful influence upon visibility, the results being the same as though the eyes were good or bad instead of normal. Any other seeing factors might be similarly considered.

jects of the order of one or two minutes visual angle, as will be obvious from the visual size of the common objects which are given in Table XIV.   These considerations are of basic importance in determining the significance of various criteria for appraising conditions for seeing in practice. In many cases, the criterion of minimum perceptible brightness-difference is far more applicable than that of visual acuity for the appraisal of conditions for seeing.

In terms of normal vision. It is of interest to determine the influence of changes in level of illumination and in brightness-contrast upon the visibility of objects as a percentage of normal vision. In ophthalmology, it is assumed that the normal eye is capable of discerning a black letter, upon a white background, whose critical detail subtends an angle of one minute at the eye. When such an object is barely recognizable, the vision of the observer is expressed as 100 per cent. Thus, if the size of the critical detail must be increased to two minutes visual angle before it is recognizable, the vision of the observer is rated as 50 per cent normal. However, this designation of vision is not to be confused with that of *visual efficiency.* The latter is discussed in Chapter V. The letters of a common form of the Snellen Chart, and their corresponding ratings in terms of normal vision, are reproduced (not to scale) in the left-hand part of Fig. 43. The data given in the right-hand portion are interpretations of the effect of changes in illumination (footcandles) and contrast expressed as a percentage of normal vision. The assumption is made that the recognition of an object of 100 per cent contrast (black on white), one minute in visual size, illuminated to an intensity of ten footcandles and exposed to view for 0.17 second (average fixational pause) also represents normal or 100 per cent vision. Thus, the two assumptions of normal vision differ essentially only in the form of test-object used and, secondarily, in the fact that both intensity of illumination and time of exposure are limited in the latter case.

It will be noted that the variation in threshold visibility of objects of 100 per cent contrast, produced by a change in level of illumination from 1 to 100 footcandles, is equivalent to a change in vision from 77 to 135 per cent of normal vision. These values may be visualized by translation to the reproduction of the test-chart in Fig. 43. If the contrast between the object and its background is reduced to 50 per cent, it will be noted that the equivalent of normal vision (as determined by the Snellen Chart) is not obtained until the illumination exceeds 50 footcandles. If the contrast is lowered to 20 per cent, the equivalent of only 79

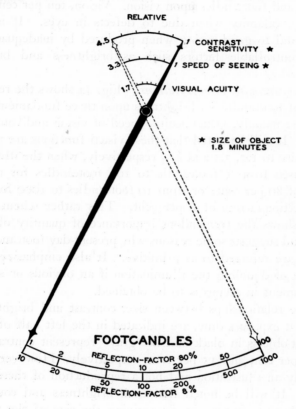

FIG. 44.—A schematic presentation of the relative influence of level of illumination upon three fundamental visual functions.

per cent normal vision is obtained at 100 footcandles. Although the factors of illumination and contrast are mutually complementary, it is obvious that the influence of higher levels of illumination is inadequate to entirely offset the disadvantage of low contrasts. However, the visibility of low-contrast objects may be increased *severalfold* by the use of higher levels of illumination which are within the range of economic and technical attainment. A careful study of Fig. 43 will reveal some startling influences of contrast and footcandles upon vision. Vision, ten per cent of normal, is a calamity when due to defects in eyes. It is just as detrimental to good seeing when produced by inadequacy of external controllable factors such as brightness and brightness-contrast.

Diagrammatic interpretations. Fig. 44 shows the relative influence of footcandles or brightness upon three fundamental visual functions: namely, visual acuity, speed of vision and contrast sensitivity. It will be noted that these visual functions are improved from unity to 1.7, 3.3 and 4.5, respectively, when the illumination is increased from 1 footcandle to 100 footcandles for reflection-factors of 80 per cent; or from 10 footcandles to 1000 footcandles for reflection-factors of 8 per cent. This rather schematic chart clearly shows the tremendous importance of quantity of light in seeing and suggests some reasons why present-day footcandle-levels indoors are referred to as primitive. It also emphasizes the importance of doubling the illumination if an obvious or significant improvement in seeing is to be obtained.

The relationships between size, contrast and brightness, for a constant exposure-time, are indicated in the left half of Fig. 45. The test-objects in black and in "gray" represent contrast values of 100 per cent and 15 per cent, respectively. However, Fig. 45 is merely an illustration and not a reproduction of these contrast values. It will be noted that both brightness and contrast are very effective factors in determining the size of the threshold stimulus. At the right are shown the relationships between size, contrast and exposure-time for a constant level of brightness. It is obvious that exposure-time, in comparison with brightness and contrast, is a factor of relatively small importance in determining the threshold size of the stimulus. In this case, it is significant that the range in exposure-time, as given in Fig. 45, corresponds to that of the fixational-pauses in seeing.

ENERGY THRESHOLDS

As the white field comprising the background of the test-object used for determining the data of Fig. 37 may be considered to be indefinite in extent, it is convenient to express the energy of the stimulus in terms of the energy per unit area subtracted from the visual field by the darker elements of the object. The energy in this case may be termed subtractive (or negative) for it represents the quantity subtracted when a unit area of the test-object elements replaces an equal area of the white field. Hence

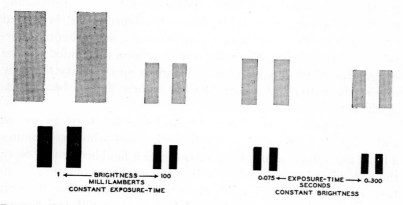

FIG. 45.—Demonstrating the relationships between size, brightness and time of exposure for threshold visibility of this test-object of two brightness-contrasts, 18 and 100 per cent, respectively. The two objects in each vertical column are of equal threshold visibility for the conditions indicated in each case.

we have assumed, as a unit of energy, an amount equivalent to the energy subtracted from a visual field, having a brightness of one millilambert, by a square of perfect black subtending an angle of one minute at the eye of the observer when viewed through a pupil of one square millimeter in area for 0.17 second.[66] Therefore, the relative subtractive or negative energy may be computed from the formula, $E = S^2 CBP$, where S is the width of the bars of the test-object in minutes visual angle; C, the brightness-contrast expressed as a fraction; B, the brightness of the visual field in millilamberts; and P, the area of the pupil in square millimeters.

[137]

Obviously, this method of computing the energy of the visual stimulus is an empirical one.

The relationships between visual size and subtractive energy of the threshold stimulus for various brightnesses of the visual field are shown in Fig. 46. In general, it will be noted that the subtractive energy for threshold vision increases with the brightness of the visual field, as might be supposed from a consideration of retinal adaptation phenomena. It will also be noted that the energy of the threshold stimulus is a minimum for an object of a particular size. The increase in subtractive energy required for threshold visibility of objects smaller than those corresponding to minimal energy is probably due to the blurring of the retinal image as a result of diffraction and chromatic and spherical aberration. In addition, the relatively few cones included in the image of a small object and their irregular spacing may seriously distort the pattern of the test-object. These factors become insignificant for much larger objects.

Energy and perception. The relationship between extent and brightness-contrast for any liminal visual stimulus indicates a finite asymptotic value of contrasts for each field-brightness. Since the test-object becomes indefinitely large as the asymptote of contrast is approached (Fig. 42) the threshold value of contrast is essentially a datum expressing minimum perceptible brightness-difference. The differences between the asymptotic values of contrast, which were observed at various field brightnesses, are in accord with the results of other researches which reveal discrepancies in Weber's law.

These data indicate that a definite brightness-contrast must exist between the background and the test-object, regardless of the area of the latter, in order to give rise to a sensation of brightness-difference. Therefore, the asymptotic value of contrast may be considered to represent a functional threshold of brightness-difference which is imposed by an "all-or-none" characteristic of visual response. The broken-line curve of Fig. 47 indicates the subtractive energy required to attain the threshold of perceptible brightness-difference for objects of various areas appearing upon

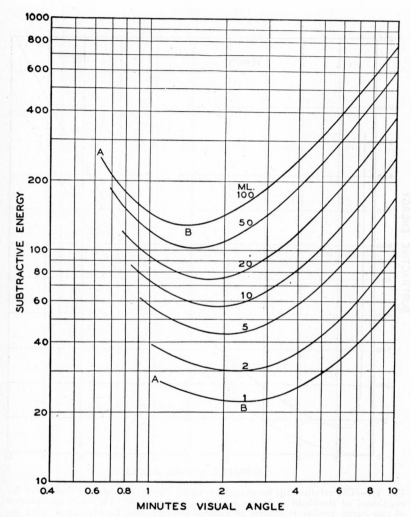

FIG. 46.—The relation between subtractive energy and size of test-object for various brightnesses of the background. All points on all curves represent conditions of threshold visibility. The left extremities, *A,* of the curves represent black test-objects on white backgrounds. For threshold visibility the contrasts of the objects with their backgrounds decrease as size increases. The lowest points *B* on the curves represent the points of transition from size to contrast as the primarily important variable of the visual threshold.

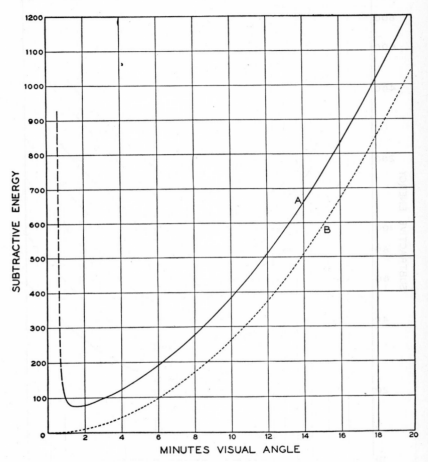

FIG. 47.—The relationship between subtractive energy and size of test-object for conditions of threshold visibility is shown by curve *A*. The solid-line portion of this curve applies to objects of various contrasts less than 100 per cent; the broken-line portion of the same curve applies to objects of contrasts greater than 100 per cent, as determined by extrapolation. Curve *B* indicates the subtractive energy required for the perception of minimum brightness-difference. Both curves apply to a brightness-level of 20 millilamberts and an exposure-time of 0.17 second.

a background illuminated to a brightness of 20 millilamberts. The values of subtractive energy for curve B are computed from the formula, $E = S^2 CBP$, where C is the threshold of contrast and has a fractional value of 0.0128. For brightness-levels of 1 and 100 millilamberts, the threshold values of contrast are 0.0137 and 0.0086, respectively. These values apply only to the test-object used.

The solid-line curve, A, of Fig. 47 represents the total sub-tractive energy required for a resolution of the elements of the test-object pattern. A part of this energy, curve B, is required to bring the image of the object to the threshold of brightness-contrast discrimination, and the remainder provides additional energy evidently necessary for the resolution of the elements of the test-object. The difference in energy between these thresholds is obviously a function of such factors as the complexity of the pattern and the definition of threshold vision as used in this work. It is conceivable that a more intimate insight into the nature of the integrational process might be obtained from similar analyses involving a series of test-objects of greater geometrical complexity.

Cortical integration. Although the difference in subtractive energy indicated by curves A and B of Fig. 47 is not the same for all sizes of test-object, it is nearly so in view of the wide range in number of retinal elements involved in the images of the different objects. Actually, the energy-difference increases less than threefold for a tenfold increase in the width of the elements of the test-object, or for a hundredfold increase in area. Such a variation in subtractive energy indicates (1) that the integrational process for objects of a simple pattern is a highly efficient one and (2) that the efficiency of the process decreases somewhat with increases in the size of the retinal image of the test-object. The influence of brightness-level upon the efficiency of the integrational process is indicated by the data of Table XI for representative cases arbitrarily selected. The reason for selecting the point of minimum energy is obvious in Fig. 47. It will be noted that the ratio of the subtractive energy difference for the smaller test-object to that for the larger test-object increases as the field-brightness increases. In general, it may be assumed that the integrational process, as the area of the retinal image is increased, is less efficient at the higher brightness-levels.

TABLE XI

The Difference in Subtractive Energy Required to Recognize the Photometric and Geometric Characteristics of the Parallel-Bar Object for Brightness-Levels of 1, 20, and 100 Millilamberts, Respectively.

Size of Object	Subtractive Energy Difference		
	1 ml.	20 ml.	100 ml.
For minimum energy	20	68	117
20 minutes	31	179	553

VARIOUS PERCEPTUAL THRESHOLDS

Three stages of visual perception. The several successive visual thresholds which follow progressive changes in the intensity of the stimulus may be defined with sufficient clearness to permit quantitative determinations of their respective values. For example, Helson and Fehrer [67] have determined the liminal brightnesses required for (1) the recognition of presence, (2) bare perception of form and (3) certain perception of form of luminous test-objects of various shapes and equal areas. These measurements involved foveal fixation and conditions of dark-adaptation. Since the liminal brightnesses are functions of the area of the objects, as well as of other factors, their absolute values possess little significance. For this reason, the data of Table XII are expressed in relative terms.

TABLE XII

Relative Liminal Brightnesses Required for Three Types of Visual Perception. As a Basis for These Comparisons, the Liminal Brightness Required to Recognize the Presence of the Circle Is Arbitrarily Assigned a Value of Unity.

Threshold	Circle	Triangle	Square	Rectangle	Semicircle	Angle
Recognition of presence	1.00	1.02	0.96	1.00	0.85	1.02
Bare perception of form	13.6	14.1	14.1	10.1	20.8	23.2
Certain perception of form	30.0	28.8	24.8	12.6	37.7	47.2

It will be noted that the relative liminal brightnesses for the recognition of the presence of the various objects are substantially identical. In other words, all forms appear alike—and more or less "formless"—under conditions corresponding to the most elementary of the several types of visual perception. Obviously, the conclusions which may be drawn from these data are directly applicable to many visual situations encountered in practice. For example, seeing on the highway at night involves many situations in which the driver is concerned only with the presence or absence of obstacles upon the road.

The relative brightnesses required for the three stages of visual perception are approximately 1, 16 and 30, respectively, if the values for all forms are averaged. Expressed in another way, the sensitivity of the subjects in this investigation is approximately 30 times as great to just noticeable light as to certain form. Thus upon the highway, for example, approximately 30 times as much light would be required to raise the visibility of an obstacle from that of mere recognition of presence to certain recognition of form. However, this datum is considered as an indication of order of magnitude rather than an accurate empirically determined constant.

As the requirements for seeing progressively become more critical, the diversity among the liminal brightnesses for the various objects also increases. Helson and Fehrer summarize their results as follows:

1. The rectangle requires the least amount of light for perception.
2. The triangle is the form reported the largest number of times on the barely perceived level.
3. The rectangle is the form confused the least number of times with other forms.
4. The circle is the form appearing neither superior nor inferior according to any criteria.
5. The rectangle seems superior to other forms on the basis of all criteria.

Recognition of presence versus resolution of detail. The relationship between the thresholds of (1) recognition of the presence of an object and (2) the recognition of an object by the resolution of distinguishing details of form is shown in Fig. 48. Actually, the determination of the relationship between these two criteria of threshold vision involved the recognition of a dot and the resolution of the bars of our standard test-object. These specific forms were selected as test-objects since (1) the dot is a simple object possessing but one critical dimension; and (2) the parallel-bar test-object is one of the simplest objects involving the resolution of details. Obviously, the relationship shown in Fig. 48 is quantitatively significant in specific situations only to the extent to which the empirical characteristics of the data are representative of the specific cases. However, these data pertain to objects of elementary geometrical design and hence it seems reasonable to consider them as typical.

It will be noted that the detection of the presence of the dot and the resolution of the parallel bars are accomplished when the critical dimension of each object subtends an angle of one minute at the eye, as shown in Fig. 49. In this case, the contrast of both objects is maximal; that is, the objects are black and are seen against a white background. As the areas of the test-objects are increased, their brightnesses and contrasts must be decreased simultaneously in order to maintain threshold conditions. These photometrical changes were accomplished by viewing black objects of various sizes through the Luckiesh-Moss Visibility Meter, which is described in Chapter V. When the size of the critical details of the parallel-bar object is increased to 20 minutes, it will be noted from Fig. 48 that the diameter of the dot must be increased to 55 minutes in order to be of the same threshold visibility. Thus, the ratio between the diameter of the dot and the width of the parallel bars increases from one to about three, as the size of the objects is increased (with concomitant decreases in brightness and contrast) from the smallest discernible to the largest encompassable by the fovea. The test-objects illustrated in Fig. 49, at the left and right, respectively, correspond in size to those at the two ends

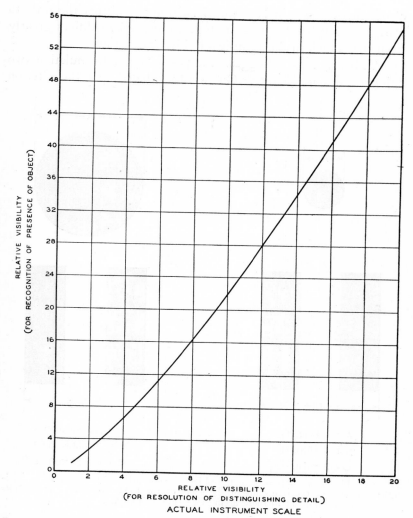

FIG. 48.—A chart for obtaining values of relative visibility based upon the criterion of recognition of the mere presence of an object (ordinates) from the
actual instrument scale values (abscissae) which are based upon the criterion
of resolution of critical details of the object. This refers particularly to the
Luckiesh-Moss Visibility Meter.

of the curve shown in Fig. 48. It will be noted that the scale to which the left-hand objects in Fig. 49 are drawn differs greatly from that to which the right-hand objects are drawn.

This relationship suggests the possibility of formulating two rational scales of visibility. One would be based upon the criterion

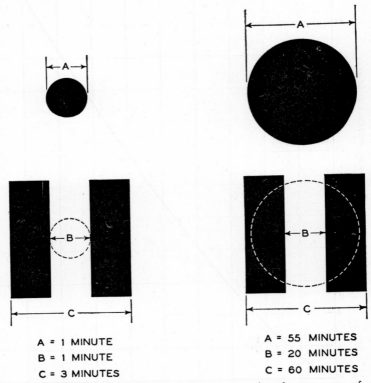

A = 1 MINUTE

B = 1 MINUTE

C = 3 MINUTES

A = 55 MINUTES

B = 20 MINUTES

C = 60 MINUTES

FIG. 49.—Threshold sizes of two test-objects representing the two types of visibility criteria for the two ends of the scale of the L-M Visibility Meter. The data correspond to those at the two ends of the curve in Fig. 48.

of recognition of presence, and the other upon the resolution of details of objects. Thus it would be logical to use the test-objects shown in the left half of Fig. 49 as standards of unit visibility, respectively, for the two scales, since these objects are of threshold visibility for normal vision. In practice, the first scale is the more applicable, for example, for the appraisal of seeing conditions on the highway at night, in certain types of inspection, and in other cases in which details of form are relatively unimportant. The second scale is obviously the more appropriate for appraising the visibility of types and other objects and visual tasks which involve the discrimination of details of form.

It may be assumed that the difference between these two scales of visibility, as represented in Fig. 48, is due to such factors as the density of receptors in the retinal mosaic, errors in the re-fractive system of the eye, the integration of the responses of the retinal receptors, phenomena associated with the borders [68] of the retinal image and others. That these complex anatomical and physiological factors are summated by simple measurements of visibility, emphasizes the significance of our approach to the com-plex problems of seeing by means of measurements of end-product results.

Visual acuity thresholds. It may be assumed from theoretical considerations that the minimum space-interval which may be dis-criminated must contain one cone which is not adequately stimu-lated. The diameter of the foveal cones, as determined by aver-aging the data of a number of investigators, is of the order of 0.0032 millimeter. Thus the average foveal cone subtends an angle of 44 seconds of arc for an eye having a focal length of 15 millimeters. Hence, two objects separated by less than this dis-tance could not be resolved. It will be noted from the data of Fig. 38 that the smallest space-interval between the parallel bars of our standard test-object which could be resolved subtended an angle of about 40 seconds of arc. In view of the uncertainty as to the diameter of the cones, it may be concluded that these experi-mental values are in agreement with the theoretical values com-puted from histological data. However, it is also a fact that a displaced segment of a line can be discriminated, as in reading a vernier scale, when the displacement is as little as five seconds of arc or visual angle. Various explanations of this observed fact have been offered, but none of them is entirely satisfactory.

The data of Table XIII indicate that the size of the smallest object which may be recognized in detail is about one minute visual angle as determined by several investigators. However, the absolute threshold depends upon many factors such as the configuration of the test-object, its brightness characteristics, and the method by which it is presented to the subject.

TABLE XIII

The Smallest Object That Can Be Distinguished as Determined by Various Investigators. (After F. H. Adler.)

	Value at Retina in Microns	Visual Angle in Seconds
Lister	4.6	64
Hirschmann	3.6	50
Bergmann	3.8	52
Helmholtz	4.6	64
Uthoff	4.0	56
Cobb	4.6	64
	Average	58 seconds

The relationship between illumination and visual acuity, as determined by Koenig, is shown in Fig. 50. It will be noted that this function of vision varies from a minimum value of about 0.04 to a maximum of 1.70. In general, the range in visual acuity from 0.04 to about 0.2 is mediated by rod-vision and beyond the value of 0.2, by cone-vision. Thus for the totally color-blind, a maximum visual acuity of 0.2 (on Koenig's scale) would be expected and has been found to be the case by direct measurement.[69] In view of the relatively low visual acuity of the color-blind, it is of interest to recall that Dalton, the great English physicist, did not discover that he was color-blind until the age of twenty-six. This case illustrates the unreliability of introspective appraisals of "how well we see."

Koenig has also shown that visual acuity for black objects upon white, red, and green backgrounds, respectively, is substantially the same and about twice as great as it is for blue backgrounds. In addition, it has been shown by others that the same values of visual acuity are obtained with black objects on white backgrounds and with white objects on black backgrounds. In this case, it is to be assumed that irradiation and induction phenomena are unimportant.

It is seen from the curves of Fig. 32 that visual acuity, under constant levels of brightness or illumination, is definitely a function

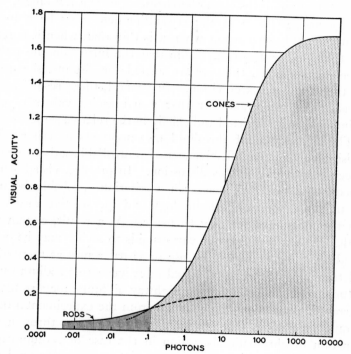

FIG. 50.—The relationship between visual acuity and retinal illumination as determined from the statistical distribution of the sensitivity of the rods and cones. These curves are derived from Koenig's data. (After Hecht.)

The photon is the unit of visual stimulation and is defined as that illumination upon the retina which results when a surface brightness of 1 candle per square meter is seen through a pupil of 1 square millimeter area.

of stimulus-distance.[47] Furthermore, it is seen that the relationship between acuity and stimulus-distance is similar for the two types of test-objects used in the investigation although the absolute values are distinctly different. Since one of these objects consisted of many opaque lines upon a luminous background which were alterable in width, but not in length, and the other consisted of white bars upon a black background and simultaneously alterable in all dimensions, it may be concluded that the existence of the anomaly of visual acuity as a function of stimulus-distance does not depend significantly upon the character of the test-object. It has been suggested [70] that the crystalline lens may be a more efficient refracting instrument when it is thin than when it is relatively thick. It is also conceivable that the image on the retina may be steadier when the eyes are fixated for distant-vision than when they are for nearer vision. In general, these results again emphasize the important fact that visual acuity values possess meaning only in a restricted and chiefly in the relative sense.

The significance of threshold measurements as criteria for appraising the relative effectiveness of controllable aids to seeing has been emphasized in this discussion. In practice, visual acuity has been used extensively as such a criterion—probably because of its universal use in ophthalmology and the relative ease with which the measurements may be made. As a result, certain appraisals of the effectiveness of various aids to seeing may be quite misleading. For example, the use of visual acuity as a criterion for determining the relative visual effectiveness of sodium-vapor and tungsten-filament light for highway lighting may result in unwarranted conclusions being drawn from the experimental data. It should be obvious that the gain in visual acuity, through the elimination of chromatic aberration in the case of sodium-vapor light, is not necessarily an advantage for the recognition or detection of large objects upon the highway. On the other hand, if the effectiveness of eyeglasses or higher levels of illumination for such visual tasks as fine engraving is to be appraised, it follows that visual acuity is the appropriate criterion for the purpose.

The physical size and the visual size (at a distance of 14 inches from the eyes) of a few common objects involving small details are presented in Table XIV. Thus it will be evident that most visual tasks of a critical nature involve details much larger than that corresponding to the ultimate resolving power of the

[150]

normal eye under favorable conditions for seeing. However, the threshold of resolving power may be increased from about one minute visual angle to many times this value when the detail of regard is of low contrast with its background. Many inspection tasks of the work-world might be cited as examples of the latter situation.

TABLE XIV

Illustrating the Relation of Visual Size (Minutes Visual Angle) to Physical Size (Thousandths of an Inch) of the Critical Details of Various Common Objects Viewed at a Distance of 14 Inches from the Eye.

Object	Size Visual (minutes)	Physical (0.001 in.)	Critical Detail
Type:			Space between dot and letter in
6-point	1.7	7	the letter (i)
8-point	3.9	16	
10-point	4.9	20	
12-point	6.4	26	
14-point	7.8	32	
18-point	17.0	52	
Steel Scale:			
¼₄ inch divisions..	1.7	7	Space between adjacent rulings
Half-Tone Patterns:			
65-screen	3.5	14	Space between dots constituting
100-screen	2.5	10	the pattern
120-screen	1.7	7	
Needles:			
Large	4.6	19	Width of the eye of the needle.
Small	2.5	10	Needles from each package of assorted sizes

The actual effectiveness of various aids to seeing is a function not only of the extent to which they are utilized, but also is a function of the particular visual threshold used in appraising their apparent effectiveness. For example, it will be noted from Fig. 38 that an increase in brightness from 1 to 100 millilamberts results in a decrease in the size of the threshold stimulus from

1.10 to 0.63 minutes visual angle for objects of maximal contrast. The latter characteristic is usually assumed in socalled visual acuity measurements. However, it will also be noted that the same increase in brightness results in a decrease in threshold size from 20 to approximately five minutes for objects of two per cent contrast. In other words, as the size of the stimulus approaches its minimum threshold value, the influence of higher brightness, or any other aid to seeing, progressively decreases.

Brightness thresholds. The minimum radiation visually perceptible varies not only with the size of the pupil, but also with attention and the physiological condition of the observer at the time of measurement. Furthermore, such factors as ideo-retinal light and the involuntary movements of the eyes tend to make such measurements unreliable. From the viewpoint of the science of seeing, these data are of rather academic interest since the condition of complete dark-adaptation seldom exists in practice. The data pertaining to the absolute sensitivity of the eye as determined by Reeves [71] together with those of Ives and Russell for star magnitudes, are summarized in Table XV.

TABLE XV

Minimum Radiation Visually Perceptible as Determined by
Various Investigators

	Threshold	Area of pupil in sq. cm.	Ergs per second Per sq. cm.	Through pupil
Reeves	0.0072 ml.	0.54	3.16×10^{-9}	17.1×10^{-10}
Ives	$6^M.0$	0.28	1.35×10^{-8}	38.0×10^{-10}
Russell	$8^M.5$	0.57	1.35×10^{-9}	7.7×10^{-10}

The studies of Langmuir and Westendorp [72] on the thresholds of radiation visible under practical conditions of observation are summarized in Table XVI. In applying these data to the problems of signalling, these investigators concluded that candlepowers at least 30 times greater than those presented should be used. This conclusion is in general agreement with the results of Helson and Fehrer which have been presented in a previous section of this

[152]

chapter. The present results and conclusions again emphasize the necessity of applying relatively large factors of safety to threshold data.

T A B L E X V I

Visibility of Point Light-Sources in Clear Air and at a Distance of Ten Kilometers

0.11	candle is visible with complete darkness
0.85	candle is visible with starlight
5.	candles are visible with moonlight
85.	candles are visible with twilight
8500.	candles are visible with daylight

Under conditions of dark-adaptation it is probable that a reciprocity relationship exists between area and intensity as variables of the threshold stimulus. Such a conclusion is in accord with Ricco's law and is experimentally supported by the data of Table XVII. Although the area of the image upon the retina is increased about four million times, the quantity of light incident on it necessary to produce excitation remained substantially constant.

T A B L E X V I I

These Results Involve Dark-Adaptation and a Pupillary Area of 45 Square Millimeters

Angle Subtended by Radius of Disk in Minutes	Intensity of Illumination, in Photons	Quantity of Light Falling on Image in Arbitrary Units
0.175	174.	2.25
0.35	43.4	3.23
0.70	10.9	3.91
1.40	2.72	2.35
2.80	0.680	3.42
5.59	0.170	2.74
13.76	0.0280	3.81
21.84	0.0112	3.08
43.67	0.0028	2.47
349.4	0.000044	3.19
699.		11.3
1000.		30.8

Brightness-contrast thresholds. Since the visual mechanism must discriminate differences in brightness in all visual tasks, the limitations or capabilities of the eyes in this respect are of immediate importance in the practical situation. This characteristic of visual function, for various states of retinal adaptation, is shown by the data of Fig. 18. These data indicate the minimum perceptible brightness-difference when the eyes are adapted to a field of uniform brightness except for the relatively small test-field and, from the viewpoint of physiological optics, may be considered as representative of the simplest fundamental situation under which the factor of brightness-contrast may be studied. However, the visual situation is seldom so simple in practice. For example, the task may require the recognition of the brightness-difference between two relatively small areas which are seen within a far larger field, as in the case of certain tasks of inspection. In the latter case, the data of Cobb,[73] Fig. 51, are the more applicable.

These experimental results, and others, invariably indicate that the threshold of minimum perceptible brightness-difference is a function of the ratio of the brightnesses of the relatively small central field and the very much larger surrounding field. It will be noted from Fig. 51 that the decrease in visual sensitivity is rapid for brightness-ratios (central/surroundings) between one and 0.1 and more precipitous for ratios less than 0.1. A comparatively small decrease in sensitivity is also obtained for ratios between one and ten. In general, it may be concluded that a brighter surrounding field is more detrimental than a darker one. This fact might be suspected from philosophical considerations since it is well known that the human eye inherently tends to fixate the brightest object within the field of view.

It is to be expected that rather wide differences in the thresholds of brightness-contrast are found even among a group of subjects possessing socalled normal or near-normal vision.[74] For example, an analysis of the data obtained from a group of fifteen subjects indicated that the threshold values of brightness-contrast for monocular vision through an artificial pupil varied from 0.066 to 0.158 millilambert, respectively, for an adaptive brightness of one millilambert. However, it will be noted from Table XVIII that the variation in retinal sensibility, for these subjects, is of the same order of magnitude as the variations in the areas of the natural pupils. A statistical analysis of these data gave a coeffi-

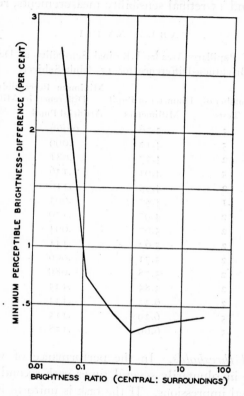

Fig. 51.—The relationship between minimum perceptible brightness-difference and the ratio of the brightness of the central visual field to the brightness of the surrounding field.

cient of correlation between retinal sensibility and pupillary area of 0.61 with a corresponding probable error of 0.11 and hence the correlation may be considered as well-defined. Therefore, it may be concluded that subjects with the larger pupils very generally have the lower sensibility and *vice versa*. It is also conceivable that low retinal sensibility is an *a priori* cause of large natural pupils, since the receptors for the pupillary light reflex and vision are considered identical. The various tests of each individual were made on different days. Each test represented a series of ten pupillary and 15 retinal sensibility measurements, respectively.

TABLE XVIII

A Comparison of Pupillary Area and Retinal Sensibility as Determined by Brightness-Difference for 15 Adult Subjects

Subject	Number of Tests	Diameter of Pupil Millimeters	Minimum Perceptible Brightness-Difference in Millilamberts	
			Artificial Pupil	Natural Pupil
1	5	3.76	0.066	0.043
2	5	4.12	.099	.042
3	2	4.27	.081	.041
4	5	4.91	.136	.041
5	2	4.95	.116	.061
6	1	4.95	.093	.047
7	2	4.97	.120	.044
8	2	5.07	.094	.034
9	2	5.62	.141	.057
10	2	5.71	.096	.039
11	2	5.78	.089	.057
12	2	5.85	.125	.072
13	2	6.22	.132	.043
14	5	6.29	.115	.041
15	5	6.69	.158	.055

Temporal thresholds. In the performance of visual tasks, the eyes pause involuntarily several times each second for the reception of visual impressions. If the task is uniform in character, as in reading, the eye-movements and fixational-pauses become more or less rhythmical through training. In fact, rhythm in eye-movements is considered to be a direct criterion of ability to read rapidly and easily. Furthermore, it is obvious that *any* operation or task guided by sight, touch or hearing should be capable of being performed faster when the external conditions are so adjusted that less time is consumed in the functioning of the sense organs which direct the performance of the task. In addi-

tion to the possibility of increasing the rate of seeing and working, it is also possible that the augmentation of any aid to seeing
would minimize (1) the frequency of cases in which an object
was not seen but which should have been seen and (2) the inter-
ruptions of the habitual sequence of eye-movements due to the
necessity of regression.   As an example of the former, it will be

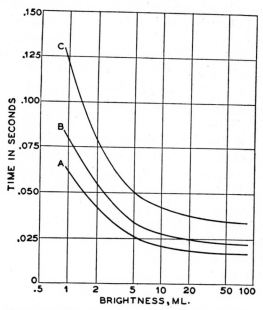

FIG. 52.—The relationship between time of exposure and brightness for various
criteria of threshold visibility.   Curve C represents the relationship when the
object is seen correctly practically every time it is presented; and Curves B and
A represent the relationship when the object is seen correctly in 80 per cent and
50 per cent of the trials, respectively.

recalled that Theodore Roosevelt lost the sight of one eye due to
an injury received in a boxing contest at the White House.   In
view of our recent survey of the lighting of the White House, it
is quite possible that this injury was the result of inadequate conditions for quick and clear seeing.

The relationship between the intensity and the duration of
the threshold stimulus is shown in Fig. 52.   These data involve

[157]

the resolution of the parallel bars of our standard test-object and, therefore, are applicable to various situations which demand critical seeing. Curve C shows the relationship between the two variables when the experimental criterion requires the recognition of the test-object with certainty. Hence these data are of primary importance from the view point of efficiency and safety. The same relationship is also shown for B, the recognition of the object in 80 per cent of the trials, and A, in 50 per cent of the trials.

The data of curve C indicate that the temporal threshold for critical vision is decreased from 0.125 to about 0.035 second when the brightness is increased from 1 to 100 millilamberts. Obviously, these temporal threshold values are also functions of the size and contrast of the object of regard as well as of its brightness. However, it will be noted from Fig. 37 that the relative influence of the factor of duration of the stimulus is substantially the same for wide variations in each of the other three factors. In general, it will be noted from Fig. 52 that the threshold exposure-times are quite exactly in the ratio of 1, 1.31, and 2 for the least to the maximum certainty of seeing, respectively.

These data may be interpreted in several ways. For example, since the shortest fixational-pauses usually occurring in critical seeing are of the order of 0.075 second,[38] it seems reasonable to conclude that brightnesses greater than two millilamberts would be required by the fastest observers, although this value does not include a factor of safety. Obviously, a factor of safety should be included, since the eye-movements and fixational-pauses do not occur with machine-like precision. If a factor of "2" is assumed, it follows from the data of curve C that the test-object should be illuminated to a brightness of at least 50 millilamberts. A factor of this magnitude seems to be a conservative one in view of the fact that the data of Fig. 52 were obtained under ideal conditions for observation; that is, in the absence of distractions with the eyes accurately fixated upon the test-field, and the attention of the observer focused upon the latter immediately prior to the presentation of the stimulus. These favorable conditions for observation are not characteristic of visual conditions in practice. Finally, these data and their interpretations again indicate the visual desirability of much better conditions for seeing than those usually provided.

As an end-product in seeing often involves muscular reactions to the stimulus, the reaction-times presented [75] in Table XIX are of interest. Although there are many variables involved in the determination of reaction-time, it may be assumed, *a priori,* that the average of the results of Table XIX are fairly representative of the socalled general case. These data, at least, establish the order of magnitudes of the reaction-times to sensory stimuli. In our work on the duration of fixational-pause we found that the average was 0.17 second. This merely involved the time required to recognize the object and did not involve other muscular activity such as pressing a button with the finger. Still, the average fixational pause, 0.17 second, is about the same as the average reaction-time to visual stimuli, 0.19 second, in Table XIX.

TABLE XIX
Reaction-Times to Visual, Auditory and Tactual Stimuli

Observer	Visual	Auditory	Tactual
Hirsch	.200 sec.	.149 sec.	.182 sec. (hand)
Hankel	.225	.151	.155
Donders	.188	.180	.154 (neck)
Von Wittich	.194	.182	.130 (forehead)
Wundt	.175	.128	.188
Exner	.151	.136	.128 (hand)
Auerbach	.191	.122	.146
Von Kries	.193	.120	.117

There are numerous situations in which a short flash of light must be observed, as for example, in signalling. Blondel and Rey [76] and others have determined the probable relationship between the intensity and the period of short flashes of light for producing a minimum perceptible sensation. Since the observers naturally vary in keenness of sight, these investigators expressed the intensity as a ratio, E/E_o, where E is the minimum perceptible intensity of the flashing beam and E_o is the minimum perceptible intensity of constant illumination. Their data are summarized in Table XX.

TABLE XX

The Relationship Between the Duration of Short Flashes of Light and the Ratio of the Minimum Perceptible Intensity for Flashing and Constant Lights

Period of Flash in Seconds	Ratio of Intensities, E/E_0
.01	22.
.025	9.4
.05	5.2
.10	3.1
.20	2.05
.30	1.70
.40	1.52
.60	1.35
.80	1.26
1.0	1.21
2.0	1.10
3.0	1.07

If an object is moving, it is obvious that there are both upper and lower thresholds for the direct perception of the motion, as regards the angular velocity. Furthermore, Aubert and Bourdon found that the threshold of perception of motion increases as the image of the moving object travels towards the periphery of the retina. Their data are presented in Table XXI. In addition, Dodge states that a moving object which is pursued by the eyes yields a subjective speed three times as great as that going with an unpursued peripheral object having an equal velocity. This fact again emphasizes the necessity of considering the subjective phases of seeing.

TABLE XXI

The Velocity Thresholds for the Perception of Motion for Various Positions of the Test-Object with Respect to the Line of Regard

Angle with Line of Regard	Velocity Threshold (per second)
1° 15′	1′ 30″
2° 15′	3′ 0″
5° 0′	5′ 37″
9° 0′	13′ 0″
20° 0′	34′ 0″

Chromatic thresholds. Although any attempt at completeness in discussing various chromatic thresholds would lead to endless variety and complexity, it seems desirable to present certain
more or less fundamental and representative aspects. For example,
various chromatic thresholds of intensity discrimination are shown
in Fig. 53. It will be noted from these data that the differential sensitivity for the various colors is quite different. Furthermore, these
values are obviously a function of the luminous intensity. However,
as Sheard [77] has pointed out, the same curve would be obtained for

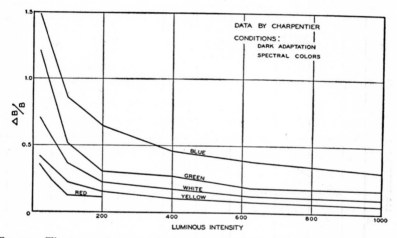

Fig. 53.—The temporal course of adaptation for lights of various spectral qualities in terms of brightness threshold.

all colors if the threshold values of color sensation rather than the
minimum light-sense values were taken as a basis. In other words,
the differential sensitivity is the same for all the colors on a basis
of equal brightnesses, the unit being defined for each of them by
its chromatic minimum.

The temporal characteristics of chromatic adaptation are shown
in Fig. 54. These data indicate that the temporal course of adaptation is quite similar for the various colors. It will also be noted
that the brightness-threshold for red is much higher than for other
colors throughout the course of adaptation. In addition, these data

[161]

show that the optimum sensitivity to red would be obtained in less time for the latter than for the other colors.

THE EFFECTS OF ATTENTION AND DISTRACTION UPON VISUAL THRESHOLDS

The threshold values of visual function which have been presented define the ultimate capabilities of the visual mechanism

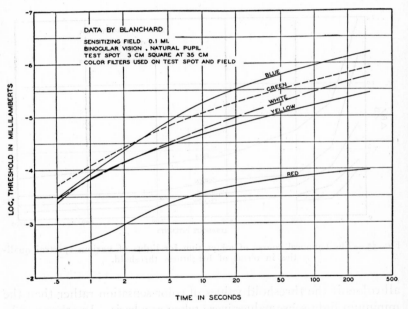

DATA BY BLANCHARD

SENSITIZING FIELD 0.1 ML.
BINOCULAR VISION , NATURAL PUPIL
TEST SPOT 3 CM SQUARE AT 35 CM
COLOR FILTERS USED ON TEST SPOT AND FIELD

LOG, THRESHOLD IN MILLILAMBERTS

TIME IN SECONDS

FIG. 54.—The temporal course of adaptation for lights of various spectral qualities expressed in terms of minimum perceptible brightness-difference.

under ideal laboratory conditions for observation. The latter include much more than favorable objective conditions for seeing. An approaching automobile, for example, may not be seen in broad daylight if the attention is elsewhere. Thus through subjective control, the efficiency of vision may be altered from that of maximum keenness to an equivalent of blindness. Although this fact may be recognized it is evident that it is lost sight of in most discussions and considerations of highway safety. From even a casual survey of the visibility of traffic signs, the lighting of hazardous locations and other situations in which human safety depends upon seeing, it is obvious that the influence of attention in seeing is not adequately appreciated. In general, it may be concluded that threshold data of visual function are valueless from the viewpoint of human welfare unless they are associated with adequate factors of safety. In many cases these must be enormous, if attention is to be adequately commandeered. Even when the attention is consciously directed to a sensory stimulus, socalled "fluctuations in attention" occur. For example, if the attempt is made to hold continuously under observation something which is just above the threshold of perceptibility, such as a small object, it will appear and disappear alternately.[78] The same phenomena also occur in auditory sensation, as may be demonstrated by listening to the ticking of a watch when it is barely audible. This emphasizes that seeing is a human activity and that human factors must be adequately considered. These human factors are not taken into account in the science of vision which has so dominated considerations of seeing that the human aspects have been lost sight of. The measurement and emphasis of these is a major responsibility of the science of seeing. Their importance is not lessened by reason of their ambiguity.

Many investigators have shown that distractions may inhibit or facilitate the simple sensory reaction.[79] According to Heyman's law of inhibition, the threshold value of visual stimuli is increased proportionately to the intensity of the inhibitory stimulus, when an inhibitory stimulus is offered.[80] The effects on the reaction-time to a visual stimulus produced by visual, auditory and tactile distractions, as determined by Evans,[81] are summarized in Table XXII. If these data are representative of the general case, it follows that distractions inhibit the reaction to a visual stimulus far more frequently than they facilitate the reaction. However, even in such investigations the distractions can scarcely be entirely unexpected. Therefore, the results cannot be directly transferred into everyday activities where the element of unexpectedness is important.

TABLE XXII

The Effects of Distractions on Reaction-Time

Kind of Distraction	Observer	Times Reactions to Light Stimulus Were Inhibited and Facilitated	
		Inhibited	Facilitated
Light	A	20	19
Sound	"	9	1
Touch	"	10	0
Light	B	16	3
Sound	"	4	4
Touch	"	7	0
Light	C	9	0
Sound	"	35	2
Touch	"	7	0
Light	D	9	5
Sound	"	10	1
Touch	"	5	4
Light	E	3	4
Sound	"	9	1
Touch	"	4	3

CHAPTER V

Visibility of Objects

On every hand and in many ways measurements and analyses reveal that conditions for seeing are far from ideal. The frequency of accidents and the prevalence of defective vision are particularly emphatic in this respect. These human errors and deficiencies are appreciated largely because they are clearly revealed by statistics and by measurements, respectively. Owing to their seriousness, efforts are made to minimize this waste of human resources. Hence, it seems reasonable to assume that statistics and measurements pertaining to deficiencies in the physical conditions for seeing would likewise be effective in revealing the generally unfavorable conditions under which seeing is done. Not many data of this kind are available although methods for obtaining them have recently been developed and applied to some extent. In the light of these new data the frequency of accidents, the prevalence of defective vision and various effects of poor seeing are less surprising.

The present discussion of the visibility of objects and visual tasks is an extension of the subject of visual thresholds in which single test-objects of elementary design and uniform surroundings are replaced by more complex patterns of objects and brightnesses. This generalization is based upon the fact that "visibility" must necessarily be appraised through the media of threshold measurements of visual function. Furthermore, since an absolute scale of visibility is not available, measurements or calculations of visibility are to be interpreted in a relative sense; and an acceptable unit and scale of visibility must be developed if possible.

In certain cases in which the physical characteristics of the objects of regard are definitely determinable, it is possible to compute the relative visibility of different tasks with considerable exactness from the relationships between the fundamental variables of the visual threshold. For example, let us suppose that the relative visibilities of the letters of a given telephone directory and a book involving letters of the same size, but excellently printed upon a good grade of white paper, are to be appraised. Since the factors of size and time for seeing are the same in both cases, and the respective brightnesses can be made equivalent through a consideration of the reflectances of the two kinds of paper, it is only necessary to measure the contrasts between the printed characters and their backgrounds. From these data it is possible to determine their relative visibilities by reference to the relationships presented in Fig. 38. The results obtained in a typical analysis of this sort indicated that the illumination should be about three times as great upon a page of the telephone directory as upon a page of the well-printed book to produce the same degree of threshold visibility. However, it should be obvious that the physical characteristics of many objects and tasks can neither be defined nor measured with such exactness. In addition, numerous modifying factors such as light, lighting, color, motion and distractions which may be encountered in practice obviously are not accounted for in such a procedure. For these reasons, the determination of the visibilities of objects and visual tasks in practice must depend upon measurements which may be made under conditions approximating those actually present. These considerations reveal the need for a "visibility meter."

THE MEASUREMENT OF VISIBILITY

The measurement of relative visibility [9] involves (1) the attainment of threshold conditions for the particular object of regard and (2) the rating of the visibility of the object upon a rational and appropriate scale. Actually it is theoretically possible to accomplish both of these objectives in at least four different ways; that is, by altering the size, contrast, brightness, or duration of exposure of the object and expressing visibility in terms of any one of these variables of the visual threshold. Thus if we consider the alteration of but one variable at a time, it follows that a visibility meter could involve sixteen different combinations of operation and calibration. Other combinations resulting from the simultaneous altering of two or more variables of the visual threshold will be obvious. However, a consideration of the mechanical and optical factors involved as well as the practical significance of the various possible calibrations, definitely limits the number of important combinations. A brief discussion of these factors follows.

Size. Assuming that it would be possible to *approach* the visual threshold by altering the size of the object of regard, it follows that this technique would result in serious distortions in the scale of visibility. Obviously, aberrations and diffraction phenomena would be disproportionately effective in cases involving objects of small threshold sizes, as will be noted from Fig. 46. On the other hand, a *scale* of relative visibility expressed in terms of the size of the threshold stimulus possesses certain definite advantages since it is one which is readily comprehended and understood.

Brightness. The attainment of threshold conditions by means of a photometric wedge or gradient filter interposed in the line of vision can be accomplished with mechanical simplicity. Obviously, extremely large changes in the brightness of the retinal image would be required in order to obtain even a rather narrow range in visibility, as will be noted from Fig. 50. Hence the factor of retinal adaptation might become a variable of some importance in the determination of the visual threshold. However, a scale of relative visibility, calibrated in terms of brightness or illumination on the object of regard, would be appropriate in practice since this is the variable in seeing which is universally controllable.

Contrast. The Bennett-Casella Visibility Meter [82] provides a means for obtaining threshold conditions by interposing a series of slightly ground glasses in the line of vision thus altering the contrast between the object and its background without serious alterations in brightness. While it might be possible to make a gradient filter of this character, the technical difficulties involved would probably be a serious handicap to its use in practice. However, a filter which would alter contrast but not brightness would be desirable from the theoretical viewpoint. Although the attainment of threshold conditions by varying contrast would emphasize the importance of the factor of retinal sensitivity, this characteristic is not particularly disadvantageous. For example, if the objects to be appraised were of high visibility due to large sizes, it follows that low contrasts within the retinal image would be involved, and thus variations in retinal sensitivity would be emphasized. However, the seeing specialist is not particularly concerned about objects of high visibility. It also seems reasonable to assume that a scale of relative visibility, calibrated in terms of contrast, would not be readily appreciated by the average person concerned with improving conditions for seeing.

Time. The mechanical difficulties encountered in controlling the duration of the exposure seem to outweigh the advantages of using this variable. However, for use in appraising conditions for seeing upon the highway, such a technique would possess many advantages due to the fact that high speeds of vehicles result in extremely brief periods for seeing. It has some other important applications as discussed elsewhere.

In general, the visibility meter designed by the authors is a result of a compromise among the factors which have been discussed.

THE LUCKIESH-MOSS VISIBILITY METER

This instrument, illustrated in Fig. 55, consists essentially of two colorless photographic filters with precise circular gradients in density which may be rotated simultaneously in front of the eyes while looking at an object or while performing a visual task. The observer holds the instrument in approximately the same position that eyeglasses are worn, and with a finger of the right hand slowly turns a disk which rotates the circular gradients until the visual threshold or limit in the performance of the visual task is reached. The procedure is quite similar to that employed in operating a visual photometer. Individual measurements of visibility may be made in a few seconds even by untrained observers. Obviously, the reliability of the appraisals of the relative visibility of various objects is proportional to the number of observations involved, assuming of course that certain precautions are exercised.

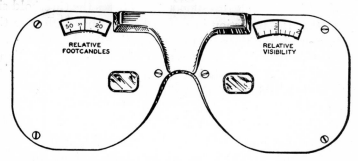

FIG. 55.—The Luckiesh-Moss Visibility Meter. A new instrument for appraising the visibility of various objects and visual tasks and for specifying practical levels of illumination for visual tasks upon a rational basis. The illustration shows the side of the meter towards the eyes.

The gradient filters illustrated in Fig. 56 not only reduce the apparent brightness of the visual field due to absorption, but also lower the contrast between the object of regard and its background

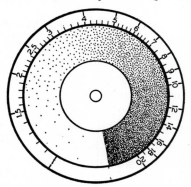

FIG. 56.—One of the two gradient filters of the L-M Visibility Meter. The scale shown is calibrated in terms of the threshold size of our standard parallel-bar test-object visible through corresponding regions of the filter. This calibration is based upon the assumption of normal vision; and for a standard level of ten footcandles upon the test-object.

due to the slightly diffusing characteristics of the photographic film which produce the effect of a "veiling" brightness over the field of view. The brightness of the retinal image may be varied

[169]

by the actual filters used, over a range sufficient to alter the size of the threshold stimulus by a factor of two. Since the maximum range of the instrument corresponds to 20 times the threshold size, it is seen that the reduction in contrast is far more effective than the reduction of brightness in producing threshold conditions. It is also obvious that the state of retinal adaptation is a function of the density of the filters before the eyes. However, since this variable is present in both the calibration and the use of the instrument, it does not introduce differential effects in the measurement of relative visibility. Furthermore, the gradient filters of this visibility meter are so designed that equal spatial changes in adjustment result in approximately equal logarithmic changes in the stimulus. Thus the mechanical operation of the instrument is similar, or nearly so, throughout the entire range of relative visibility.

Since the visual field is restricted by the apertures of the instrument, the influence of the entire peripheral field is not included as a variable in the measurement of relative visibility. However, it has been shown that the brightness characteristics of the surrounding fields, excluding glaring light-sources, are not important when the area of the central field exceeds that subtended by an angle of approximately 30 degrees.[83] This was taken into account in designing the present instrument. The field of view for each eye subtends horizontal and vertical angles of 30 and 24 degrees, respectively. Hence the critical portion of the peripheral field is within the field of view. These conclusions pertaining to the distribution of brightnesses within the peripheral field are based upon considerations of threshold visibility and do not include the undesirable psychophysiological effects which may be produced by improper lighting outside the central field.

The instrument is provided with two rational scales:

Relative Visibility .... Scale range, 1 to 20
Relative Footcandles .... Scale range, 1 to 1000.

The scale termed "relative" visibility can be "absolute" visibility by definition. In fact, it is as absolute as visibility can be. The scale of relative footcandles is rational with respect to illumination as a variable of the visual threshold.

Scale of relative visibility. Although relative visibility may be expressed as a function of any one of the four fundamental variables of the visual threshold, the factor of areal extent or size possesses certain inherent advantages for this purpose. In ophthalmology, the angular size or extent of the threshold stimulus has long been used as a criterion for appraising the efficiency of the visual mechanism. Thus the adoption of this basis for appraising the influence of external physical variables in seeing facilitates the establishment of correlations between the internal and external realms of seeing. In addition, such data are easily translated into relative distances at which the various objects are just visible. Hence the significance of visibility data so expressed will be obvious to the vast majority of non-technical persons, whose achievement and welfare depend upon seeing and who generally exercise control over seeing conditions in practice. While the basis for calibrating the visibility meter is a comparatively simple one, there are numerous specific factors to be considered in order to evolve a scale which is not only rational, but also quantitatively related to the visual ability of the observer in a fundamental manner.

Since the angular size of the threshold stimulus is a function of the fixation-distance,[47] this factor is specified in the calibration of the visibility scale. In general, critical visual tasks are performed either at distances within arm's reach, as in reading, or at much greater distances, as in driving an automobile. The ophthalmologist usually assumes that distances of about 14 inches and 20 feet, respectively, are representative of these two cardinal distances. The same assumptions have also been made in calibrating the visibility meter. Thus the visibility scale may be calibrated for both near-vision and distant-vision; and for (1) the detection of the presence of an object and (2) the resolution of critical details of the object, respectively, for both distances. At the present time, these calibrations have been made for distant-vision. As normal vision is assumed, it follows that somewhat similar scales of relative visibility would be obtained for near-vision. However, due to the fact that near-vision calibrations are influenced to a much greater degree by anomalies of accommodation and convergence, it is probable scales so derived would be generally less appropriate than the distant-vision scales for appraising the relative visibility of objects and visual tasks. The latter conclusion is based upon the consideration of visibility as an attribute of the object of regard. On the other hand, if we were primarily concerned with the characteristics of the visual organs, both the near-vision and distant-vision scales would possess clinical significance in revealing anomalies in accommodation and convergence. For example, such scales would facilitate the diagnosis of progress made in correcting pseudo-myopia.

The calibration of the scale of relative visibility, assuming distant-vision, also depends upon the characteristics of the test-object or objects. If the visual pattern presented for observation consists of more than one object, such as a line of letters on the usual Snellen Chart, the relative visibility of any one letter may be a complex function of many rather extraneous variables. For example, the recognition of a given letter may be facilitated by comparing it with other letters more easily recognizable. On the other hand, the presence of the other letters may serve as distractions or confusion patterns and thus tend to lower the visibility of the object of regard. For these reasons, we have calibrated the distant-vision scales of relative visibility through the use of single objects of simple geometric patterns. The actual test-objects used were our standard parallel-bar object and a dot, respectively, for both the scales of resolution of detail and of recognition of presence of an object.

It will be noted from Table XIII that normal human eyes are able to resolve, under favorable conditions for seeing, two objects which are separated approximately one minute in visual angle. In cases of exceptional visual acuteness, a critical detail subtending an angle of about 30 seconds may be recognized. In general, it may be assumed that a black object upon a white background, whose critical detail subtends a visual angle of one minute at a distance of 20 feet, represents an object of threshold visibility

when the white background is illuminated to ten footcandles. The
validity of this assumption is indicated by the data of Fig. 40.
The visibility of an object of this description represents *unity* on
our scale of relative visibility for the recognition of detail. From
a formal technical viewpoint, this specification of unit visibility
is somewhat arbitrary. However, in the world of seeing it is
rational, quite exact and of basic derivation. Besides, arbitrariness
is a common attribute of units and terms throughout science and
practice.

On the visibility scale for the resolution of detail, the value
"1" indicates that the standard test-object, whose critical detail
subtends a visual angle of one minute, is of threshold visibility
when viewed by a person possessing average normal vision, through
the corresponding region of the filter. Hence any object, under
any conditions, which is barely visible through this portion of
the gradient filter is assigned a value of unity in visibility. The
scale value "2" indicates that the visibility of the object of regard
is equivalent to that of our standard test-object when the critical
detail of the latter subtends a visual angle of two minutes. Other
cardinal scale-values were obtained by a similar method and have
a similar significance. Thus the scale-values of relative visibility
are directly proportional to the visual size of the standard test-
objects under threshold conditions. According to this scale an
object twice as large as another is twice as visible, provided other
factors are constant. However, this does not mean that the visibility of the larger object is such that it serves the human seeing-
machine in the ratio indicated. For example, let it be assumed
that the visual rating of two subjects by means of the Snellen
Chart is 20/20 and 20/40, respectively. Thus the threshold size
for the first subject is one-half of that for the second subject.
Hence from physical considerations, it might seem reasonable to
suppose that the visual ability of one subject is twice as great
as that of the other. This supposition is contrary to experience
of eyesight specialists.[84]

The essential characteristics of the actual calibration of the
scale of relative visibility may be recapitulated as follows:

1. A fixation-distance of 20 feet. This distance is approximately equivalent to optical infinity.

2. A series of parallel-bar test-objects varying in size from 1 to 20 minutes.

3. An extended white field as a background for the test-objects illuminated to ten footcandles.

4. Subjects possessing normal vision.

5. The assumption that a one-minute parallel-bar test-object represents the smallest object which may be recognized under these conditions.

Thus the visibility of any object regardless of its size, configuration, brightness or contrast, will be equivalent to that of our parallel bar test-object of a definite size. Hence the principle is similar to that of appraising the value of any object in terms of a definite amount of gold.

The rationality of the calibration of the instrument, as it pertains to certain photometric characteristics of the test-objects, was also tested by comparing the visibility measurements of our standard parallel-bar test-object corresponding to (1) black bars upon white backgrounds and (2) white bars upon black backgrounds. The two methods of calibrating resulted in nearly identical scales of relative visibility. Therefore, the scale of relative visibility may be assumed to be rational for both types and all degrees of contrast less than 100 per cent.

It is obvious that a person who is handicapped by visual deficiencies requires more favorable conditions for seeing than does the subject possessing normal vision. Furthermore, it is conceivable that one person may require more favorable conditions for seeing than does another for purely physiological or psychological reasons. In the specification of conditions for seeing, it would seem immaterial whether the visual limitations were imposed by morphological, physiological or psychological factors. Hence, the values of relative visibility obtained with this instrument are *inherently proper* for the person who appraises the conditions for seeing.

In certain situations the recognition of the mere presence (or absence) of an object may be a more important criterion of visibility than the resolution of details of the object. Usually such situations involve distant-vision, as on the highways, although there are exceptions involving near-vision such as inspection tasks in the work-world. If the visibility of an object is gradually lowered, the thresholds of resolution, form and presence are successively reached. In the last stage of visibility, test-objects in the form of squares, triangles, circles or ovals appear merely as blurred patches which are more or less circular in shape. Hence a circular test-object is a rational one for developing a scale of relative visibility

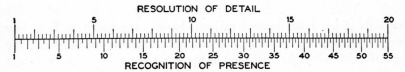

Fig. 57.—A diagrammatic representation of the relationship between the scales for the resolution of detail and the recognition of the presence of the object, respectively. These scales are drawn from the relationship presented in Fig. 48.

which is based upon the recognition of the mere presence of an object.

The data of McCallie [85] and of others indicate that a black circular object (dot) upon a white background is of threshold visibility for average normal eyes when it subtends a visual angle of approximately one minute. This value is in close agreement with the result we obtained in calibrating the visibility meter by the criterion of the recognition of the presence of the test-object. Hence an object of this description illuminated to ten footcandles is assigned a value of unity on our scale of relative visibility pertaining to the recognition of the presence of an object. Thus value "1" corresponds on both scales of visibility to the same density of the circular gradient. However, from this point the results of calibrations for the two criteria of visibility depart from each other. The relationship between these scales of relative visibility is presented in Fig. 57. We have provided two visibility

[175]

scales for these two types of visibility on our visibility meter for special investigations, such as on the highways.

Scale of relative footcandles. Since brightness or illumination is one of the four fundamental variables of the visual threshold, it is obvious that the visibility meter may also be calibrated in terms of this variable. Thus the visibility of any object under any level of illumination is expressible in terms of the level of illumination upon a standard test-object. If the illumination incident upon various objects of regard is constant, and equal to that under which the instrument was calibrated, the scale values represent the footcandles required upon such objects in order to produce the same degree of threshold visibility as that of the standard test-task. Therefore, it is now possible to specify footcandles for various visual tasks upon a rational basis. Inasmuch as light is a very controllable factor in our complex civilization, in which the specification of light has been largely a matter of guesswork and lighting has been little more than a crude art, the usefulness of our visibility meter is greatly extended by providing a rational scale of relative footcandles.

The technique of calibrating the scale of relative footcandles involves the following steps: (1) a determination of the relationship between density of the gradient filter and level of illumination corresponding to threshold visibility of the test-task; (2) the assumption of a given intensity of illumination as a basis for the scale of footcandle values and (3) a transition from *threshold* to *relative* levels of illumination. The technical details of these phases of the calibration process are briefly discussed in this order.

Critical visual tasks are usually performed at distances within arm's reach. This distance is about 14 inches for adults and was used in calibrating the scale of relative footcandles. It is obvious that the tasks performed at distances greater than 14 inches are visually more difficult than they would be at shorter distances. Hence correspondingly higher relative footcandles will be obtained. The distance of observation at which this visibility meter is used in practice is independent of that used in calibrating it. However, the observation distance at which it is used in practice for determining the relative footcandles for a given visual task should be sensibly the same as the distance from the eyes to the task as it is commonly performed. Those not used to thinking in terms of "visual size" are reminded that the distance from the object is just as much a factor as the actual physical size of the object.

Reading is a universal near-vision task, and since it is a critical, uniform, describable and controllable visual task, it possesses distinct advantages as a standard of comparison for calibrating the scale of relative footcandles. Many of our researches have involved reading as the visual task and, therefore, much pertinent knowledge and experience is available as a sound basis upon which to build. In addition, the fact that the printed words lie in a single plane minimizes the influence of possible variables due to quality of lighting or distribution of light and brightness. Since the visual threshold may be approached by gradually increasing the density of the filters before the eyes while reading, it is possible that continuity in the text may be a factor in the determination of threshold conditions. Ambiguity due to this cause was minimized by inserting irrelevant words (numerals) throughout the text. The reading matter consisted of several paragraphs printed in black 8-point Bodoni book-type on an excellent grade of non-glossy white paper. This particular size and style of type-face was selected because of its prominence in typography. It is further assumed that the visual pattern presented by the individual letters (or words) is comparable in visual difficulty to that of many tasks of the world-work although, of course, many tasks are far more difficult.

The relationship between density of the gradient filter and level of illumination upon the test-task was determined for threshold conditions of seeing for various levels of illumination between 0.1 and 100 footcandles. Since the filter density, for threshold conditions, is proportional to the visibility of the object of regard, a correlation between visibility and footcandles may be derived from these data. The rationality of the resultant scale relating these factors, for various types of visual tasks, has also been investigated and established by methods which are discussed later.

It has been definitely established that levels of illumination of at least 100 footcandles are desirable for such a visual task as reading ordinary black print upon white paper. This conclusion is firmly based upon the results of extensive researches in the physiological effects of seeing and is in harmony with philosophical considerations and experience. Hence, the arbitrary selection of an illumination of 10 footcandles for such a visual task, *for purposes of calibrating* the scale of relative footcandles seems to be an appropriate and a conservative one.

The method of converting threshold footcandles into relative footcandles may be explained by an example. If an object X is of higher visibility than the standard test-task S, under the same intensity of illumination, then X would require a denser filter than S in order to produce threshold conditions. Obviously, this differential in density may be expressed in terms of footcandles upon the standard test-task S by reference to the data determined in the first phase of the calibration process. Let it be assumed that the threshold densities for the two objects correspond to threshold levels of illumination of 20 and ten footcandles, respectively. Since the differential in visibility between X and S is of such magnitude as to require a factor of two in footcandles in order to produce an equality in threshold visibility, it follows that five footcandles should be recommended for X if ten footcandles are considered suitable for S. This relationship may be expressed by the formula, $R = 10/T \times 10$, where R and T are the relative and threshold footcandles, respectively; and the constant ten is the level of illumination upon the standard test-task used in the calibration of the scale of relative footcandles.

The rationality of this procedure for relating threshold and relative footcandles has been investigated by direct methods. For this purpose four tasks were selected differing greatly in size of the object of regard, in brightness-contrast, in color-contrast, and in the interpretation of the visual stimulus. These tasks were diffusely illuminated to a level of ten footcandles, the instrument adjusted for threshold seeing, and the value of relative footcandles for each task was read from the scale. The validity of these foot-candle values was then checked by illuminating the individual objects to their respective values of footcandles and again adjusting the instrument for threshold seeing. If the method of relating threshold and relative footcandles is a rational one, it is obvious that a scale value of ten footcandles should be obtained for all the tasks. It will be noted in Table XXIII that this requirement is fulfilled within the limits of accuracy of the instrument. The differentials between Items A and D are, therefore, considered as errors of measurement primarily, rather than as indications of irrationality in the calibration of the instrument. Furthermore, it will be noted that errors of these magnitudes have little significance when appraised upon a basis of the quantitative effectiveness of level of illumination as a factor in seeing.

TABLE XXIII

These Data Present the Specification of Relative Footcandles for Four Diverse Visual Tasks and Evidence of the Rationality of the Values Obtained

	Visual Tasks			
Order of Procedure in Checking Rationality of Transition from Threshold to Relative Footcandles	Use of Steel Scale, 1/64 Inch Divisions	Reading Newspaper Stock Quotations	Dark Gray Print Upon Lighter Gray Background	Typing on Dark Blue Paper
Measurement				
A. Footcandles on visual tasks. (Standard for calibration.)	10	10	10	10
B. Relative footcandles for particular task indicated by meter	160	84	171	88
Check				
C. Footcandles on tasks determined in Step *B*	160	84	171	88
D. Footcandles read from scale. These values should correspond to those of Step *A*....	10	11.5	13.4	11
Per cent error (*D/A*)	0	15	34	10

In view of the relatively few observations involved in the summary presented in Table XXIII and, particularly, in view of

[179]

the basic fact that footcandles must be altered in geometric ratio in order to alter visibility or visual effectiveness in arithmetic ratio, the per cent error in any case in Table XXIII is insignificant. With these facts in mind, these data appear to establish the rationality of the scale of relative footcandles determined from a single type of test-task (8-point Bodoni type) for objects of diverse physical characteristics.

Hence the relative footcandles for various tasks correspond directly to the scale values when the measurements are made under an illumination of ten footcandles by persons possessing average normal vision. When the measurements are made under an actual level of illumination, A, which is different from that (ten footcandles) for which the instrument is calibrated, a correction-factor must be applied to the scale values. It is obvious that the actual footcandles, A, under which any observation is made, is equivalent to T in the calibration formula, $R = 10/T \times 10$, already discussed. Therefore, the scale values of relative footcandles must be multiplied by the factor $A/10$ or $0.1\ A$. For example, if an object is observed or a task is performed under an illumination of one footcandle, and a scale value of 50 footcandles is obtained, the relative footcandles will be one-tenth of 50 footcandles or five footcandles. If the actual level of illumination under which measurements are made in another case is 20 footcandles and a scale value of 50 footcandles is obtained, the relative footcandles will be twice 50 footcandles or 100 footcandles.

The essential characteristics of the calibration of the scale of relative footcandles may be recapitulated as follows:

1. A fixation-distance of 14 inches. This represents the so-called normal distance for close work.
2. Reading as a standard task.
3. 8-point type (Bodoni Book Monotype) well printed upon white paper.
4. Subjects possessing normal vision.
5. The arbitrary selection of an intensity of ten footcandles as a basis for calibration. It is not implied that this level of illumination is recommended for reading 8-point type.

[180]

Thus the visibility of any object is compared to that of the 8-point Bodoni Book Monotype illuminated to a definite footcandle-level; and since all objects will be compared to the same standard, their relative visibilities will be related to the corresponding values of relative footcandles read from the meter.

T A B L E   X X I V

The Data in the Second Column Show the Relative Visibilities of Various Tasks as Determined with the Luckiesh-Moss Visibility Meter Under a Constant Illumination of Ten Footcandles. The Data of the Third Column Show the Footcandles Required on Each Task in Order That All Tasks Will Be of Equal Threshold Visibility. These Values Are Relative and Are Based Upon an Assumed Value of Ten Footcandles for Reading the Standard 8-Point Type.

Task	Relative Visibility	Relative Footcandles
12-point type	5.1	5
10-point type	4.3	7
8-point type	3.6	10
6-point type	3.1	17
Own handwriting in pencil	2.8	20
Newspaper text matter	2.5	30
Bookkeeping	2.4	35
Drafting	2.30	40
Business machines	2.14	50
Medium-grade assembly and inspection	2.02	63
Metal buffing	1.88	80
White thread on white crepe cloth	1.78	100
Metal finishing—surface grinding	1.57	170
Using steel scale—1/64 inch divisions	1.56	180
Fine sanding and finishing	1.49	220
Distinguishing black thread on black cloth	1.31	425
Precision die making	1.20	700

Visibility meter measurements. In view of the fact that the specifications of conditions for seeing in the world of practice are usually prepared in the absence of quantitative data regarding the visibility of the particular task to be performed, the method of obtaining this information is emphasized in this discussion. The latter is a phase of the science of seeing which is now in the process of development. Hence, details of methods and discussions of the usefulness of such data are more important than a recapitulation of the fragmentary data now available. Furthermore, practical methods of appraising the specific situation are proposed in order to avoid the usual ambiguity encountered in applying data of a socalled general character to the problems presented by the specific situation. The data presented in Table XXIV are examples of the application of such a method to a number of practical visual tasks.

These data indicate, for example, that the relative visibilities of the critical details of the 12-point type are more than four times as great, in terms of equivalent size, as the visibilities of critical details to be recognized in precision die-making. In other words, if the 12-point type and a 5.1-minute parallel-bar test-object were placed side by side and viewed through our visibility meter, the same reduction in brightness and contrast would be required to attain threshold conditions in both cases. Similarly, the critical details to be seen in die-making would be equivalent to a 1.2-minute parallel-bar test-object. Obviously, it cannot be definitely stated that these objects are equal in visibility under supra-threshold conditions. Since unity on the scale of relative visibility represents the limit of the normal eye in visual acuity, it follows that the visual tasks in die-making are of a near-threshold order under an illumination of ten footcandles.

THE VARIABILITY OF THRESHOLD MEASUREMENTS

Since a threshold measurement or determination of visual function represents the end-product of innumerable biological factors, it seems rather remarkable that such measurements are as consistent as shown in the following tables. However, it may be stated that "consistency" is not a descriptive term which would be applied to such data by those who are accustomed to measurements in the physical sciences. As a result, illuminating engineers and others who exercise control over visual conditions are often discouraged in their attempts to specify conditions for seeing upon a rational and scientific basis and are inclined to ignore psycho-physiological methods of appraising visual situations. Hence, it is to be emphasized that if great variability is obtained in formal measurements of visual phenomena, these variations likewise exist in the world of seeing. In fact, the variability of such measurements indicates the minimum factor of safety which should be applied to all measurements of visual performance.

TABLE   XXV

The Relative Visibility of 8-Pt. and 18-Pt. Type as Determined from a Single Series of Five Measurements and from the Average of Several Series Involving a Total of 250 Measurements

Subject	Number of Observations					
	250		First 5		250	First 5
	8-Pt.	18-Pt.	8-Pt.	18-Pt.	8/18	8/18
1	3.72	9.12	3.51	8.55	0.41	0.41
2	4.64	9.10	4.67	9.80	0.51	0.48
3	3.22	9.06	3.09	9.00	0.35	0.34
4	5.39	12.38	5.05	11.20	0.43	0.45
5	4.32	9.72	4.44	10.40	0.44	0.43
6	3.04	5.95	3.34	6.54	0.51	0.51
7	1.63	3.08	1.75	3.07	0.53	0.57
8	3.53	10.20	3.61	10.30	0.35	0.35
9	3.32	9.12	3.04	7.78	0.36	0.39
10	3.65	9.20	3.51	7.93	0.40	0.44
Mean	3.64	8.69	3.60	8.46	0.43	0.44
Per Cent Mean Variation	19	19	17	20		

PRECISION   OF   VISIBILITY
MEASUREMENTS

Number of measurements. Obviously, the precision of the average value of visibility obtained for a given object or task depends upon the number of measurements involved and the care taken in making them. Our experience with our visibility meter indicates that a satisfactory degree of reliability for practical purposes usually may be obtained from a series of five measurements for each situation, as will be noted from Table XXV. These

[183]

data show that substantially the same average values are obtained from the first five measurements as from the total of 250 measurements. However, the probable errors of the average values obtained from the larger number of measurements are much smaller than those obtained with a few measurements. In general, in comparing two or more visual tasks it is always advisable to repeat the measurements, in a reverse order, for the purpose of minimizing any progressive effects of learning and practice. Also, two series of five measurements each are preferable to a single series of ten measurements.

Since subjects differ in their conceptions of carefulness and accuracy in making measurements and in their ability to obtain consistent results, the optimum number of observations in each series depends upon the characteristics of the individual observer.

TABLE XXVI

The Relative Visibility of a Black Parallel-Bar Test-Object, the Details of Which Subtend an Angle of 3.95 Minutes

This object appeared in a white field which was illuminated to an intensity of ten footcandles. The data are arithmetic averages of series of five observations taken on five different days with the visibility meter.

Subject			Series			Arith.	Mean Variation
	1	2	3	4	5	Mean	Per Cent
1	2.89	2.89	3.04	3.15	2.62	2.92	4.9
2	3.45	3.04	3.58	4.49	4.19	3.75	12.6
3	4.85	3.80	3.18	4.85	4.80	4.30	15.0
4	4.24	7.69	5.15	7.17	5.05	5.86	21.4
5	4.04	5.26	4.28	4.85	4.24	4.53	9.2
6	4.85	5.00	4.15	4.53	5.05	4.72	6.4
7	2.67	2.86	2.47	2.95	2.20	2.63	9.0
8	5.60	7.53	5.10	6.80	6.54	6.31	12.2
9	4.85	6.80	4.85	5.32	5.10	5.38	10.5
10	3.65	4.58	3.95	3.34	3.25	3.75	10.9
11	2.97	3.95	2.86	3.58	2.23	3.12	16.6
12	1.96	2.04	2.16	1.94	2.23	2.07	5.0
13	4.90	5.94	6.00	5.32	5.94	5.62	7.3
14	6.36	6.05	4.85	7.69	8.45	6.68	16.7
Mean	4.10	4.82	3.98	4.71	4.42	4.40	11.3

Although the actual values of visibility obtained by the individual subjects are quite different, it will be noted from Table XXV that the ratios of the visibility of 8-point and 18-point type are quite consistent.

Variability from test to test. Since reproducibility of results is an essential characteristic of any method of measurement, it is important to examine the L-M Visibility Meter in this respect. It will be noted from Table XXVI that the mean variation of five series of measurements taken upon five different days is approximately 11 per cent for the average of the 14 subjects, with extreme variations of about 5 and 20 per cent for the best and poorest subjects, respectively. Although these subjects are consid-

TABLE XXVII

The Individual Data Represent the Mean Variation of a Series of Ten Measurements Each on Four Different Days. The Concave-Bar Test-Object (Fig. 113), Illuminated to Ten Footcandles, and Viewed from a Distance of 20 Feet Was Used in All Cases. The Ten Individual Measurements Were Taken in Two Series of Five Measurements Each, and in the Interval Between These, a Series of Observations Involving Another Test-Object Was Taken. The Latter Data Are Not Given in the Table.

| Subject | Series | | | | | Probable |
	1	2	3	4	Average	Error
1	9.0	4.7	7.9	2.9	6.1	1.7
2	10.8	8.7	2.5	2.7	6.2	1.8
3	6.3	4.9	2.0	3.4	4.2	1.2
4	4.2	3.2	1.9	1.6	2.7	0.8
5	4.7	2.5	2.9	1.6	2.9	0.8
6	22.0	11.3	7.7	5.1	11.5	3.2
7	4.0	4.7	9.8	3.4	5.5	1.6
8	9.1	4.1	3.2	2.5	4.7	1.3
9	7.1	3.9	3.7	2.4	4.3	1.2
10	7.2	2.6	1.5	1.5	3.2	0.9
11	4.2	2.4	3.3	4.4	3.6	1.0
12	5.2	2.8	3.1	1.3	3.1	0.9
13	8.1	1.7	8.5	3.0	5.3	1.5
14	11.7	6.6	3.1	5.7	6.8	1.9
15	6.2	3.5	2.1	2.4	3.5	1.0
Mean	8.0	4.5	4.2	2.9	4.9	1.5

ered as typical, with respect to visual efficiency, it will be noted that rather wide variations are found in their appraisals of the visibility of a given object. This fact emphasizes the necessity of using a number of subjects when the scale values of the visibility meter are to be used in the absolute sense.

Variability within a single series of measurements. It will be noted from the data presented in Table XXVII that the variability of the measurements taken during a single test-period is exceedingly small as is indicated by an average mean variation of 4.9 per cent and a corresponding probable error of 1.5 per cent. It will also be noted that the variability of the initial series of measurements is considerably greater than that obtained in the next series. For various reasons, largely psychological, it is usually advisable to discard one or two measurements at the beginning of any test-period. The subject is unfamiliar with the appearance on the threshold object; the entire situation is freshly new to him; and his attention may not yet be entirely under his control. He can scarcely do his best until he has settled down to the job.

Trained and untrained subjects. The preceding discussion of precision has been based upon data obtained from subjects who have had previous experience not only in operating the visibility meter, but also as subjects in visual researches. The results obtained by these subjects (Group A) are compared (Table XXVIII) with those obtained by subjects without previous experience in the use of the instrument (Group B). This comparison is all the more interesting since the latter subjects were handicapped by serious visual defects. The data of Table XXVIII show that there is little difference between the two groups in ability to make the settings for threshold visibility in a consistent manner. For example, both groups obtained a ratio in visibility between 18-point and 24-point type of 0.75, with a mean variation of about eight per cent for each group. However, it will be noted that this ratio was obtained from markedly different degrees of visibility in the two cases. For Groups A and B, respectively, 15.6 and 16.3 footcandles upon 18-point type produced the same

[VISIBILITY OF OBJECTS]

TABLE XXVIII

Group A Represents Ten Stenographers and Engineers Trained in the Use of the Visibility Meter and with Previous Experience as Subjects in Behavioristic Experiments. Group B Represents Twenty-Eight Pupils from the 7th, 8th and 9th Grades of Sight-Saving Classes. All of the Latter Group Had High Degrees of Myopia and, in Addition, Were Somewhat Below Normal Upon an I-Q Basis.

Relative Visibility of 18-Point and 24-Point Type

Group	18-Pt.	24-Pt.	Ratio 18/24	Mean Variation of Ratio
A	8.69	11.68	0.75	8.5 per cent
B	5.22	7.00	0.75	7.3 per cent

Footcandles for Equal Visibility

A	10 f.c. on 24-pt. equivalent to 15.6 ± 1.7 f.c. on 18-pt.
B	10 f.c. on 24-pt. equivalent to 16.3 ± 2.4 f.c. on 18-pt.

degree of visibility as did ten footcandles upon 24-point type. The difference between these footcandle values is not significant in comparison with the variability of the data. These data emphasize the precision with which *relative measurements* may be made even under very adverse conditions. The facility with which the untrained subjects made the measurements is indicated by the fact that the total time required to receive instruction in operating the meter, and then to make three series of ten measurements each, averages 19 minutes per subject.

Lighting. One of the practical uses of our visibility meter is to specify footcandles or quantity of light on a rational basis for various visual tasks in order that they may be approximately of the same visibility and perhaps of comparable difficulty to average normal human seeing-machines. The visibility meter is the first scientific attempt to reduce guesswork and to introduce rationality into the specification of light or footcandles. It is equally useful in appraising the effects of lighting. The visibility of a three-dimensional object is largely a matter of highlights and shadows. Even a casual experiment will reveal enormous effects upon visibility by changes in quality of lighting; that is, by changes in the distribution of light and brightness. Without

[187]

measurements of visibility, the specification of lighting has little or no scientific foundation as far as resultant seeing is concerned.

By illuminating the three-dimensional objects involved in a visual task by light coming from different directions and from light-sources of different sizes (subtending different solid angles at the objects), one can determine the effects upon visibility by simple measurements with the visibility meter. The variations in visibility due to quality of lighting will be found to vary greatly throughout the range from invisibility to high visibility. Certainly without providing controlled light properly directed upon the work, particularly when it involves the visibility of three-dimensional objects, the best is obtained from lighting only by accident. Thus it is seen that both light and lighting influence visibility throughout the world of seeing. These are discussed in later chapters.

HUMAN CHARACTERISTICS AND DEFICIENCIES

It is convenient to discuss the visibility of a visual object or task as if it were a matter quite apart from the human seeing-machine and quite fixed in value under certain standard conditions of light, lighting, vision, etc. In fact this is quite true for practical purposes of discussion. Actually, however, there is no such thing as visibility apart from the human being, just as sound and other human experiences are not isolated from the human being. For the purposes of fundamental standardization and measurement, all influential factors are controlled as far as possible and some are eliminated. However, in everyday seeing many factors influence visibility. Major ones are listed in Chapter II which should be referred to at this point. From that list one will see how many factors were controlled or eliminated in the development of our visibility meter in order to have a standard reproducible condition. Likewise, one will see how many factors can be controlled or eliminated in the practical use of this device. In some cases one may be interested in the effect of this or that factor upon visibility. In everyday visual tasks this visibility takes into account many factors and yields measurements of visibility which are sorely needed and are not readily available from any other source at the present time.

Certainly human beings differ inherently in speed, accuracy and certainty of seeing even though they may possess average normal vision. They vary considerably in absolute retinal sensitivity and in pupil size even under standard conditions. They vary in their perceptual faculties particularly in threshold measurements and in their interpretations of visual sensations. They vary markedly in various human characteristics which influence their behavior and, therefore, their appraisals of the visibility of objects and tasks under many conditions. In other words, human seeing-machines differ considerably because they are human.

A common measurable deficiency of human seeing-machines is that due to optical defects of vision. These are commonplace. In Table XXVIII is presented the average visibility of a test-task for a group of school children of markedly defective vision. It is seen that for this deficient group the average visibility of the test-task was 60 per cent of the average value for a group of persons possessing normal or near-normal vision. It is not likely that light alone could compensate completely for the deficiency in visibility, but if it could, it would require at least three times as much light for the deficient group to enjoy the same visibility of the test-task as the normal group.

Another example is seen in Table LXXIX. Ten subjects possessing normal vision were provided with glasses in error by one-half diopter. Under these conditions the visibility of a test-task was 75 per cent of the value without the glasses. It would require about twice the amount of light (footcandles) to overcome the deficiency in vision due to a refractive error of one-half diopter.

Such examples not only reveal the effects of human deficiencies, but also give some idea of light as a compensatory factor for minor refractive errors. They also suggest that the refractionist who prescribes glasses should know something of the value of other aids to seeing. In general, it may be emphasized that inasmuch as our visibility meter measures the influence of various controllable factors, it also reveals how these factors can be used to compensate, at least partially, certain human deficiencies.

VISUAL FACTORS OF SAFETY

The values of relative visibility presented in Table XXIV may be considered as visual factors of safety expressed in terms of equivalent size. Thus an object with a visibility rating of "1" is of threshold visibility and a reduction in magnitude of any of the four fundamental variables of the visual threshold would cause it to become invisible. Distractions and fatigue would produce a similar effect. Obviously, the factor of safety would be unity in this case; and the margin of safety would be zero. In bridge design, factors of safety of ten are usual; and in the design of dirigibles, a factor of safety of two is as great as is usually obtainable or considered practicable. We have measured the factor of safety in seeing pedestrians on one of the best lighted streets in Cleveland and, for a distance of 150 feet, seldom found factors as high as two. Furthermore, it is to be emphasized that factors of safety of this low order were obtained with subjects possessing normal vision, free from distractions, and with the attention directed to the time and place where the pedestrian was to appear. However, the motorist has other tasks than seeing; his vision is often defective, and his attention must be directed to many regions of the visual field. Thus a highway department, when making road repairs, almost invariably uses more than one red lantern to warn traffic of dangerous conditions.

Since human efficiency, safety, and welfare depend so largely upon seeing clearly and quickly, even while some attention is given to other matters besides seeing, the technical value of known factors of safety in seeing is obvious. Acceptable or adequate factors of safety for the tasks of the home, school, work-world, on the highway and in other situations where critical seeing is involved, are yet to be determined. The visibility-meter technique offers a practical and rational basis for measuring these factors, but it cannot determine the "proper" margins of safety. This must be done empirically, since the values which will be useful in practice involve compromises between desirability, practicability, and cost. Obviously, an optical device cannot appraise these variables.

In determining acceptable factors of safety for critical visual tasks of the work-world, for example, the following technique seems both practical and rational. An acceptable standard of type-size is definitely indicated by the characteristics of good typography, since these standards have been evolved as a result of mass experience for generations. Furthermore, it seems reasonable to conclude that normal vision has been assumed in the design of type-sizes. Hence the fact that 10-point or 12-point type is used in the better grade of books may be considered as an indication of the desirability of these sizes. Furthermore, it may be assumed that 12-point type represents a practical maximum, since 14-point type is rarely used for the solid text-matter of books designed for adults. If 12-point type, illuminated to ten footcandles, represents a satisfactory standard of visibility, it will be noted from Table XXIV that a factor of safety of "5" is indicated. Furthermore, it will be noted from these data that none of the diverse tasks listed involve a factor of safety of this order—yet it is not unreasonably high for the task of reading, as anyone may determine for himself by reading types of various sizes.

Certainly the assumption of 8-point type illuminated to ten footcandles represents a most conservative standard of visibility, in view of the fact that most persons will actually select over a hundred footcandles for this task if given the opportunity. Thus 8-point type under ten footcandles involves a factor of safety of 3.6. It will be noted that the work-world tasks listed in Table XXIV do not involve factors of safety as high as the conservative value of 3.6. However, if the levels of illumination are increased to the values shown in the table, the margin of safety will be equivalent to that provided by 8-point type under ten footcandles. It might be asked: Does one see an object possessing an equivalent areal factor of safety of four "twice as well" as he sees an object having a factor of safety of two? Obviously, this viewpoint leads from a consideration of the objective characteristics of the visual object or task to the subjective phases of its perception. Although an absolute scale is not available for determining the ultimate significance of various values of visibility, the empirical relationships derived from mass experience for years in the field of ophthalmology may be assumed to be appropriate for the purpose, at least until another relationship is shown to be more appropriate.

In 1925, the Ophthalmological Section of the American Medical Association [84] adopted the relationship between reciprocal visual acuity and *visual efficiency* shown in Fig. 58. This relationship is widely used as a basis for awarding compensation for loss of vision due to eye injuries sustained in industry. In general, it will be noted that "visual efficiency" is not directly proportional to the visual acuity ratings or their reciprocals. For example, a decrease in visual acuity from 20/20 to 20/40, or a change from one to two minutes in the size of the threshold stimulus, corresponds to a decrease in visual efficiency from 100 to 83.6 per cent. In other words, if the threshold stimulus size is two minutes visual angle instead of one minute which is considered normal, visual efficiency is considered to be lowered 16.4 per cent and not 50 per cent, as might be assumed from a consideration of visual acuity. We may now rate the visual tasks of Table XXIV in a similar manner.

In making these calculations, it will be helpful to recall that the scale values of the visibility meter correspond to various sizes of our standard test-object. Thus, for example, a standard test-object which subtends a visual angle of two minutes will be of threshold visibility under the following conditions: (1) when it is observed by a person with a visual rating of 20/40; or (2) when it is observed by a person with normal vision through the portion of the gradient filter corresponding to a scale value of "2." In both cases, the loss in visual efficiency is 16.4 per cent. In the one case, this loss is due to subnormal vision; and in the other, it is due to the interposed filter. The relationship of Fig. 58 enables us to interpret the loss in visibility due to the filter in the light of the experience of the ophthalmologist. It is obvious that an object of threshold visibility when viewed through a given filter would constitute an object of supra-threshold visibility without the filter.

Since it has been shown that the influence of the filter is equivalent
to a definite loss in visual efficiency, we now have a means for

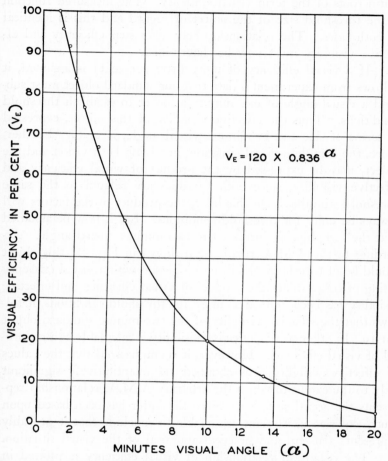

$$V_E = 120 \times 0.836^{\alpha}$$

FIG. 58.—The relationship between the size of the threshold stimulus and visual
efficiency as adopted by the American Medical Association.

determining the degree of supra-threshold visibility of an object
for normal vision.

The ophthalmologist has designated the loss in vision due to
visual anomalies in terms of *visual efficiency*. Similarly we have

designated the loss in visibility due to an interposed filter in terms of *effective visibility*. This term is derived from a reversal of the Latin roots of the term visual efficiency. The measured function is the threshold size of the object of regard and this is identical in both cases. The relationship between visual efficiency and effective visibility must now be determined.

If a visual efficiency of unity (100 per cent) is assumed, it follows from experimental data that our standard object must subtend a visual angle of one minute in order to establish threshold conditions. Thus the effective visibility of this object, expressed in terms of size and in minutes visual angle, is unity. Furthermore, the complete visual situation, involving both vision and the object, may be expressed by the product of visual efficiency and effective visibility, since both variables are related to the same threshold stimulus. On this basis, the product of the factors will always be unity for threshold conditions. Let it now be assumed that the test-object is increased to two minutes visual angle. According to the A.M.A. relationship shown in Fig. 58, this object would be of threshold visibility to a person with a visual efficiency rating of 0.84. Since the product of visual efficiency and effective visibility has been defined as unity for threshold conditions, it follows that the effective visibility of the two-minute standard object is 1.19. In other words, effective visibility is calculable as a reciprocal of visual efficiency. However, it is emphasized that the values of effective visibility thus obtained are quantitatively significant only to the extent to which the arbitrary A.M.A. relationship represents the actual situation. Since the latter has been based upon much experience, it seems reasonable to conclude that it probably represents a useful and practical appraisal of the visual situation.

The reciprocal relationship of visual efficiency is plotted in Fig. 59. In this figure, the abscissa values correspond to the scale values of the visibility meter and the corresponding ordinate values denote the effective visibilities of the objects of regard. The broken-line of Fig. 59 represents the relationship between relative visibility (visibility-meter values) and effective visibility upon the assumption that these values are directly proportional. The solid-

line curve represents the relationship between these variables interpreted in the light of the experience of the ophthalmologist. Thus
it will be noted that a standard test-object of ten minutes visual

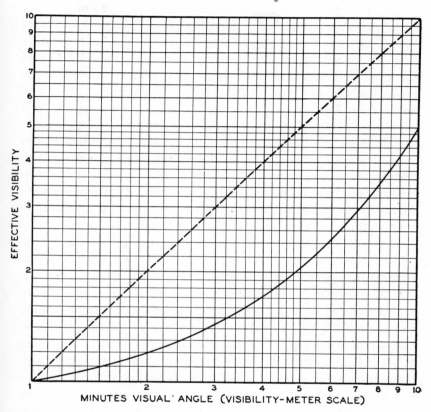

FIG. 59.—The solid-line curve shows the relation between relative visibility (our
visibility-meter scale) and effective visibility. The latter is assumed to be the
reciprocal of visual efficiency as used by the A.M.A. The broken-line shows the
relation between these factors if it is assumed that effective visibility is directly
proportional to relative visibility.

angle, or any object of equivalent visibility, has an effective visibility of five on the latter basis. In other words, its "effective size"
is five times greater than the smallest which may be seen under
favorable conditions.

As a practical example, it will be noted from Table XXIV that 12-point type, under standard conditions for observation and measurement, has a relative visibility rating (actual visibility-meter reading) of 5.7. The corresponding rating in terms of effective visibility is approximately 2.3, as will be noted from Fig. 59. Hence the effective factor of safety may be considered as 2.3 rather than 5.7, as would be obtained upon a basis of threshold size of the equivalent standard test-object. It is also of interest to appraise the 12-point type in terms of visual efficiency. It will be noted from Fig. 58 that this type would be barely visible to a person with a visual efficiency rating of about 43 per cent.

It is not claimed by the authors that the relationship shown in Fig. 59 is a fundamental one. However, we believe that it represents an approximation which has considerable significance in seeing. We have proposed this interpretation of relative visibility values for reasons quite similar to those which led the ophthalmologist to translate visual acuity data into terms of visual efficiency. It is conceivable that the relationship shown in Fig. 59 may be revised eventually when many measurements of the relative visibilities of common tasks are available.

The restricted significance of any particular scale of visibility is also revealed by a further analysis of the data of Table XXIV. For example, it will be noted that, for approximately equal visibility, the visual task of precision die-making requires 140 times as much light as does the task of reading 12-point type, although these tasks differ only by a factor of about four when appraised in terms of equivalent threshold size. · However, each criterion possesses certain unique characteristics from the practical viewpoint. In die-making, as in other tasks of the work-world, the sizes and contrasts of the critical details are fixed. The controllable factors are light, lighting, eyeglasses and others. Hence the relative foot-candle values are helpful in estimating the quantity of light, for example, which will enable the task to be accomplished with a reasonable degree of ease.

VISIBILITY AND EASE OF SEEING

Although the relative visibilities of two dissimilar objects or critical details of a visual task may be identical, it is not be to assumed that the two visual tasks may be performed .with equal ease. For example, the relative visibilities of two kinds of news-print involving rather bold-face type and somewhat larger type of a less bold character, respectively, were found to be identical. However, when readers were asked to appraise the relative "ease of reading" in the two cases, they invariably reported that the larger type was the superior. In this particular case, the news-paper that made the change in type-size in the interest of "eye-comfort" for the reader failed to take full advantage of the possible benefits from the larger type since the reduction in the bold-ness of the type-face apparently was unnecessarily great.

Visibility and ease of seeing are obviously related, but the relationship, *a priori*, is not one of direct or complete proportion-ality. In general, measurements of visibility do not take into account all the factors in seeing from those of the external physical world to those involved in perception and ultimate achievement. Some of the factors which are either ignored or inadequately evaluated in the measurement of the relative visibilities of visual tasks are:

1. The muscular effort required in fixation and convergence,
2. The influence of pre-exposures and post-exposures,
3. The degree of comprehension of the objects seen.

The influence of these factors on the ease of seeing in performing visual tasks may be discussed by assuming the cases presented by the two forms of newspaper typography which have been mentioned. It is evident that the smaller letters require a more precise fixation than do the larger ones. Thus the effect of eye-movements in blurring the objects to be seen becomes more serious as the size of the characters is decreased. In fact, it may be assumed that the image of the object of regard is seldom, if ever, stationary upon the retina as is indicated by the activity of the extrinsic muscles shown in Fig. 28. Furthermore, a fine or precise degree of fixation is much more difficult to acquire and maintain than a coarser one. This fact will be demonstrated if the attempt is made to point a pencil accurately at small and large objects, respectively, for a few seconds.

It has been demonstrated [68] that one border of a visual pattern influences the threshold characteristic of an adjacent image. Hence it follows that the greater the extent of the white area about each printed character, the less serious will be the influence of adjacent patterns. It also seems reasonable to assume that the transient eye-movements will be less likely to introduce pre-exposure and post-exposure patterns in the case of the larger separation between adjacent letters. Since seeing involves the growth and decay of visual sensations in rapid succession, the introduction of confusion patterns, as shown by the researches of Cobb,[64] may be quite detrimental.

As the text-matter becomes more difficult to comprehend, the number of fixational-pauses and regressions increases as will be evident from the data of Fig. 128. Thus the muscular effort involved in reading may be quite different in the two cases, although the visibilities of the printed characters may be identical. Hence it may be concluded, for these and other reasons, that visibility and ease of seeing are not necessarily synonymous. However, the measurement of visibility goes a long way toward establishing knowledge and rational practice in the world of seeing in which guesswork and introspection have been almost entirely relied upon.

Introspective appraisals of ease of seeing. In general the appraisal of the relationship between controllable visual factors and ease of seeing has been based upon data from physiological criteria. However, the subject has also been investigated by the introspective method of experimentation and both interesting and significant results have been obtained. In a recent research a number of adult subjects were asked to select, by actual trial, the level of illumination considered as ideal for reading black print on white paper for long periods. The selection was made solely upon the basis of their own criteria of comfort afforded by the lighting. The average footcandles selected by 82 subjects was about 100 footcandles. Owing to the indefiniteness of the criteria it is not surprising that the maximum and minimum selections were 1000 and 10 footcandles, respectively. Such a result provides experimental evidence of the conservative character of the footcandle recommendations indicated by physiological considerations, although this

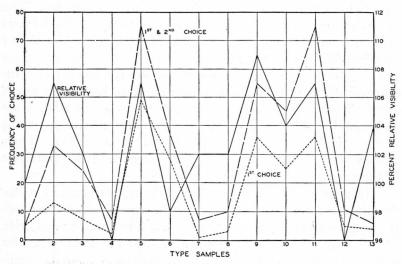

FIG. 60.—The solid-line shows the relative visibilities of 13 different type samples as determined with the visibility meter. The broken-line indicates the number of first and second choices of each type-face made by several hundred readers of a newspaper. The dotted-line shows the number of first choices of each type-face.

kind of experimental attack is by no means desirable for laying a scientific foundation for seeing. In fact, human beings are very poor judges of seeing conditions. They are poor seeing-meters. However, an experiment of this sort is sometimes of value in a corroborative sense. At least the results show that persons apparently satisfied to read under one or two footcandles choose an average of nearly 100 footcandles if they have an opportunity and are divorced from the commonly distorted and inadequate economic considerations.

Introspective appraisals versus visibility measurements. The correlation between threshold measurements of relative visibility and introspective appraisals of ease of seeing under supra-threshold conditions is indicated by the data of Fig. 60. The solid-line graph represents the relative visibilities of 13 different samples of types currently used in newspapers. These types varied in size from 6¾-points to 7½-points and also in the boldness of the type-faces. In relative visibility they ranged from 96 to 109 per cent. The latter data were obtained with the visibility meter by five subjects who made two series of five measurements each for each of the 13 samples. The agreement between the two series of measurements was excellent. The dotted-line graph shows the number of readers preferring each sample, respectively; and the broken-line graph shows the total of the first and second choices of the readers for each sample. These data summarize the introspective appraisals of the samples of types by approximately 200 readers. Their average choices are in remarkable agreement with the visibilities of the various specimens of printing.

In general, it will be noted that the results obtained under threshold and supra-threshold conditions, respectively, are in qualitative agreement; that is, the samples which were rated as superior by the visibility-meter technique were also the most generally preferred by the readers. A statistical analysis of these data indicated a coefficient of correlation between the frequency of the combined choices and relative visibility of 0.64, with a corresponding probable error of 0.15. Thus it may be assumed that there is a significant correlation between these two factors. In view of the fact that the differences in visibility among the various samples were rather small, it is of interest to note that both methods of appraisal indicated that samples 2, 5, 9, and 11 were superior among these types.

CHAPTER VI

Physiological Effects of Seeing

The definite expansion of the narrower viewpoint of vision into the more appropriate and extensive viewpoint of seeing revealed a new field of research which aimed to discover and evaluate suspected psychophysiological effects of seeing. It also renewed effort and freshened the attack upon the problems of eyestrain and eye-fatigue. Considerations of the latter represent almost entirely the previous efforts in the realm of physiological effects of seeing. Even the psychological approach through sensation and perception is extended and somewhat clarified by the concepts and objectives of the science of seeing. This psychological approach has been the only past recognition of seeing as a human activity, but even this had the effect of expanding the viewpoint of vision rather than of replacing it with the present conception of seeing. In other words, the older approaches were closely allied to the restricted viewpoint of vision as an organ and with the visual sense as a part of the entire complexity of sense-organs and sensations. They did not clearly recognize the human seeing-machine as such, or that the human being is complexly penalized by poor seeing conditions and may be as complexly benefited by conditions of quick, certain and easy seeing. The present discussion reveals new approaches to an understanding of seeing as an activity of the human being rather than merely of the eyes and the visual sense.

The usefulness of an adequate criterion of ocular fatigue as one means of determining optimum conditions for easy seeing is obvious and such criteria have long been sought. Numerous attempts have been made to detect and to appraise the degree of ocular fatigue by measurements of visual function such as, for example, the measurement of visibility by means of the visibility meter at frequent intervals during a period of reading. Notwithstanding the fact that the reading was continued in this experiment for more than two hours, no significant changes in the visual abilities of the subjects were observed. Furthermore, extensive researches indicate that the decrement in visual acuity, resulting from a period of eight hours of critical near-vision work, is of the order of two or three per cent.[86] Obviously such a differential in visual function is of no practical use in relating ocular fatigue with the visual conditions under which the critical seeing was performed. With this limitation it cannot be expected even to indicate more deep-seated effects of seeing.

If the brain is as hard a task-master for the eyes as it is known to be for the heart, the failure to detect ocular fatigue by measurements of visual function is easily understandable. As stated by Starling [25] "even when the heart in consequence to disease is scarcely able to carry on the circulation, the arterial pressure (carotid) undergoes little or no alteration. Any other tissue of the body, even the heart itself, may suffer, but the brain at all costs must receive its proper supply of blood." It is conceivable, a priori, that the brain likewise demands clear and effective vision even though the ocular mechanism has been considerably fatigued by prolonged critical visual effort. This possibility is at least in harmony with certain observed facts. As has been stated, no statistically significant difference in visual function was noted as a result of continuous reading for two hours, although a decrement in convergence reserve of over 12 per cent in prism diopters was observed after reading only one hour under similar conditions.

The strain and fatigue which accompany severe visual effort become evident after viewing the pattern of Fig. 22 for a few seconds, and are indicated by the prevalence of defective vision in occupations which require critical seeing, as will be noted from the data of Fig. 5. Of course, it might be argued that in the former case, the visual task is so unusual that the demonstration is merely of scientific interest. However, statistical data on the prevalence of defective vision are indisputable evidence that modern visual tasks, and likewise the physical conditions under which they are performed, are far from desirable from the viewpoint of ocular hygiene. Obviously, for the purposes of research, the visual test-task should be comparable to usual tasks and the criteria for appraising the effects of seeing should be capable of revealing these effects in a reasonable length of time. Furthermore, it should be appreciated that the effects of seeing may extend far beyond the visual mechanism. If such psychophysiological effects are unobvious they are none the less important to human welfare.

The development of the picture, in the camera analogue to vision, completes the process. However, in human vision the development of countless images in sensation not only produces physiological changes in the visual mechanism itself, but it also leaves its imprint upon the psychological pattern of human experience. We shall now describe invasions of these realms of sensory functioning and of sensory experience by formal research methods. A major objective has been to establish correlations between the physical variables of the external world and the psychophysiological effects of seeing. In general, various effects of seeing are discussed here as functions of illumination, as a controllable variable in seeing. Obviously, the same criteria and experimental methods are also applicable for appraising the influence of other controllable aids to seeing, such as eyeglasses, backgrounds, size of type, and others.

NERVOUS MUSCULAR TENSION

Experimental criterion. It is a matter of everyday experience that nervous tension and fatigue commonly cause a tightening of certain muscles. For example, a pencil may be held more tightly when one is nervous or after the muscles of the hand or arm have become fatigued from a long period of writing. In the latter case, the effect of the fatigued muscles is indicated by the reaction of those muscles. It may also be observed that muscular energy is often wasted as a result of strain or fatigue which originates remotely from the place where it may manifest itself. An automobile driver commonly grips the steering-wheel more tightly at night on a poorly-lighted street than on a well-lighted one. In this case, an inadequacy in conditions for seeing is manifested in tenseness and in the useless expenditure of muscular effort. The importance of nervous tension in general fatigue of human beings is likewise obvious.

The muscular strain, using the term in its usual sense, produced by fatigue or strain is referred to as *nervous muscular tension* in the present discussion. Measurements of this factor are designated as *indicated nervous muscular tension*, since we have no means of knowing the completeness or the accuracy with which this criterion appraises or measures these internal psychophysiological reactions. Obviously, any criterion selected to appraise the amount of human energy wasted in useless work is to be regarded as a relative rather than as an absolute method of appraisal. Therefore, the value or usefulness of such a criterion corresponds to the directness with which it may be interpreted. Nervous muscular tension is to be regarded as an arbitrary, convenient and useful "measuring-stick" for appraising complex psychophysiological reactions to light, lighting, visual tasks and various conditions for seeing.

Experimental procedure. The utilization of nervous muscular tension as a criterion for the appraisal of energy expended in useless work permits a wide choice of methods for its measurement. However, there are certain fundamental restrictions which are to be observed. It is obvious that the true purpose of the research should be concealed from the subjects in order that their reactions might not be altered by a consciousness of the objectives of the experiment. Hence, this requirement practically eliminates the possibility of attaching apparatus directly to the body of the subject in order to measure muscular tension. The method evolved and used consisted in measuring the changes in muscular tension as registered by fingers of the left hand which rested naturally and lightly upon a large flat knob of a concealed key as shown in Fig. 61. Level of illumination (brightness) was selected as the experimental variable and all extraneous factors eliminated or reduced to a minimum. Tests were conducted at each of three levels of illumination—1, 10 and 100 footcandles, respectively.

The subjects were instructed to read at their *natural rate* during the 30-minute test-period, and cautioned against considering the problem as a "speed-test." In addition, they were instructed to rest the index and second fingers on the left hand upon the knob of the key and to press this key firmly down as they read the last word on each page. This manual task served to justify the presence of the key and at the same time concealed the real purpose of the key. Even at the conclusion of the research, which was in continual operation for about six months,

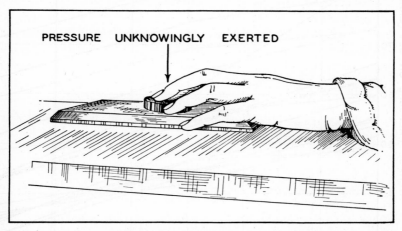

PRESSURE UNKNOWINGLY EXERTED

FIG. 61.—Showing the position of the hand and fingers with respect to the key by means of which measurements of muscular tension in the fingers of the left hand were made.

none of the 14 subjects, who completed the entire series, was aware of the real purpose of the research.

During each 30-minute test-period, the reader was alone in a room separate from the experimenter and recording apparatus. Hence, he was not disturbed or influenced by the recording of the data, the adjustment of apparatus, noise or other distractions. The apparatus which automatically recorded the variations in pressure upon the key was placed in sound-proof cases even though it was located in a room adjacent to the one occupied by the subject. The reading was performed steadily, quietly and continuously throughout the test-period, excepting for a rest-period of a half-minute inserted at the middle of the test-period.

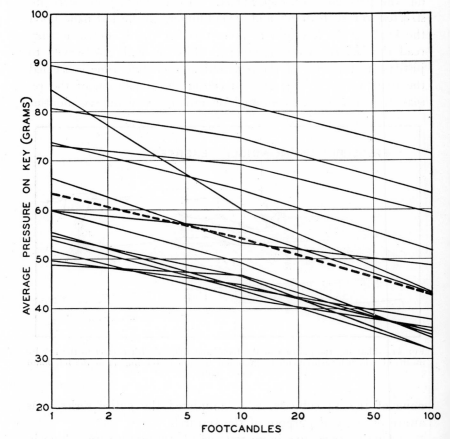

FIG. 62.—The relationships between indicated nervous muscular tension and level of illumination for each of the 14 subjects. The broken-line represents the geometrical mean of the results of the 14 subjects. The probable errors of the average values of nervous muscular tension are less than one per cent.

Reading was selected as the visual task because of its obvious advantages as a universal, uniform and desirable visual problem. The book chosen was "Why We Behave Like Human Beings" by Dorsey. The reading matter consisted of 12-point Bodoni book-type printed well on excellent book-paper. Visually, this task was about as easy as reading can be. Each subject began reading at the beginning of the book and progressed through it during the 24 reading periods for each subject, which were once a week for nearly every subject. As the subjects were interested in the contents of the book, attention was drawn from the key and natural reactions were expected.

The results. The experimental results are summarized in Fig. 62 for each subject and for the entire group. During each 30-minute period of reading under one of the three levels of illumination 360 measurements of the pressure exerted upon the key were automatically recorded. There was a total of 308 test-periods of 30 minutes' duration, each involving 360 measurements of pressure. Of the 308 tests, the results of nine tests were excluded from the calculations in accordance with Chauvenet's criterion. It will be noted from the summaries of these data that the *indicated nervous muscular tension*, developed incidental to reading, decreased from 63.2 grams to 43.0 grams as the illumination was increased from 1 to 100 footcandles.

The individual data and the corresponding probable errors are presented in Table XXIX. The relative probable errors are derived in each case from the separate serial values. The relative probable error of the mean E_m is derived from the 14 corresponding individual values E, by the formula $E_m = 1/N \sqrt{\Sigma E^2}$, in which $N = 14$. The variations due to the systematic differences between the subjects are, therefore, not included. Relative probable error is defined as the probable error of the mean divided by the mean.

Since the relative probable errors of the average values of indicated nervous muscular tension are of the order of one per cent, these data possess a high degree of reliability from the statistical viewpoint. It will also be noted from Fig. 62 that *each subject yielded similar results*; that is, the pressure unconsciously exerted upon the key was definitely less for each increase in illumination for every subject. Such agreement among different subjects is not always obtained in researches upon human behavior. The consistency among the results for the several tests upon the same

TABLE XXIX

The Relationship Between Indicated Nervous Muscular Tension and Intensity
of Illumination; Also a Statistical Analysis of the Reliability of These Data

Indicated Nervous Muscular Tension
(Grams Pressure Unknowingly Exerted on Key)
E Is Individual Probable Error in Per Cent

Subject	1 Footcandle		10 Footcandles		100 Footcandles	
	Pressure (Grams)	E (Per Cent)	Pressure (Grams)	E (Per Cent)	Pressure (Grams)	E (Per Cent)
1	55.4	1.8	44.0	1.6	38.0	2.4
2	48.8	2.6	46.6	2.7	34.9	2.1
3	54.7	2.2	46.4	3.0	31.8	1.9
4	53.9	1.5	43.5	2.6	31.7	1.9
5	51.7	2.7	42.0	2.1	36.2	2.0
6	49.8	2.5	44.6	1.5	35.6	1.9
7	89.4	2.5	81.7	3.1	71.6	3.0
8	66.4	0.9	53.1	2.0	48.9	3.4
9	80.6	3.3	74.6	2.1	63.4	4.6
10	73.8	3.1	63.9	2.8	51.9	3.8
11	59.9	1.8	49.1	3.0	34.2	2.1
12	73.3	4.6	69.1	2.3	59.3	2.2
13	84.4	2.7	59.9	3.6	43.5	2.8
14	59.9	2.5	56.0	3.0	42.8	5.3
Mean	63.2*	0.7	54.1	0.7	43.0	0.8

* Geometric mean of the individual results.

subject, as indicated by the individual probable errors, is additional
evidence bearing upon the reliability of these data and upon the
value of this method in studying the effects of conditions which
influence seeing. The absolute values of pressure exerted on
the key have no significance beyond the fact that some fingers
rested more lightly or heavily upon the knob of the key than
others.

The integrated frequencies of the pressure measurements in
per cent are plotted in Fig. 63 as ordinates on a normal probability
integral scale. The abscissae are various degrees of pressure which
the subjects unknowingly exerted upon the key while reading. The
graphs of the data are substantially straight lines, thus indicating

a normal or Gaussian distribution of the individual pressure measurements for each of the three levels of illumination. Hence it follows that uncontrolled or uncontrollable variables of the experimental situation did not disproportionately influence the results in the three cases.

The rate of reading, in pages per minute, is given in Table XXX for the various subjects. Since the subjects were carefully instructed to read at their natural rates, it is significant that the average rate of reading for the group increased consistently for

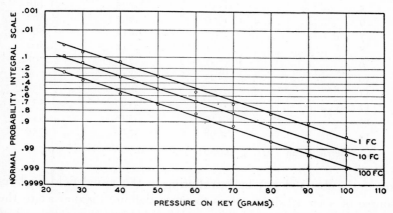

FIG. 63.—The relationships between pressure on the key and the integrated frequencies of the various levels of pressure which were recorded. The latter are plotted on a normal probability integral scale. These plots indicate a normal distribution of pressure values for each of the three levels of illumination.

each increase in the level of illumination. That the increase in rate of reading is rather small may be interpreted as indicating that the visual task was relatively easy; otherwise, a comparatively large increase would have been obtained,[5] as will be noted from Curve *B* of Fig. 80.

Discussion of results. A preliminary experiment [87] established the important fact that an increase in the pressure unknowingly exerted upon the key by the reader (indicated nervous muscular tension) is a result of unfavorable conditions for seeing and for comfort. For example, increases in pressure upon the

TABLE XXX

The Effect of Intensity of Illumination upon Rate of Reading under the Conditions Specified in This Research

Subject	Pages Read per Minute		
	1 Footcandle	10 Footcandles	100 Footcandles
1	.476	.569	.533
2	.594	.644	.637
3	.687	.724	.746
4	.631	.614	.622
5	1.346	1.265	1.446
6	.920	.867	.882
7	.762	.812	.800
8	.691	.742	.802
9	.701	.729	.708
10	.893	.810	.799
11	.790	.817	.839
12	.531	.497	.531
13	.310	.348	.352
14	.698	.750	.759
Geometric mean	0.680	0.700	0.712

key were obtained (1) by introducing in the visual field a glare-source of such a brightness as to cause definite discomfort to the reader and decreased visibility, and (2) by lowering the level of illumination until seeing became difficult and trying. In this research, the subjects were required to steadily observe a rotating test-object and to press a key at certain intervals as prescribed by the position of a detail of the test-object. The test involved extremely difficult visual work and the relatively easy mechanical task of operating the key. The task, as a whole, was of such an exacting nature that the subjects instinctively rested their fingers upon the knob of the key continuously during the test-period of ten minutes. It was thus possible to record changes in the pressure which the subjects unknowingly exerted upon the key. The changes in nervous muscular tension, as indicated in the fingers of the right hand which operated the key, were correlated with changes in the experimental variables of preventable glare and level of illumination. A

[210]

detailed description of the test-object and auxiliary apparatus is given elsewhere.[88]

The key was so constructed that an auxiliary circuit was closed when the pressure upon it exceeded a certain predetermined value. This critical pressure was determined empirically for each subject and remained constant throughout the entire series of tests. The gap between the auxiliary contacts was so small that the closing of these contacts was not indicated to the subject by the sense of touch nor could they be seen since all parts of the key except the knob were concealed. The standard or ordinary contacts of the key were connected to electric counting devices which recorded the accuracy with which the visual task was performed. The auxiliary contacts were connected to an electromagnetic device which recorded the opening and closing of the auxiliary circuit upon the drum of a kymograph. However, the subjects were not aware of this arrangement.

Levels of illumination of one and five footcandles, respectively, were produced at the test-object and at the eyes by a lamp placed 20 degrees above the line of vision. Therefore, this lamp served as a source of illumination for the test-object and also as a glare-source in relation to the eyes. The direct light from the lamp to the eyes (preventable glare) was eliminated by an opaque screen to provide the "glareless" condition. Since this investigation was not concerned with the influence of the location of the glare-source within the visual field, this factor was held constant. The brightness of the glare-source and its angular position with respect to the line of vision are the same as used in a previous and extensive investigation [89] of the effects of glare upon visibility.

The subject was seated at a table with the index finger and usually the second finger resting naturally upon the broad knob of the concealed key. Since the weight of the hand was supported by the table, the fingers normally exerted but a slight pressure upon the key. As the test progressed, it was found that the subject unconsciously varied the pressure on the key and the auxiliary circuit was opened and closed in an irregular manner. The summation of the times the auxiliary circuit was closed is assumed to be an indication of nervous muscular tension. Level of illumination and preventable glare were the experimental variables, and other factors which might affect the performance of the subject were carefully controlled.

Measurements of indicated nervous muscular tension were made for levels of illumination of one and five footcandles, respectively, without preventable glare, and at a level of illumination of five footcandles at the object and five footcandles of preventable glare at the eyes. A series of five measurements, arranged in an order to equalize the influence of learning, was made for each of these three experimental conditions and for each of ten observers. The results are summarized in Table XXXI. The values given for muscular tension denote the time in seconds during which the pressure unknowingly exerted upon the key exceeded a fixed value. The probable error of the mean is computed from the ten individual values.

TABLE XXXI

The Influence of Illumination and Preventable Glare upon Indicated
Nervous Muscular Tension

Subject	1 F.C. on Test-Object No Preventable Glare		5 F.C. on Test-Object No Preventable Glare		5 F.C. on Test-Object 5 F.C. Preventable Glare	
	Indicated Muscular Tension	Relative Probable Error Per Cent	Indicated Muscular Tension	Relative Probable Error Per Cent	Indicated Muscular Tension	Relative Probable Error Per Cent
1	117	16.2	94	12.7	231	27.5
2	121	21.2	63	18.5	131	14.1
3	228	9.0	138	23.4	292	15.3
4	170	8.4	109	18.0	160	18.4
5	298	7.9	77	9.4	200	11.4
6	153	6.2	150	31.1	154	9.2
7	95	16.6	61	20.0	119	16.2
8	236	27.2	68	22.5	255	22.2
9	130	4.9	75	19.1	102	10.8
10	103	9.6	41	11.5	101	17.6
Mean	154*	4.6	82*	6.2	163*	5.4

* Geometric mean.

These data indicate that the deleterious effects of the glare-source were comparable in magnitude to the effect produced by decreasing the level of illumination from five footcandles to one footcandle as appraised by the criterion of nervous muscular tension. It is also obvious that the results are significant when compared to their corresponding probable errors. An analysis of the data on a basis of accuracy with which the tests were performed indicated no differential among the three experimental conditions. This is additional evidence that the human seeing-machine is often able to operate under severe handicaps without influencing the accuracy of its performance, but, doubtless, at a cost to it which at present is unappreciated or at least unmeasured.

It is apparent that the differences among psychophysiological reactions resulting from reading under different levels of illumination are of such definiteness and magnitude that they are capable of creating muscular strains which are measurable. Human energy expended in nervous muscular tension, in this case, is wasted, since it accomplishes nothing useful. This *indication* of the waste of human energy due to relatively low levels of illuminations compared with daylight intensities outdoors may be considered as a conservative appraisal of the actual conditions. Certainly, it is measured at a point remote from its origin. Apparently it can indicate nothing else than an effect of greater ease in performing a relatively easy visual task under footcandle-levels greatly above the threshold requirements.[90]

The average values of indicated nervous muscular tension (in grams) and footcandle-levels are plotted in the upper part of Fig. 36. It will be noted that the data may be represented approximately by a straight line when the footcandle values are plotted on a logarithmic scale. This indicates that the relationship between nervous muscular tension and level of illumination is generally logarithmic in character. The same relationship also exists between level of illumination and the several fundamental variables which influence visibility. In the lower part of Fig. 36 the relationship between footcandles and the contrast required for threshold visibility (of an object equivalent in size to the book-type) is presented for comparison. The similarity between visibility relationships obtained by direct measurement and psychophysiological relationships appraised indirectly is obvious and very important in the development of the science of seeing. It encourages us to have confidence in an approximate relationship between visibility and ease of seeing.

The importance of these new data obtained in the psychophysiological realm may be readily seen by reference to Fig. 8. They may be regarded as data which seek to establish optimum conditions for seeing.

VISUAL EFFORT AND THE HEART-RATE

Since the heart responds to numerous physiological and psychological stimuli, it seemed possible that the expenditure of human energy in critical seeing might also be revealed or indicated by changes in the heart-rate.[91] Thus if critical visual effort produced "reverberations" in the central nervous system, which spread excitation to the peripheral system, it follows that the heart-rate should be affected. Hence the investigation of the effects of seeing upon the heart-rate serves as a check, *a priori*, upon the conclusions derived from the experiment on tenseness. This was the primary consideration of our researches upon the heart-rate, although in the light of the results obtained, it now seems advisable to extend the significance of the latter criterion, beyond that of an independent check of the tenseness research.

Experimental procedure. Reading was selected as the visual task because of its obvious advantages as a universal and uniform visual problem. The reading-matter chosen was "The Outline of History" by Wells. This work seemed to be ideal for the purposes of the research since the text is generally of uniform interest throughout and adequate in length for an extended investigation. Each subject began reading at the beginning of the book and progressed steadily through it during succeeding test-periods. The subjects were instructed to read at their normal rate and cautioned against considering the problem as a "speed-test." The extent of the investigation was such that any possible effects due to the novelty of the situation were quickly dissipated by the routine of the procedure. Physically, the conditions under which the reading was done were made as comfortable as possible for the subjects. These conditions are described and illustrated elsewhere.[90] During each test-period, the reader was alone in a room separate from the experimenter and the recording apparatus. Hence, he was not disturbed or influenced by the recording of data or the adjustment of apparatus.

Each of seven male subjects, varying in age from 25 to 35 years, completed a series of 20 one-hour tests. They were technically trained men with previous experience as subjects in behavioristic researches. All were in good health and possessed normal or nearly normal vision. Hence, the research pertains to normal subjects performing a common visual task which is an easy one compared with many performed for long periods in the work-world.

The tests were conducted at illuminations of 1 and 100 foot-candles, respectively. These footcandle values represent a range in intensity of illumination comparable to the range between prevalent levels of illumination indoors and those which can be recommended at present as practicable and desirable for reading. Obviously, in a research of this type there are uncontrolled variables such as ambient temperature, distractions, temporary physical condition of the subjects, and many others. Although these extraneous factors may have a significant effect upon the absolute values derived, they can scarcely be considered important from a relative viewpoint in a research which involves repeated tests under the same physical conditions. Therefore, level of illumination is regarded as the only systematic variable.

The heart-beat was recorded by means of a cardiotachometer adjusted to operate only upon the R phase of the pulse-curve. One electrode was located in the region of the base of the heart and the other near the apex. Errors in the automatic recording of the heart-beat due to occasional disturbances in the input circuit of the cardiotachometer were noted, by visual observation of a milliammeter placed in the output circuit of the amplifier, and manually recorded. This combination of methods of recording resulted in an exact count of the number of heart-beats. An accurate measurement of time-intervals made it possible to determine the heart-rate with exactness during each successive five-minute interval.

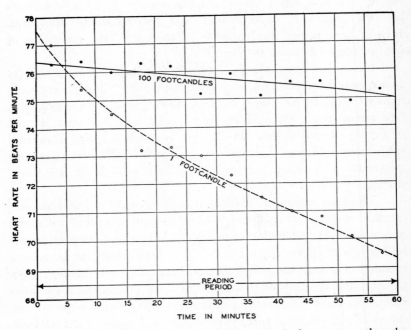

FIG. 64.—Showing the average progressive decrease in the heart-rate as the subjects read for one hour under illuminations of one footcandle and 100 footcandles, respectively.

After the electrodes had been attached, the subject was allowed a ten-minute rest-period in order to attain an approximately constant state of physical composure and retinal adaptation. An auditory signal inaugurated the reading period which continued without interruption for one hour. The footcandles were then altered to the other standard value and, after a ten-minute rest-period, the experimental procedure was repeated. Thus each test involved two one-hour periods of reading which were preceded

by ten-minute rest-periods. The order in which the two levels
of illumination were presented was reversed on alternate tests.
Ten such tests involving two one-hour reading periods were made
for each of the seven subjects. The tests were made at the same
hour of the day for each subject and the interval between successive tests was approximately one week.

The results. The influence of visual effort upon the heart-
rate is clearly indicated by the relationships presented in Fig. 64.
The important facts revealed by these data are (1) that the heart-
rate progressively decreased as the duration of the visual task
increased and (2) that this decrement in heart-rate was much
greater under one footcandle than it was under 100 footcandles.
It is particularly significant that *all subjects show such decrements
in heart-rate while reading,* as will be noted from Table XXXII.
The slopes of the composite curves of Fig. 64 indicate that the
heart-rate would be further depressed if the reading were continued for longer periods.

The statistical reliability of these data is indicated by the fact
that the relative probable errors are about 0.5 of a beat per
minute. These relative probable errors of the values plotted in
Fig. 64 are derived from the relative probable errors of the heart-
rates of the individual subjects, and hence do not include variations
due to systematic differences in heart-rate among subjects. A
statistical analysis of the results obtained from individual subjects
is presented in Table XXXII. Since the decrements in heart-
rate observed after an hour of reading are several times as great
as the corresponding probable errors, they are real and significant.

It will be noted in Fig. 65 that the heart-rates at the beginning of the first reading-period, which immediately followed the
first rest-period, are essentially equal. Hence, it may be assumed
that any change in the heart-rate during the first rest-period pro-
ceeded at the same rate in both cases since the initial rates, on a
basis of probability, were identical. However, it will be noted that
the rates changed abruptly when the subjects began reading. This
result is obvious in both the first and second periods of reading.
Therefore, it is concluded that the variations in heart-rate are due

TABLE XXXII

The Average Heart-Rate for Each Five-Minute Interval of the One-Hour Period of Reading. The Individual Values Represent Averages of the Ten Tests under Each Level of Illumination.

Time Minutes	A	B	C	D	E	F	G	Geometric Mean	Relative Probable Error
			100 Footcandles Heart-Rate in Beats Per Minute						
0– 5	84.3	82.6	77.8	80.0	70.1	64.2	63.1	74.1	0.54
5–10	84.6	82.2	78.0	79.7	69.5	63.4	63.2	73.9	0.50
10–15	84.5	81.1	77.1	79.2	69.3	64.3	64.7	73.9	0.50
15–20	83.9	81.1	76.5	80.2	70.5	64.2	64.5	74.0	0.53
20–25	85.2	81.2	76.5	78.2	70.4	64.0	63.3	73.7	0.57
25–30	84.7	80.1	76.4	77.9	69.5	63.1	64.1	73.3	0.47
30–35	84.5	80.4	75.9	78.3	69.6	62.7	64.6	73.3	0.53
35–40	82.8	81.1	75.8	78.3	69.2	62.5	62.3	72.7	0.54
40–45	82.7	81.9	75.8	78.6	69.2	63.1	62.7	73.0	0.51
45–50	83.4	81.8	75.3	78.9	68.9	64.3	64.1	73.4	0.48
50–55	82.4	81.0	76.0	78.9	67.4	64.8	63.2	73.0	0.51
55–60	82.7	81.7	75.9	79.4	67.2	66.6	62.8	73.4	0.47
Arithmetic Mean	83.8	81.4	76.4	79.0	69.2	63.9	63.6	73.5	0.14
			1 Footcandle						
0– 5	88.7	84.7	78.4	79.3	70.8	64.5	66.3	75.6	0.45
5–10	86.5	83.7	77.0	78.1	70.1	62.9	64.6	74.2	0.45
10–15	85.7	81.7	77.3	76.8	68.6	61.9	63.6	73.2	0.45
15–20	83.8	80.6	75.7	76.1	66.3	62.4	62.8	72.1	0.45
20–25	83.9	79.7	74.4	76.7	66.3	61.2	63.3	71.8	0.46
25–30	82.8	81.4	73.2	76.2	66.4	60.4	62.3	71.3	0.46
30–35	82.1	80.6	72.0	75.9	67.2	59.7	62.0	70.9	0.48
35–40	82.5	79.9	71.1	74.7	65.5	59.7	61.5	70.2	0.48
40–45	79.9	79.5	71.2	75.5	64.7	60.5	62.5	70.1	0.42
45–50	78.4	78.8	70.4	76.0	64.3	60.4	61.8	69.6	0.44
50–55	78.7	78.4	70.3	75.4	63.3	60.4	61.0	69.2	0.42
55–60	77.9	77.9	69.4	74.6	62.9	59.5	60.2	68.5	0.42
Arithmetic Mean	82.6	80.6	73.4	76.3	66.4	61.1	62.7	71.4	0.12

to differences in ease of seeing in the two cases rather than to differences in photic stimulation. It was also experimentally shown that the introduction of an intense glare-source into the visual field while the subject was reading did not produce an observable change in either the heart-rate or the form and magnitude of the pulse-wave during the next minute. These results indicate that the heart is not appreciably affected by temporary changes in the brightness of the visual field.

Apparently, the commencement of the visual task inhibits the recovery from a depressed heart-rate even though the conditions for seeing are such as to exert but little influence upon the heart. For example, the heart-rate tends to approach the normal initial value during the second rest-period after being depressed due to reading for one hour under one footcandle, as will be noted from Fig. 65. However, it begins to decrease immediately, although

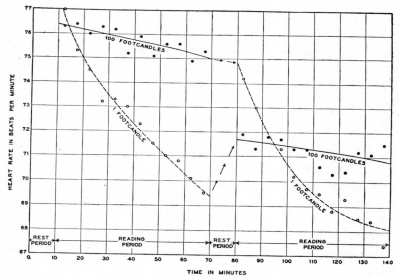

FIG. 65.—The relationship between heart-rate and duration of the reading for each successive 5-minute interval of the entire test-period. Each plotted point represents an average of 70 test-periods. The probable errors of these data are generally less than 0.5 of a beat per minute.

slowly, when the visual task is resumed under 100 footcandles. In view of the fact that reading under 100 footcandles is shown to have little effect upon the heart-rate, a rise rather than a fall in the heart-rate curve in this period might be expected since the heart-rate is so far below the normal initial value. However, the experimental results show that the reverse is true. This relationship between the effects of visual effort and relaxation may eventually prove to be a useful criterion in the field of ocular hygiene.

Superficially one might suppose that the greater decrement in heart-rate under the lower level of illumination was due to a natural psychological association between dim illumination and relaxation or the onset of sleep. The validity of this supposition is doubtful for several reasons. (1) It is not supported by the introspective reports of the subjects. (2) The experimental results show that the subjects read nearly as rapidly under the lower level of illumination as under the higher although it was in no sense a speed test. The observed difference in rate of reading is to be expected due to the lower visibility of the printed matter under the lower level of illumination. (3) Measurements of nervous muscular tension developed as a result of reading (Fig. 62) show that tenseness is decisively greater under one footcandle than under 100 footcandles. It appears that this established fact also definitely rules out relaxation as an explanation of heart-rate decrement.

Theoretical considerations. Boas [92] in summarizing the literature on heart-rate concludes that it is very questionable whether the heart-rate is affected by purely intellectual processes. In the present discussion it has been shown that mere photosensory stimulation, in the absence of critical visual effort, does not primarily affect the heart-rate. However, in reading a definite depression of the heart-rate was noted as the visual work progressed. This result is indirectly supported by the researches of Rihl [93] which indicate that attention to visual stimuli produces such a result. Shepard [94] also finds that the heart-rate is decreased by sensory attention and suggests that this result is due to a decrease in the rate and amplitude of respiration. However, Gillespie [95] concludes that the heart-rate is accelerated by mental effort. These results, which are typical examples from the literature of the subject, emphasize the difficulty of formulating generalizations concerning the influence of various sensory and psychological stimuli upon the heart-rate.

The depression of the heart-rate due to reading may be explainable on the basis of a reflex stimulation of the cells of the central nervous system arising from mental or visual processes which stimulates the inhibitory nerve of the heart. This very general explanation of the depression of the heart-rate while reading is also pertinent to the cause of the development of tenseness while reading. In the latter case it is assumed that various motor nerves are stimulated through the media of reflex arcs. In brief, these effects may be considered as reverberations in the central nervous system due to sensory stimulation. A less complicated explanation of these phenomena, in terms of simple physiological effects, does not appear possible at present.

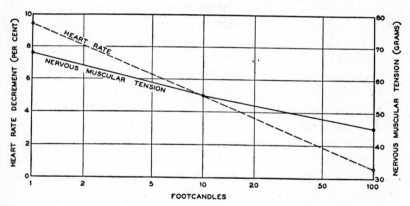

Fig. 66.—The solid-line shows the decrement in indicated nervous muscular tension as the level of illumination is increased. The broken-line indicates the decrement in heart-rate for similar changes in the illumination. These relationships suggest that the two effects have a similar or common origin.

The fact that a relatively large depression in heart-rate was observed under the lower level of illumination, but not under the higher, is interpreted as indicating that the sensory processes were abnormally taxed in the former case. Emphasis is thus placed upon the sensory processes rather than upon the mental phase, since it is reasonable to assume that the latter is not a variable in this particular problem. The variations in tenseness and heart-rate with changes in level of illumination, for the task of reading, are shown in Fig. 66.

Obviously the changes in the heart-rate of the order shown in Fig. 65 are small in comparison to those which occur as a result of physical exercise. Furthermore, it seems reasonable to assume that the heart has been evolved to mediate such increases without deleterious effects to itself. However, the decrements in heart-rate which are due to the performance of prolonged critical visual tasks cannot be so casually explained. These visual tasks are abnormally severe and unnatural in character and it follows that the heart and the vascular system in man have not been developed through evolutionary processes to adequately compensate for the physiological changes these tasks produce. Thus a depression of the heart-rate of at least ten per cent due to reading for one hour under unfavorable conditions for seeing is *unnatural* in that it is brought about by artificial conditions imposed by man. If such tasks are performed eight hours or more a day throughout a period of years, the integrative effects may be definitely deleterious from both the physiological and neurological viewpoints. In addition, it may be emphasized that the decrement in heart-rate due to reading, as shown in Fig. 65, was obtained for healthy young men.

A recent study of occupational morbidity and mortality by the United States Public Health Service revealed that in one company, with approximately 6000 workers doing precision assembly of small parts, almost 80 per cent of the mortality cases in five years involved heart trouble. The trend with the rest of the 59,000 industrial workers whose occupational and illness records were studied was quite similar. It is conceivable that the reflex effects of critical seeing and the prevalence of mortality cases from heart trouble in occupations demanding critical seeing may be related. Certainly heart failure is a common cause of disability and death. Its cause or causes must also be commonplace. The subnormal conditions under which unnaturally critical and prolonged seeing is performed over the course of years and even lifetimes are worthy of the most serious examination, particularly in the light of the present scourge of heart ailments and failure.

THE EYELID REFLEX IN CRITICAL SEEING

The conclusions of Ponder and Kennedy [96] that the "rate of blinking is closely related to the mental tension of the subject at the time and that the movements constitute a kind of relief mechanism whereby nervous energy, otherwise unutilized, passes into a highly facilitated path" suggests the possibility that this phenomenon may serve as a measure of human energy expended in critical seeing. In fact, Litinsky [97] has proposed the recording of winking as a method of study of ocular fatigue in children resulting from reading. Ponder and Kennedy also concluded that the eyelid movements are centrally originated and controlled, although they may be influenced along certain secondary paths, such as the second, fifth and eighth nerves. It has been shown that the performance of critical visual tasks produces certain reflex effects which are considered to be of central origin and which may be correlated with the expenditure of human energy in seeing. In general, our experimental results indicate (1) that nervous muscular tension, developed as a result of continuous reading for a period of 30 minutes, decreases as the task of reading is made easier; and (2) that the heart-rate progressively decreases as the duration of the visual tasks increases and that this decrement in the heart-rate is also increased when the reading is made more difficult. Hence it may be supposed that eyelid movements, since they are supposed to be centrally controlled, may also be caused by "reverberations" in the central nervous system and hence correlated with factors pertaining to the expenditure of human energy in seeing.

We have investigated this possibility directly with many subjects by observing the rate of blinking under the following experimental conditions: (1) during the first and last five minutes, respectively, of an hour of continuous reading, (2) during reading types of different sizes, (3) during reading with and without a glare-source within the visual field, (4) during the performance of a visual task requiring rapid and alternate fixation of two different test-objects, and (5) during reading while wearing eye-

[223]

glasses of improper prescription. Our data were obtained by visual observation and in accordance with the technique described in detail by Peterson and Allison.[98] The experimental results are summarized in Table XXXIII.

TABLE XXXIII

Rate of Blinking While Performing Various Tasks Under Various
Visual Conditions

Visual Situation	Relative Rates of Blinking	
A. Reading for one hour under:[1]		
1 footcandle	First 5 min.	100
	Last 5 min.	171
10 footcandles	First 5 min.	100
	Last 5 min.	131
100 footcandles	First 5 min.	100
	Last 5 min.	108
B. Performing a visual task requiring rapid alternate fixation of test-objects separated 30 degrees [2]	First 5 min.	100
	Second 5 min.	146
	Third 5 min.	171
C. Reading types of different sizes under 10 footcandles [3]	12-pt. type	100
	6-pt. type	148
D. Reading with and without glare. Glare-source at 20 degrees with line of vision [3]	Without glare	100
	With glare	156
E. Reading while wearing various ophthalmic lenses in addition to regular eyeglasses (when worn)[2]	$+\frac{1}{2}$ d. spheres	152
	Plano lenses	100
	$-\frac{1}{2}$ d. spheres	145

[1] 11 subjects; 2 series of measurements.
[2] 18 subjects; 1 series of measurements.
[3] 18 subjects; 2 series of measurements.

Results. In general, it may be concluded from the data of Table XXXIII that the rate of blinking is increased without exception when the *specific* visual task is made more difficult or more prolonged. However, this generalization may not be extended to include various *types* of visual tasks; that is, the reflex blink is not necessarily an adequate criterion for comparing two tasks which are radically different in character. For example, the visual task required in Test B (rapid alternate fixation) is introspectively more severe than that required in Test C (reading 12-point type), yet the actual rate of blinking is slower in Test B as will be noted from Table XXXIV.

T A B L E   X X X I V

The Values Given Are the Number of Blinks Occurring in Five-Minute Periods. The Data for Test A Are Presented in Table XXXVI

Subject	B. Alternate Fixation Period			C. Type-Size		D. Glare		E. Corrections		
	1st	2nd	3rd	6-pt.	12-pt.	With	Without	+.50d	0	—.50d
1	23	24	27	46	32	25	19	41	29	46
2*	11	18	24	40	28	26	18	40	31	39
3*	17	24	24	47	30	32	19	21	22	25
4*	41	56	72	56	35	40	30	73	58	70
5	10	14	17	30	20	52	28	28	17	21
6	15	24	28	70	50	107	80	80	55	80
7	11	10	13	18	14	12	6	26	19	24
8	18	23	26	26	16	22	18	29	15	22
9	30	37	41	22	16	32	19	40	20	33
10	12	17	17	38	28	19	12	57	39	67
11	5	10	13	18	8	20	10	8	11	13
12	6	7	8	10	10	18	14	21	11	22
13	3	7	10	33	26	56	34	29	18	18
14*	13	24	31	22	18	17	11	15	8	16
15*	33	34	26	52	42	50	33	38	29	42
16*	9	11	11	10	6	11	5	11	8	13
17*	19	27	33	31	25	52	38	60	36	30
18*	8	16	15	28	18	32	22	28	14	27
Arith. Mean	15.8	21.3	24.2	33.2	23.4	34.4	23.1	35.8	24.4	33.8
Av. Variation	7.8	9.1	10.5	13.0	10.0	11.2	6.0	15.8	11.8	15.7
Probable Error	1.6	1.9	2.2	2.7	2.0	2.3	1.2	3.2	2.4	3.2

* Correction worn.

Test A. Since it is axiomatic that fatigue increases with the duration of the task, it follows from the results of Test A and Test B, Table XXXIII, that the rate of blinking is a function of the duration of the task and a measure of the fatigue induced by performing the task. Without exception, the subjects blinked at a faster rate at the end of the test-period than at the beginning. In Test A an effort was made to provide physical conditions favorable for easy reading, and in addition, the subjects were allowed to select books which interested them. Under such conditions the task of reading for an hour was not a difficult one when appraised introspectively. However, large increases in the rate of blinking were observed.

Test B. The performance of this test involved severe ocular muscular effort of a character described in detail elsewhere.[99] The subject had to look back and forth from one field to another of the same brightness and to distinguish a letter which appeared in each field. The letters were changed with each alternation. It will be noted that the average rate of blinking during the second five-minute period increased 46 ± 6 per cent over that of the first five-minute period or by an amount equal to that resulting from an hour of reading. During the third five-minute period the rate of blinking was 71 ± 9 per cent faster than it was during the first five-minute period.

It was also observed that the number of blinks during the first period of Test B is definitely less than in the experiments involving reading. Since the lateral displacement of the point of fixation requires a voluntary innervation of the third nerve, which also supplies the levator palpebrae superioris, it is to be expected that the antagonistic orbicularis palpebrarum would reflexly be inhibited, resulting in an initial lowered rate of blinking. It is also conceivable that the observed decrease in the rate of blinking is due to the fact that excessive blinking interferes with the performance of this rapid and exacting visual task. In any event, the criterion of eyelid response is applicable for appraising the relative difficulty of various visual tasks only after allowance is made for any change in the base rate of blinking due to such reflex effects. The experimental results of Telford and Thompson,[100] Table XXXV, apparently corroborate this conclusion in a qualitative manner.

TABLE XXXV

The Mean Number of Eye-Blinks Per Five-Minute Period as Obtained from 36 Subjects

Occupation	Number of Blinks	Standard Error
Mental Arithmetic	54.4	4.0
Reading	14.4	2.7
Conversation	44.5	1.6

Telford and Thompson suggest that the decreased blinking during reading compared with the other two tasks is not due to the mental activity involved, but possibly to several other factors such as the

[226]

visual fixation involved in reading, the eye movements, and other variables. The latter may either increase or decrease the socalled normal rate of blinking.

Test C. Since the fixation and perception of small objects is known to be more difficult than that of larger objects, this phase of visual difficulty was investigated by requiring the subjects to read matter printed in 6-point and 12-point types, respectively. The test-periods were five minutes in duration and so arranged that errors due to the order of the tests were eliminated. The number of blinks while reading the 6-point type was 48 per cent greater than for the 12-point type, with a corresponding probable error of four per cent. These data, indicating that the reading of 6-point type is much more difficult than reading 12-point type, are in harmony with the empirical fact that 6-point type is generally regarded as unsatisfactory for printed matter which is read for rather prolonged periods.

Test D. It has been demonstrated that a glare-source within the visual field augments the development of nervous muscular tension [87] incident to the performance of a critical visual task. In view of the data already presented, it is to be expected that such a situation would also increase the rate of blinking. The data of Test D verify this supposition. In this experiment a 50-watt inside-frosted lamp was placed at a distance of one meter from the eyes of the subject and at an angle of 20 degrees with the line of vision while reading. This glare-source having a brightness of approximately 25 lamberts was more annoying than uncomfortable, according to the introspective reports of the subjects. Thus the glare-source is considered as a distraction whose influence is due to the inherent tendency of the human eye to fixate a bright peripheral object. The number of blinks with and without glare-source was 34.4 and 23.1, respectively, during the five-minute period with corresponding probable errors of 2.3 and 1.2, as will be noted from Table XXXIV. Thus the presence of the glare-source increased the rate of blinking 56 per cent. The conclusion that the increase in the rate of blinking is due to the distracting influence of the glare-source rather than to direct photic stimulation is in agreement with a statement of Ponder and Kennedy to the effect that a sudden illumination of the eyes, as by a bright light concentrated upon them, may produce a few rapid blinks, but after a very short time the rate falls to about the normal for the individual.

Test E. The criterion of the reflex blink was also applied to the appraisal of the effects of refractive errors in the optical system of the eye. The number of blinks during a five-minute period of reading was counted with the subject wearing (1) plus ½ diopter spheres (2) plano lenses and (3) minus ½ diopter spheres in addition to his usual correction, if any. These additional corrections resulted in either blurring the retinal image or dissociating the normal relationship between accommodation and convergence. It is obvious from the data of Table XXXIII (Test E) that the condition of maximum comfort or minimum strain and fatigue was obtained with the prescribed corrections as worn by the subjects as a group. This conclusion applies to the majority of the subjects. In the case of Subject 17, for example, it will be noted that the minimum rate of blinking was obtained when minus ½ diopter spheres were added to the correction worn, and a refraction without mydriatic indicated that this subject needed such a refractive correction. An analysis of other individual results presented in Table XXXIV indicates that not all subjects were perfectly corrected, if minimum rate of blinking be accepted as a criterion of the accuracy of the ophthalmic corrections. However, the errors are relatively small, and in view of the meagerness of the data further quantitative interpretation is not warranted. Nevertheless, it seems reasonable to conclude that the reflex blink may prove eventually to be a significant diagnostic criterion in the science of refraction, particularly if the data were automatically recorded for rather extended periods. The authors have such an investigation and development in progress.

Level of illumination. Owing to the need for all possible criteria and data pertaining to proper levels of illumination, we have studied, and are continuing to study, blinking as related to footcandles upon the visual task. At the outset it appeared pos-

[228]

sible that the higher brightnesses due to higher footcandle-levels might cause a greater rate of blinking. However, this possibility apparently is quite overshadowed by the effect of higher visibility due to higher levels of illumination.

The relationship between level of illumination and the increase in the frequency of blinking from the beginning to the

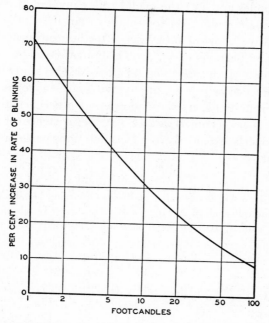

Fig. 67.—The relationship between level of illumination and the increase in the rate of blinking as a result of reading for one hour. The increase in rate of blinking was determined from the number of blinks occurring during the first and last 5-minute periods, respectively, of the hour of reading. This relationship is approximately a logarithmic function of the level of illumination. It is of interest to compare this relationship with that shown in Fig. 62.

close of an hour of reading is shown in Fig. 67. The data for individual subjects are presented in Table XXXVI. In general, it will be noted that the increase in the frequency of blinking is approximately proportional to the logarithm of the illumination under which the reading was performed. A similar relationship was obtained between tenseness and illumination as will be evident by comparing Figs. 67 and 62. Thus these data reveal an extremely close correlation between eyelid reflex and nervous muscular tension or expenditure of energy in reading. We consider this correlation to be highly significant from the viewpoint of ocular hygiene. Thus the criteria (1) visual acuity, (2) nervous muscular tension, (3) the heart-rate, (4) the fatigue of the extrinsic muscles and (5) the eyelid reflex invariably indicate that *reading is easier* under 100 footcandles than it is under one footcandle—and we know of no evidence to the contrary. Obviously this conclusion pertains to level of illumination under good lighting conditions. It has nothing to do with the kinds of lighting found in practice which often involve glare, abnormally bright or dark surroundings, harsh shadows and other negative factors. Since there is no technical excuse for the existence of the latter, they are properly excluded from considerations pertaining to quantity of light.

TABLE XXXVI

The Values Given Are the Number of Blinks Occurring During the First and Last Five-Minute Periods of an Hour of Reading under Levels of Illumination of 1, 10 and 100 Footcandles, Respectively.

Subject	1 Footcandle First	Last	10 Footcandles First	Last	100 Footcandles First	Last
1	39	82	39	56	35	37
2	66	90	69	79	72	77
3	15	25	15	23	17	19
4	25	46	29	40	32	37
5	24	42	19	26	18	21
6	50	116	50	89	54	68
7	62	87	66	71	66	70
8	39	70	40	50	36	40
9	42	75	34	46	40	42
10	10	16	10	14	10	12
11	9	16	10	14	10	11
Average	35	60	35	46	36	39
Per Cent Increase	71.5 ± 5		31.4 ± 3		8.3 ± 1	

Summary. These data indicate that the rate of blinking while performing critical visual tasks is a function of both the duration and severity of the specific visual task, and that an augmentation of either of these factors increases the rate of blinking. It must be considered that the initial rate of blinking is not necessarily a measure of the relative amount of human energy expended in the performance of visual tasks of different characteristics and requirements, since reflex inhibition of blinking will also be involved.

FATIGUE OF THE EXTRINSIC MUSCLES

The present investigation is primarily concerned with the effects of critical visual effort upon the tonus of the extrinsic ocular muscles. This empirical method for investigating a phase of ocular fatigue is not a new one.[101] However, it is unique in that it involves the performance of a universal visual task under conditions which are usual in practice and it deals with a variable—brightness or footcandles—the effects of which have not been studied by this criterion. The experimental data are considered as useful criteria in the field of ocular hygiene and human welfare for the specification of certain physical conditions which will be most favorable for seeing. Since our purpose is to obtain evidence which will be symptomatic of ocular fatigue, it is obvious that an analysis of the *relative* fatigue induced in the muscular systems of accommodation [102] and convergence [103] is not essential. In addition, this study is limited to cases which do not involve known pathological conditions.

The specific objectives of the research were (1) to determine the decrement in the amplitude of convergence reserve due to reading for an hour under levels of illumination of one and 100 footcandles, respectively, and (2) to investigate the duration of this effect after the cessation of the reading. Since the oculomotor, or third cranial nerve, supplies both the ciliary and internal recti muscles, it seems reasonable to assume that the effects of accommodation and convergence in reading will be revealed by measurements of convergence reserve.

Experimental procedure. The internal recti muscles were caused to contract by means of a convergence ergograph until diplopia occurred; that is, until two images were seen. This ergographic technique may be described as a repeated-effort method. A series of 20 successive contractions of these muscles was recorded on the drum of a kymograph immediately preceding and following each period of reading under one of the footcandle-levels. In addition, a third series of 20 measurements was recorded after a ten-minute period of rest during which seeing was casual. The level of illumination under which the reading was done was alternately one and 100 footcandles for the successive test-periods.

It was considered advisable, for reasons of analysis and interpretation, to maintain the same fixational distance during the periods of reading and operation of the ergograph. Accordingly, the test-object for the ergograph was placed at a distance of 14 inches from the eyes. Since the experimental data of Ferree and Rand indicate that the near-point of vision is a function of the brightness of the visual field,[104] this possible extraneous factor was eliminated by taking all ergograph measurements under identical brightness conditions. Actually, the test-object appeared upon an extended white field which was illuminated to ten footcandles. This arrangement thus introduces retinal adaptation as a variable since the reading was performed under brightness conditions differing from those of the ergograph field. However, this can scarcely be significant in the conclusions drawn from the results.

The subjects were instructed to read silently and at their natural rate during the hour of reading. They were particularly cautioned against regarding the procedure as a speed test.

Results. The average amplitude of convergence reserve of the internal recti muscles for the various experimental conditions is presented in Tables XXXVII and XXXVIII. These measurements involved adduction; that is, the turning of the eyes inward from parallelism. Decrements in the amplitude of convergence of 3.0 and 1.0 diopters were observed after reading for one hour under one and 100 footcandles respectively. Therefore, the assumption is made that muscular fatigue produced by reading, as indicated by changes in the tonicity of the internal recti muscles,

[232]

TABLE XXXVII

The Individual Data Presented Represent the Arithmetic Mean of Ten Separate Tests for Subjects 1 and 2; and the Mean of Five Separate Tests for All Other Subjects. The Corresponding Relative Probable Errors, in Per Cent, Are Given in Columns 6 to 9, Respectively.

	Prism Strength—Diopters				Per Cent Relative Probable Error			
	100 F.C.		1 F.C.		100 F.C.		1 F.C.	
Subject	Before	After	Before	After	Before	After	Before	After
	Reading		Reading		Reading		Reading	
1*	12.3	12.0	13.6	10.0	2.0	2.2	1.7	2.4
2*	19.6	18.2	20.9	15.4	1.2	1.4	1.1	1.3
3	18.3	15.4	18.1	14.8	1.1	1.3	1.0	1.3
4	25.1	25.4	25.1	24.1	1.0	0.9	1.2	1.4
5	6.9	7.4	7.7	6.4	1.4	1.5	1.0	1.2
6	19.2	18.4	17.9	16.8	0.8	1.3	1.1	0.9
7	19.0	18.0	17.2	13.9	0.8	0.8	1.0	1.4
8	10.1	8.0	13.8	9.7	2.3	2.2	3.3	2.9
9*	16.5	14.6	16.7	13.0	0.6	1.0	0.5	1.0
Geometric Mean	15.3	14.3	16.0	13.0	0.5	0.5	0.5	0.6

* Correction worn.

TABLE XXXVIII

The Individual Data Represent the Arithmetic Mean from Five Separate Tests for Each of the Subjects

| | Prism Strength—Diopters | | |
| | | 1 F.C. | |
Subject	Before Reading	After Reading	After 10-Min. Rest
1	17.1	13.9	17.0
2	23.4	18.2	22.9
3	14.6	11.6	13.3
4	......	......	......
5	7.5	6.1	7.4
6	19.6	17.2	19.0
7	16.6	13.4	16.5
8	13.8	9.7	14.2
9	16.8	12.7	16.3
Geometric Mean	15.5	12.3	15.2

is approximately three times as severe after reading one hour under one footcandle as it is after an hour's reading of the same printed matter under 100 footcandles. This conclusion is even more significant in view of the fact that the subjects read nearly ten per cent faster in the latter case even though they were asked to read at a natural rate. The relative probable errors of the average convergence reserve are considerably less than one per cent, therefore, the observed differences in convergence reserve have a high degree of statistical reliability.

Since the brightness of the pages of the book was either one-tenth that of the ergograph field or ten times as great, this factor is to be considered in the interpretation of the results. It appears reasonable to assume that the sudden transition from the higher brightness of the book to the lower brightness of the ergograph field would adversely affect the power of convergence due to incomplete retinal adaptation. This effect would not be expected when the change was from the lower to the higher brightness. Hence the conclusion regarding the relative fatigue of reading under these two levels of illumination is considered as a conservative one.

These data provide an additional link in the chain of experimental evidence which indicates that at least 100 footcandles are desirable for reading under usual conditions. This conclusion is based upon the assumption that preventable glare and other negative visual factors are not present in the lighting environment. It is obvious that this conclusion is not applicable to certain cases involving pathology.

An analysis of the data taken ten minutes after the cessation of reading indicates that these symptoms of ocular fatigue, due to an hour's reading of large type excellently printed, practically disappear during this brief period of casual seeing, as will be noted from Table XXXVIII. It is of theoretical interest at least to compare the effects of rest (from reading) upon the tonus of the ocular muscles with other physiological reactions. The data obtained in the research on heart-rate indicate that a period of at least 30 minutes of rest is required to dissipate the effects upon the heart-rate which resulted from reading for one hour under one footcandle.

It is conceivable that the time required to dissipate muscular fatigue may eventually prove to be an important datum in the field of ocular hygiene for determining the duration of rest-periods. Such data would be particularly significant when applicable to children and those with severe visual disorders.

Theoretical considerations. A possible explanation of the greater decrement in the amplitude of convergence under the lower level of illumination is that a more exact fixation is required due to the lower visibility of the printed characters. This supposition at least appears reasonable from a quantitative basis. Experimental data relating extent and brightness for the liminal visual stimulus [63] establish the fact that an object must be approximately 1.8 times as large to be visible under one footcandle as it needs to be under 100 footcandles. A differential in threshold size of this magnitude would permit considerable variation in the oculomotor habits of the reader in the two situations.

It might be contended that the greater fatigue of the internal recti muscles indicated under the lower level of illumination resulted from a larger number of fixational-pauses during the reading. It has been shown that the frequency of fixational-pauses is a function of the complexity of the objects of regard.[39] Hence, if it is assumed that decreased visibility and greater complexity are similar factors in this respect, the explanation of a differential in fixational-pauses may be given some credence. However, the fact that the subjects read nearly ten per cent faster under the higher level of illumination makes such an explanation less attractive.

Ocular fatigue from a work-world task. The change in convergence reserve from the beginning to the close of the work-day was determined for four women operators of key punch machines. As a visual task, this work is similar to typing excepting that the recognition of numerals predominates, and perhaps even greater concentration of the eyes upon the task is required. These measurements were made under two conditions of illumination: (1)

with the machines illuminated by ceiling lights which provided a general level of illumination of about ten footcandles; and (2) with the ceiling lights plus a supplementary light properly located at each machine, which produced about 60 footcandles upon the work. The supplementary lights were used on alternate weeks during the test-period of six weeks. The daily measurements of convergence reserve before and after the day's work are summarized in Table XXXIX.

TABLE XXXIX

In This Table the Caption "Light On" Indicates That the Supplementary Lights on the Machines Were Used

Subject	Prism Diopters				Relative Probable Error Per Cent			
	Light On		Light Off		Light On		Light Off	
	AM	PM	AM	PM	AM	PM	AM	PM
A	14.8	13.7	16.0	12.1	.99	.85	1.07	1.00
B	8.8	8.5	8.9	7.6	.86	.69	1.00	.93
C	8.7	8.3	9.1	7.8	1.29	1.83	1.46	1.62
Geometric Mean	10.4	9.9	10.9	8.9	.61	.71	.69	.71
D	23.3	25.2	22.4	27.3	.97	.80	1.08	.90

It will be noted that for three of the four subjects the amplitude of convergence reserve decreased nearly 20 per cent as a result of the day's work when the latter was performed under the general lighting; and only five per cent when the supplementary lighting was used. However, one subject (D) showed a decided increase in the amplitude of convergence reserve during the work-day. This interesting exception to the usual result possibly represents a case in which the subject over-compensated for the development of fatigue through a greater expenditure of nervous energy. Furthermore, the fact that this operator attained the highest speed ever recorded in this particular office during the period of the muscle-fatigue tests, may not be unrelated to the indication of over-compensation.

PUPIL SIZE AND OCULAR FATIGUE

In the performance of visual work, the size of the pupils varies with photic stimulation, with the associated movements of accommodation and convergence, and to a lesser extent, with certain other influences. These variations may be conveniently designated as temporary changes. It is reasonable to suspect that some semi-permanent pupillary change may be produced by sev-

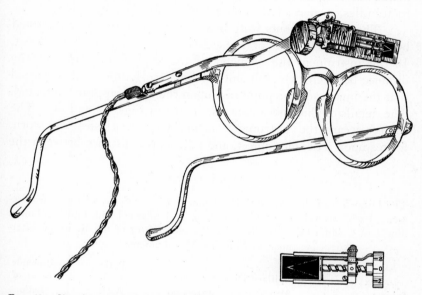

FIG. 68.—Showing the Luckiesh-Moss Pupillometer and its position with respect to the right eye. In this design, the central visual field of the right eye is obscured by the mechanism of the pupillometer.

eral hours of continuous and exacting visual work and that this pupillary change will largely disappear after a period of rest. If this is the case, a comparison of measurements of pupillary size made at the beginning and at the end of a long period of visual work should reveal such a semi-permanent change in the size of the pupil. If such a change is observed, it may be assumed to be an indirect index of ocular fatigue developed during the period of visual work.

[237]

This problem was investigated by measuring the size of the pupils of nine subjects at the beginning and at the close of a day's work.[36] During the interval between these series of measurements, the subjects were engaged in various kinds of clerical and general laboratory work. All measurements were made with the eyes adapted to the same brightness-level and with a constant state of accommodation. The room in which the measurements were made was uniformly illuminated to a level of approximately ten footcandles, as measured upon a horizontal plane.

The measurements were made with a pupillometer designed by the authors [105] and of the general type suggested by Broca. In this instrument the diameter of the pupil is measured by the distance between two pin-points of light, so located and separated that the images of the pupil cast upon the retina appear tangential. The details of this instrument are shown in Figs. 68 and 69. The subject wears the instrument as ordinary eyeglasses are worn, fixates upon a definite object, and adjusts the distance between the

TABLE XL

The Diameters of the Pupils, as Determined from 22 Series of Five Measurements Each, Are Given for Nine Subjects in the Second and Third Columns. The Last Column Gives the Relative Probable Errors of the Ratios of Afternoon to Morning Measurements.

Subject	Pupillary Diameter (mm.) 8:30–9:30	4:00–5:00	Ratio P.M. / A.M.	Probable Error of Ratio
1	6.16	6.25	1.014	.007
2	4.17	4.38	1.056	.015
3	4.97	5.54	1.115	.005
4*	7.32	7.35	1.003	.004
5	6.35	6.60	1.041	.011
6	4.83	5.14	1.065	.008
7	4.46	4.94	1.111	.015
8	5.89	6.49	1.104	.008
9	4.67	4.93	1.056	.011
Arithmetic Mean....			1.063	.010
Geometric Mean....			1.062	

* An average of 16 series of measurements.

two points of light until the retinal images appear tangential. During this procedure it is obviously essential that the accommodation remain constant.

In general, the sensitivity of this technique is such that the slight changes in pupil size due to the emptying and filling of the iridic blood-vessels are readily observable. It will be noted that the pupillometer obscures the visual field of the right eye and hence the measured diameter of the pupil is larger than it would

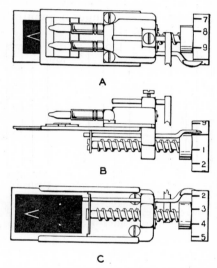

FIG. 69.—The mechanical details of the pupillometer. *A* shows the side farthest from the eye; *B,* the top view; and *C,* the side nearest the eye. (Actual size.)

be if one eye were not so obscured. However, due to the fact that light entering the unobscured eye adds its pupillomotor influence to the other, the results obtained with the pupillometer illustrated in Figs. 68 and 69 are considered adequate as relative criteria for revealing the influence of fatigue upon the size of the pupil.

It will be noted from the data of Table XL that the pupil dilated approximately six per cent in diameter, or 13 per cent in area, during the course of the day. From the statistical viewpoint this difference in pupillary size is to be regarded as significant,

[239]

since it is more than six times the probable error of the measurements. In addition, it will be noted the pupils of all subjects showed a dilatation as the day progressed.

In general, it was observed that on occasions when the subjects volunteered the information that their eyes "felt tired," there was a marked increase in the pupillary area for the afternoon period as compared with that of the morning. No attempt has been made to present this introspective data in tabular form. However, a mathematical analysis of the data gives no indication of a bi-modal distribution of the changes in pupillary area. There-

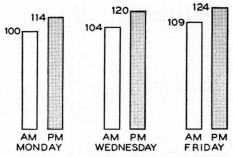

FIG. 70.—The relative area of the pupil at different periods of the work-week. It will be noted that there is a gradual dilation of the pupil as the work-week progresses.

fore, little importance may be attached to the introspective reports of the subjects.

A further analysis of the same data indicates that the size of the pupil not only increases during the day, but also slowly and somewhat irregularly increases as the week progresses from Monday to the close of the work-week on Friday afternoon. The data summarized in Table XLI, Fig. 70, are for a period of four weeks.

From these data it appears that the effect of the day's use of the eyes in the work-world is not entirely dissipated by relaxation at night, and that further relaxation from near-visual work is required. It is probable that the eyes of these subjects were not subjected to unusual variations in photic stimulation during the non-work days of Saturday and Sunday, and that the contraction of the pupils occurring during this period is chiefly a result of a reduction in the near-visual work. If this is assumed to be true, then it follows that socalled ocular fatigue is apparently due to muscular rather than retinal fatigue. Such a conclusion finds support in other independent analyses.

T A B L E   X L I

The Size of the •Pupils in the Morning and Afternoon of Each Day of the Work-Week

Subject	Monday A.M.	Monday P.M.	Tuesday A.M.	Tuesday P.M.	Wednesday A.M.	Wednesday P.M.	Thursday A.M.	Thursday P.M.	Friday A.M.	Friday P.M.
1	5.98	6.33	6.18	6.18	6.27	6.06	6.15	6.21	6.19	6.42
2	4.00	4.22	4.20	4.22	4.19	4.43	4.17	4.50	4.63	4.67
3	4.91	5.49	5.05	5.54	4.89	5.49	5.01	5.59	5.07	5.65
5	6.22	6.43	5.36	6.34	6.46	6.56	6.43	6.72	6.34	6.78
6	4.82	5.05	4.72	5.00	4.83	5.34	4.94	5.24	4.84	5.11
7	4.44	4.85	4.51	5.07	4.29	4.96	4.67	4.00	4.50	4.79
8	5.58	6.22	5.98	6.40	5.83	6.61	6.11	6.62	5.98	6.60
9	4.66	4.77	4.49	4.81	4.74	4.97	4.66	4.92	4.84	5.24
Geometric Mean	5.02	5.36	5.12	5.39	5.12	5.50	5.21	5.39	5.25	5.60

(Subject No. 4 omitted from this summary as a complete series of measurements is not available.)

It may be concluded from these data that the pupil changes in size during the course of a day's work and that this change is very generally one of dilatation. Whether this change is due to the performance of visual work or to some physiological cycle cannot be definitely determined from these data. A possible explanation is that the continuous functioning of the iridic muscles develops fatigue in these muscles which in itself may be an indirect measure of general ocular fatigue.

S U M M A R Y

The relationships between level of illumination and (1) visual acuity, (2) contrast sensibility, (3) nervous muscular tension, (4) the heart-rate, (5) fatigue of the extrinsic ocular muscles, and (6) the eyelid reflex are summarized in Fig. 11. Certainly these are diverse criteria for appraising ease of seeing as it is influenced by light and lighting. Obviously, these criteria may be applied in the determination of the effects of other factors which influence ease of seeing, such as refractive errors, small type, low contrasts and duration of critical visual tasks. It is to be emphasized that these data were obtained from normal healthy young men and women while these subjects were performing relatively easy visual tasks under relatively good conditions. Certainly many tasks of the work-world such as sewing, engraving, inspection and precision assembly are far more exacting and difficult.   •

At present, we may only surmise the import of these effects of seeing in pathological cases. It does not seem unreasonable to suppose, for example, that the development of nervous muscular tension from prolonged critical seeing would be more serious for a neurotic patient than it would be for a young and healthy subject. If a ten per cent departure from the normal heart-rate due to reading under unfavorable conditions is not considered to be a matter of great importance for our seven more or less athletic young subjects, it might be very important for those possessing certain cardiac anomalies. Furthermore, it is conceivable that the change might be greater than ten per cent in such cases. In cases involving excessive blinking, as in blepharism, the augmentation of the frequency of blinking due to unfavorable conditions for seeing may be quite serious. In general, these physiological effects developed from the performance of a common visual task are potentially important to the human seeing-machine; and in concluding, it is again emphasized that they were observed after relatively short periods of reading. We are not prepared to estimate their importance when they are continued day after day for years. Obviously, this is a subject for clinical research and it appears to be an appealing one.

VISUAL FUNCTIONS AND RATE OF WORKING

The functioning of the human machine is the result of a host of applied stimuli. Therefore, the seeing specialist is faced with a decidedly difficult task when he attempts to isolate the effect of one factor from the many that are present. The problem is difficult even in the research laboratory where elaborate precautions can be taken to minimize the number of variables and to control them. It is not unusual for the laboratory technician to take thousands of observations to determine one particular phase of the relationship between a certain controllable factor and seeing. When direct, simple, and quick measurements of seeing are attempted outside of the laboratory the pitfalls are increased and the difficulties are magnified. Not only do eyes and individuals differ greatly, but the same subject will frequently give results varying over a range several times as great as the difference sought. These wide fluctuations are likely to occur not only momentarily but from one test to another.

Another difficulty encountered when one seeks to show the visual difference between two conditions for seeing is that the eyes will temporarily compensate for the poorer conditions, at the observer's expense, and by increased expenditure of energy actually perform as well as under the more favorable condition. The following brief summary of a recent experiment illustrates this phase and also demonstrates one of the pitfalls of superficial knowledge and analysis. The eyes of the subjects were tested at the beginning and again at the close of the day's work and, in addition, the subjects were required to perform a rather difficult mechanical and visual task. The rate of working and the accuracy of and attentiveness to the work were determined. The results obtained after the subjects did their usual day's work in offices compared with those obtained at the beginning of the day were as follows:

The Eyes

> Visual acuity decreased 2 per cent.
> Eye-muscle balance changed 5 per cent.

Performance of Work

> Attentiveness to task increased 14 per cent.
> Delay in correcting errors decreased 2 per cent.
> Amount of work done increased 4 per cent.

It is to be noted that, although the eyes and the subjects showed evidence of fatigue and strain, the performance of this specially inserted work was greater at the close of the day than at the beginning. Similar results have been obtained in some other experiments. Such a situation, in which *increasing production* takes the place with *decreasing ability* to produce, forms a combination which is detrimental to the welfare of the worker and results in excessive fatigue and losses in nervous energy. It can be stated definitely that the rate of working is not necessarily an indication of fatigue, since the results often indicate the opposite effect. It is likely that quality and quantity of work done would always be unfavorably affected when fatigue of the eyes or subjects has progressed toward the extreme of exhaustion. However, when this is not true conclusions based upon work done should be drawn carefully. These experiments show the difficulty encountered in using production of work as a measure of visual efficiency, of fatigue, or of wasted human resources. The effect to be determined is often obscured, principally on account of the ability of workers to adapt themselves to widely different conditions even at the expense of greater effort and fatigue.

CHAPTER VII

Conservation and Achievement

Such sciences as ophthalmology, optometry, optics, and hygiene have made great contributions to human beings through the conservation of vision. Many other scientific activities deal with matters in which seeing is involved, and sometimes seeing is considered in extensive investigations involving human beings and in the conclusions and practices resulting therefrom. However, it appears that seeing should be taken into account in such activities to a much greater extent than it has been in the past. It is axiomatic that seeing and, therefore, the factors which aid or hinder it, play an important part in the production, fatigue, health, comfort and safety of human beings. Nevertheless, extensive studies have been made of the effects of work and work conditions upon the efficiency and welfare of workers without considering seeing at all. This is also true of many other studies dealing primarily with such matters as health, safety, and education. Doubtless this neglect of seeing is largely due to its commonplaceness and to inadequate conceptions of it.

Eye-examinations made before and during employment may well include consideration of the deleterious effects of the critical visual work done by the worker or of readily controllable factors such as light and lighting. Many opportunities for ascertaining possible improvements in eyesight, health, progress, etc., due to improvement in seeing conditions are passed by unheeded in the welfare activities in schools and in the work-world. For years, safety engineers and organizations have analyzed accidents, have perfected many effective safety devices, and have developed meritorious educational approaches. All this has contributed much toward greater safety, but seeing as a human activity and as an almost universal factor in safety has received relatively little attention.   Death and destruction on streets and highways is extensively publicized and analyzed, but poor seeing is rarely mentioned as a primary or even secondary cause.   Somehow carelessness, speed and mechanical failure are given far more attention than visibility, light, lighting and seeing.   This is unjustifiable from the viewpoint of the importance of seeing and of the limitations of the human seeing-machine, particularly at night on the highways where visibility is generally close to, and often below, the threshold.

Long ago insurance companies concluded that in about 20 per cent of the industrial accidents inadequate light or improper lighting was a contributing cause.[106]   What would this percentage actually be if the analysis were made from the viewpoint of new concepts and knowledge of light as an aid to seeing?   What was considered adequate light in past years of empirical lighting practice has been radically revised.   It is difficult to believe that seeing—easy, quick and certain—is not a major factor in safety when there is no carelessness or mechanical failure.   There are many controllable factors and in any given case it is always possible to utilize some of them to improve seeing.

Notable advances have been made in the efficiency and welfare of human beings throughout the work-world by motion-study, routing of processes, ventilation, rest-periods and the like. However, an extensive literature reveals little attention to the reduction of fatigue and the enhancement of quality and quantity of achievement of the workers by improving the seeing conditions.   It may be determined that female workers should have a ten-minute rest-period each hour or that certain workers should be switched to other work periodically.   However, even in elaborate studies and conclusions of this character generally there is no evidence of a consciousness that fatigue can be lessened and achievement can be improved through various controllable aids to seeing.   Some attention has been given to the effect of foot-candles upon production and spoilage, but not from the modern viewpoint of light and lighting as they affect visibility and ease of seeing.   Throughout the work-world the lot of the worker

[246]

has notably improved in the past score of years by approaches from many important angles, but an appropriate seeing consciousness has been notably absent or meager at best.

Psychologists have made much progress toward understanding the complexity of reaction-times and the influence of distractions upon the efficiency and efficacy of human senses. However, the conception of the human being as a seeing-machine has not clearly and adequately entered most of their considerations. Studies of the differences between old, young, normal and subnormal human beings have progressed in many directions; but the idea of compensating deficiencies due to age, for example, by means of aids to seeing, other than eyeglasses, has not penetrated far into such considerations. Age has acquired skill and wisdom. To retain the benefits of these in the work-world, it is necessary to counteract other deficiencies by means of man-made aids. It is quite evident that various controllable aids to seeing can help older persons, and even young persons whose eyesight is subnormal, and make them comparable with average adult seeing-machines by diminishing the inequalities.

On every hand in most of the activities of human beings, seeing plays a primary or prominent part. It appears axiomatic that, at least, the major factors and results of seeing should be borne in mind by those specifically interested in human efficiency and welfare. The new concepts and knowledge embodied in the science of seeing indicate that considerations of vision which have seldom been adequate in such studies should be extended considerably. In the present discussion an attempt is made to reveal something of the variety of avenues of human activity in which seeing is an important factor in the quality and quantity of human achievement. Owing to the general lack of adequate considerations of seeing in studies of human activities, there is a paucity of authentic data showing the effects of seeing conditions upon achievement. However, some examples are available for illustrating the discussion.

To freshen the approach to a consideration of achievement through seeing and its aids, hindrances and effects, Fig. 71 is

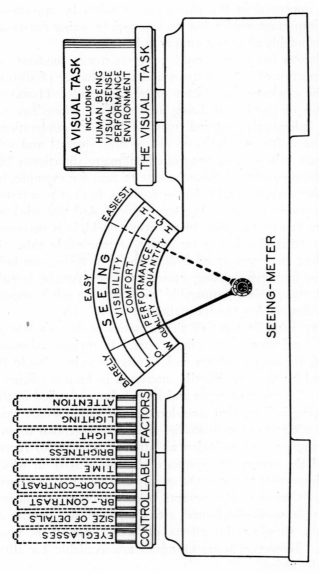

FIG. 71.—A diagrammatic view of the controllable factors in seeing balanced against a given visual task considered in its extended sense which includes the vagaries, limitations and abilities of the human being, the characteristics and requirements of performance and the environment as it affects visibility and the human seeing-machine. In any given case at least some of the factors shown on the left-hand platform are controllable. These can be utilized to increase speed, accuracy, certainty and ease of seeing.

presented. This is a conventionalized seeing-meter which suggests that controllable factors in seeing may be balanced against the results of seeing. It also suggests that the former may be used to counterbalance the latter at any point on the scales of ease of seeing, of visibility, of quality and quantity of performance. On the right-hand platform the visual task is placed. It is indicated that any given visual task involves more than the physical external characteristics of the task itself. It also includes the specific characteristics and requirements of performance, the factors of the environment such as distractions and surroundings, and the vagaries, deficiencies and limitations of the visual sense and of human beings, and various other human factors. On the left-hand platform are placed the controllable factors which influence seeing. In any given case some are usually controllable by someone. Commonly, throughout the artificial world, the combined effect of the controllable factors as they are actually associated with a visual task (in the complete sense) is illustrated by the position of the pointer in Fig. 71. If some of these factors which are controllable in an actual case are sufficiently augmented, seeing is improved as indicated by the other position of the pointer. The controllable factors indicated on this diagrammatic seeing-meter are quite inclusive. In Chapter II the various factors are described more in detail.

CONSERVATION OF VISION

The application of silver nitrate to an infant's eyes is the first contribution of medical science from the viewpoint of vision. Often the second important one is the first pair of eyeglasses that this human being receives years later. Between these two major contributions to human vision, science is capable of making various other contributions and at present education in ocular hygiene is prominent among these. From our viewpoint, the control of the external physical conditions under which seeing is done has not been adequately developed or effectively applied in practice. We would expect that two primarily important benefits in the conservation of human resources would be derived from such control:

1. The minimization of ocular deficiencies,
2. The minimization of the strain and fatigue of performing the necessary tasks imposed by civilization.

While silver nitrate may prevent infection and eyeglasses may correct refractive errors, the control of conditions for seeing has the potentiality of making seeing *easier* but not necessarily *easy*. It is not to be supposed that even the maximum possible control of modern visual tasks will eliminate defective vision or will completely compensate for the deleterious effects of prolonged near-vision tasks. Investigations have shown that primitive races possess the same sort of visual defects as do civilized peoples. However, these defects are less serious in the case of the primitive man since his visual tasks are less critical. Furthermore, these tasks do not aggravate visual deficiencies to the same degree that modern critical tasks do. In this connection it is also interesting to refer to the prevalence of defective or deficient vision among groups in various modern occupations as illustrated in Fig. 5.

Optimum conditions for seeing not only minimize eyestrain and ocular fatigue, but also conserve human energy in many unobvious ways. Some of these physiological effects are illustrated in Fig. 11 and also discussed in Chapter VI. In general, if conditions for seeing are poor, the handicap thus imposed upon the human seeing-machine may be offset to some extent by an increased expenditure of human resources. Thus the characteristics of seeing conditions in our artificial world are directly related to the willingness to expend human rather than material resources. In addition to the "normal" deterioration of the visual abilities with age, there are superposed the penalties of defective vision which may be considered to result from the use and abuse of the eyes through years of performing critical near-vision tasks. Some of these effects of age are shown in Fig. 72.

Vision. It will be noted that, as the eyes grow older, there is a progressive loss in visual acuity; the pupils become smaller and their response to changes in illumination decreases; the amplitude of accommodation decreases until it becomes inadequate for close work; and the prevalence of defective vision increases markedly. In this respect, the visual mechanism is no different from other bodily mechanisms which deteriorate or become less efficient with age. To some extent the human being alters the character of the tasks he performs in accordance with his abilities to perform them as he grows older, but visual tasks themselves

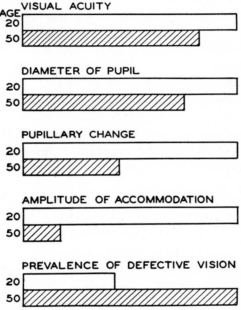

FIG. 72.—Showing the effects of age upon visual functions and visual abilities.

are not altered. At a certain age a laborer may be physically unable to continue hard manual labor, but a proofreader can usually continue with his work even though at constantly increasing effort. From the humanitarian viewpoint, the aids to seeing which science has made available should be used to compensate for the deterioration of human abilities.

As a generalization, Mills [107] has stated that eye injury usually begins in the third grade. This conclusion is adequately supported by much data showing the increase in the prevalence of myopia among school children as they grow older. An example of such data is presented in Table XLII from a compilation by the United States Public Health Service.[108] These data are given for the right and left eyes, respectively, which show that this defect is commonly present in both eyes. It will be noted that about two per cent of the pupils in the youngest group (six to eight years) are myopic. As many of these early cases of myopia are of congenital origin, it appears that the beginning of severe visual work in the schools marks the onset of defective vision. Since the character and visibility of the school tasks and their duration are controllable, it seems likely that adequate control over these factors has not been exercised, if the increase in myopia may be taken as a criterion of the efficacy of the control. However, it is not implied that optimum conditions for seeing would prevent the increase in the prevalence of myopia, but there are many reasons for believing that such conditions would minimize this and other visual defects.

TABLE XLII

The Prevalence of Myopia Among School Children in Three Age-Groups in Per Cent of the Total Examined

Age in Years	6 to 8		9 to 11		12 and Over	
Eye	Right	Left	Right	Left	Right	Left
Boys	2.6	2.6	6.3	6.3	9.6	10.0
Girls	1.7	1.7	4.5	4.5	8.5	8.9
Both	2.1	2.1	5.5	5.5	9.1	9.5

It is not surprising that the visual tasks in schools have not been graded in visual difficulty upon a rational and quantitative basis and in accordance with the visual abilities of the pupils. Such refinements can scarcely be expected as long as gross eye-defects are so often ignored. Even in cases of pupils wearing eyeglasses, it has been shown [109] that these may be in error in a rather large percentage of the cases. One would hardly expect such a refinement in ocular hygiene in schools which "test" the vision of the pupils merely with the aid of a Snellen Chart. The data of Table

XLIII indicate the extent to which visual defects were found to be accurately corrected with eyeglasses.

TABLE XLIII

Percentages of Cases in Which Visual Defects Are Neglected or Inaccurately Corrected

	Number	Per Cent
Children examined	15267	100.0
Having defective vision	1881	12.3
Having proper eyeglasses	627	4.1
Having improper eyeglasses	415	2.7

These data indicate that about 12 per cent of these school children had defective vision. These are in close agreement with those found by a nation-wide survey of some 4,200,000 school-children of the United States. It will be noted that less than 60 per cent of the cases needing eyeglasses were provided with them; and of the eyeglasses being worn about 40 per cent were in error at the time of the investigation. Although the science of refraction is highly developed it is obvious that the application of this science is far from complete. The science of seeing has revealed the benefits to be derived from other aids to seeing and these are beginning to be applied upon a rational basis. However, their use in assisting human eyes in performing the exacting visual tasks of the modern world is even less extensive than that of eyeglasses. The goal is the complete and universal use of all aids to seeing. It is probable that even if this goal is attained, the result will only minimize the deleterious effects of critical near-vision tasks. Further reduction might be achieved by other means such as rest, relaxation and exercise of the eyes.

The results obtained by Boynton[110] in studies of eye-defectiveness among college students are doubtless typical. Visual acuity was determined with the Snellen Chart for 1000 students upon entering college and before graduation four years later. This method cannot detect small differences or changes in visual acuity and probably does not detect or appraise many cases of hyperopia and moderate astigmatism. Therefore, the conclusions are perhaps conservative. Some of the data are presented in Table XLIV. It is emphasized that these data pertain only to net de-

TABLE XLIV

Decrease in Visual Acuity During Four Years in College

	Students Examined	Per Cent of Total
No change or slight decrease	790	79.0
Moderate decrease	61	6.1
Marked decrease	149	14.9

tectable change by a relatively crude method of measuring visual acuity. It is seen that about 15 per cent of the students showed a marked decrease in visual acuity, during the four years, equivalent to two or more lines on the Snellen Chart. Of the 1000 students 788 had better than 20/30 vision on entering and only 680 on leaving. On entering only 52 per cent had 20/20, or socalled normal vision, and 26 per cent wore glasses. Boynton very properly emphasizes the importance of symptoms of eye-trouble. Of 229 students in the test group that were fitted with glasses during the four years, almost as many of those with 20/20 or 20/30 vision complained of eye-trouble as those whose visual acuity markedly decreased.

Apparently it is established among school-children that defective vision reduces scholarship, achievement and progress in general. However, among college students statistics appear to indicate that better students have poorer eyesight. Boynton's work with two groups of students verifies this. An ability test given to 378 students on entering college showed that those ranking in the upper fourth had more cases of 20/70 vision or less than those in the lower fourth. This was also true in the appraisal of scholastic achievement of 194 medical students during four years.

Therefore, it is seen that sizable percentages leave college with the handicap of appreciably defective vision. Whether or not this deterioration can be reduced or eliminated, it is certain that the handicap will continue throughout life unless counter-

[254]

acted by adequate use of controllable aids to seeing. Certainly this represents unnecessary waste and disappointment, which must be partly preventable and can be largely compensated for by proper attention to various aids. An excellent verification of all this is found in the results of the United States Naval Academy a few years ago. At the time of graduation one of every eight

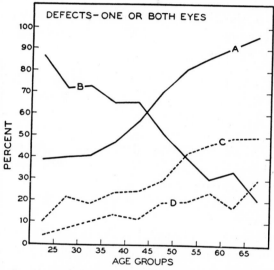

FIG. 73.—Showing the prevalence of defective vision among a group of 3000 industrial workers and the extent to which the visual defects have been corrected with eyeglasses. Curve *A* shows the increase in the prevalence of defective vision at various ages; *B*, the cases in which no effort was made to correct the visual defects; *C*, those cases with incomplete corrections; and *D*, those with complete correction.

graduates was not admitted to the Navy on account of subnormal eyesight. Those rejected, in common with all others of the class, had passed rigid eye-examinations on entering four years before. This was waste and disappointment.

The prevalence of uncorrected or improperly corrected visual defects persists through life [111] as will be noted from the data of Fig. 73 derived from the examination of 3000 employed men. Curve *A* shows the percentage of those of various ages who had de-

[255]

fective vision. Curve *B* shows the percentages who had made no effort to obtain eyeglasses. Curve *C* shows the percentages wearing eyeglasses, and Curve *D* the percentages who were wearing correct ones at the time the investigation was made. It will be noted that about 40 per cent of the youngest workers possess defective vision, and of these only about one-tenth have proper corrections although about one-fourth of them wear eyeglasses. At the age of 50, about 75 per cent have subnormal vision, and of these about one-fourth are properly corrected although more than one-half wear eyeglasses. The rather sharp increase in the number wearing eyeglasses for ages between 40 and 50 years is undoubtedly due to the onset of presbyopia, which strikingly emphasizes to the individual the need of glasses. Presbyopia generally makes eyeglasses a necessity to those doing much near-vision work. The fact that such a large proportion of the population has uncorrected visual errors emphasizes the importance of considerations of all controllable aids to seeing. All aids, excepting eyeglasses, serve all eyes, both normal and abnormal. It is even probable that a greater use of socalled magnifying glasses could be justified for visual tasks involving very small details.

There is some experimental evidence to indicate that higher levels of illumination not only increase visibility and ease of seeing, but also gradually and measurably increase the ability of the visual sense which has become impaired through years of use under unfavorable conditions for seeing. Ives [86] and his associates of the United States Public Health Service conducted an investigation of the relationship between lighting and its influence upon the welfare of the eyes of a large number of post-office employees engaged in routine sorting of mail. The average length of service of these employees as mail sorters was 16.5 years. Although about 90 per cent of these employees possessed visual defects, only 50 per cent wore glasses. Thus this situation possessed several advantages for the purposes of the research. Measurements were taken on a relatively large number of subjects performing more or less severe visual work; the prevalence of defective vision was high; the same group of subjects was available throughout the test-period which extended over a year; and the type of visual work remained fairly constant.

Visual acuity was selected as a criterion of the ocular changes which followed changes in the level of illumination at the work-places. The measurements of visual acuity were under constant conditions, before and after a day's work, throughout the entire

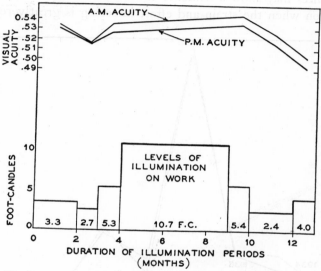

Fig. 74.—The lower part of the diagram shows the duration and the succession of certain periods of investigation and the levels of illumination under which the workers sorted mail. The upper part of the diagram shows the results of measurements of visual acuity, made in the morning and afternoon under constant conditions independent of work conditions. This indicates that level of illumination permanently affects the visual acuity of the workers' eyes.

investigation and independent of the work-conditions. It will be noted from Fig. 74 that visual acuity decreased during the day. However, it is of particular interest to note that after working under an increased level of illumination there was a measurable improvement in visual acuity, and that the change in visual acuity noticeably lagged behind the time when the change in footcandles was made. This investigation provides rather direct evidence that higher footcandle-levels may permanently benefit the visual

[257]

organs themselves when the latter have been impaired by long service under unfavorable conditions for seeing. Obviously this conclusion is not to be construed as suggesting that refractive errors such as astigmatism or axial myopia are lessened by improving the conditions under which seeing is accomplished. However, it is conceivable that certain defects such as muscular imbalances may show a tendency toward returning to the normal condition when the strain and effort in seeing is greatly reduced.

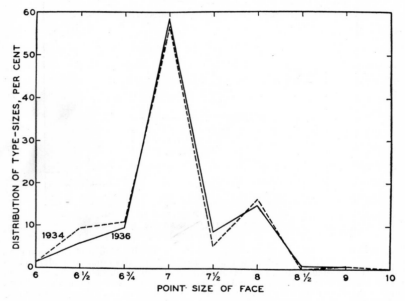

FIG. 75.—Showing the percentages of a total of nearly 500 American newspapers using types of various sizes for the years of 1934 and 1936, respectively.

It is unfortunate that it was necessary to conduct this important research at such low levels of illumination as were used. Researches in physiological optics invariably indicate that relatively large changes in illumination are required in order to obtain obvious and significant improvements in visibility and in ease of seeing. Furthermore, visual acuity is a rather inadequate criterion for revealing the many complex influences which better lighting may exert upon the behavior, efficiency and welfare of the human seeing-machine. A similar extensive research which included criteria of ease of seeing such as nervous muscular tension, heart-rate, pupil size, the reflex blink and the fatigue of the ocular muscles would undoubtedly be of great interest and importance.

Visual tasks. Optimum visibility of visual tasks as well as optimum visual efficiency of the eyes is a primary objective of the science of seeing and should also be in ocular hygiene. In general, the visibility of the visual task is usually controllable. We have shown that higher levels of illumination are effective in this manner. In view of the fact that reading is a universal and critical task, it follows that type-size is an extremely important and controllable factor for obtaining hygienic conditions in reading. However, this factor, as is the case with light, has been employed inadequately for the purpose. The data of Fig. 75 show the percentages of a large number of newspapers using various sizes of type for the body of news items. It will be noted that a large majority are using 7-point type. By reference to Fig. 76 it will be noted that a type of this size possesses a relative visibility of about 3.2. In other words, the size of the critical details is only 3.2 times as large as the smallest visible to the normal eye under otherwise favorable conditions for seeing. It will be noted from Fig. 77 that a relative visibility of 3.2 corresponds to an "effective visibility" of only 1.5. The latter appraisal is made with reference to the relationship between threshold size (relative visibility) and visual efficiency adopted by the American Medical Association.

The data of Fig. 75 indicate a slight tendency towards larger type-sizes in 1936 as compared with 1934, and a strong persistence in the use of 7-point type in a large majority of the cases. It seems significant that few books are printed in type as small as 7-point and schoolbooks should never be. It is said that early books, which could be purchased only by the wealthy, were printed in fairly large type and that much smaller types came into use as a matter of economy in making books and other printed matter available to the masses. In particular, the early

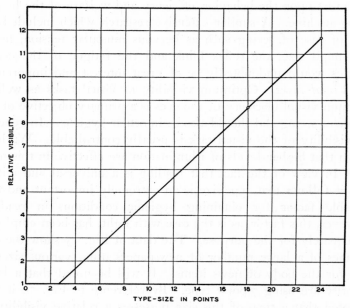

FIG. 76.—The relationship between type-size and visibility as determined with the visibility meter. The plotted points represent average values derived from 250 observations made by each of 15 subjects possessing normal or near-normal vision. The measurements were made with a level of illumination of 10 footcandles on Bodoni type printed in black ink on a background of suitable white paper.

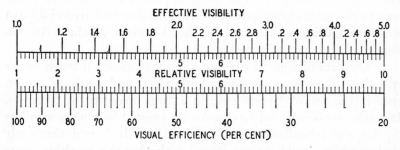

FIG. 77.—Showing the relationships between relative visibility and effective visibility, and between relative visibility and visual efficiency. The values of relative visibility correspond to the scale values of the visibility meter.

editions of the Bible were printed in small type in an effort to publish them as cheaply as possible. On this basis it would seem that small type has been inherited and that its use at the present time is founded upon rather archaic economics. Certainly it is not justifiable from the viewpoint of ease of reading.

Civilization has introduced a preponderance of critical near-vision tasks and human eyes and human beings are thereby penalized. As stated by Bishop,[112] it is a matter of common observation that continuous close work engenders fatigue, and that the liability to damage to the eyes is increased in cases involving refractive errors and muscular imbalances. In some cases there occurs a breakdown in the ability of the worker to continue his work. Certainly countless examples of damage and breakdown are obvious throughout the inorganic and organic worlds. The data of Table XLV show the severity of these penalties among habitual "near-vision" workers and among other workers not so engaged. These data were compiled from the records of 7000 patients. This provides a glimpse of conservation of health through conservation of vision and improvement in seeing conditions. Later a glimpse is provided of the conservation of life, limb and property through the same means.

TABLE XLV

Percentages of Failures Among Persons Habitually Engaged in Near-Vision Work and Persons Not So Engaged

Type of Patient	Number	Breakdowns	Damage to Eyes	Total Failures
Near-vision workers	100	38.2	15.	53.
Other workers	100	2.4	7.06	9.4

Since the character of the work with respect to distance from the eyes is not generally controllable, it follows that appropriate effort should be made to increase ease of seeing and diminish eyestrain through the augmentation of other factors favorable for seeing. In the case of school-children, it would seem advisable to limit the duration of near-vision tasks even more than is usually the custom. This should be one of the advantages of socalled visual education by means of projected motion-pictures and lantern slides, also of large charts, provided other factors were also prop. erly controlled.

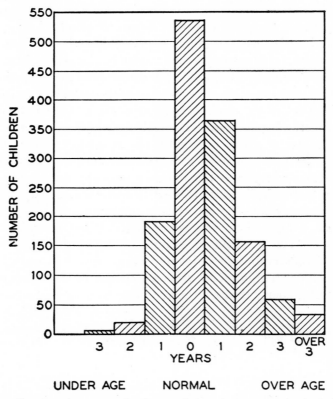

FIG. 78.—Showing the age-grade characteristics of a group of school-children possessing visual deficiencies. It will be noted that the characteristic of over-ageness predominates.

EDUCATION AND SEEING

The attempt has been made by a number of psychologists to estimate the relative influence of the visual sense in the acquisi-tion of an education. Although such estimates have little scientific value as yet, they serve the useful and important purpose of emphasizing the far-reaching significance of efficiency in seeing.

The latter, as a function of the visual conditions encountered in homes, schools, offices, factories and elsewhere is generally under the control of the layman rather than the specialist. Hence, an adequate appreciation of the influence of the visual sense upon human behavior and welfare and of the effectiveness of various aids to seeing is correspondingly important. It is this viewpoint which led us to include diagrams and illustrations in this discussion which may be readily understood by non-technical persons, who are so generally responsible for conditions for seeing.

Defective vision versus scholarship. It has been shown by numerous investigators that visual deficiencies are closely related to retardation in educational progress of school-children. For example, of 7122 school-children selected for ophthalmological examination in Baltimore, many more were chronologicaly over-age, with respect to their school-age, than were under-age. [113] The results are presented in Fig. 78. The data of Table XLVI also indicate a similar relationship between visual defects and retardation in school progress.[114] It is not assumed that the retardation is entirely a function of the visual abilities of the pupils. However, the fact that such investigations invariably reveal a greater prevalence of defective vision among the retarded school-children than among those making normal progress is statistical evidence that a real and significant correlation exists between these factors.

TABLE XLVI

Percentages of Retardation Among a Large Group of School Children

	Children Examined	Children with Defective Vision
Making normal progress	66.0	14.6
Retarded in studies	12.4	34.8
Repeating grade	21.6	50.6

The results of a visual survey among 4316 school-children in Syracuse are presented in Table XLVII. In this case, the upper limit of normal vision was designated as 20/30. The percentage of the pupils having one or more failures in their school work is

[263]

taken as the criterion of educational progress. In interpreting these and similar data, it may be assumed that the deleterious effects of visual deficiencies are not only those of lowered visual ability, but also may include the indirect effects which often result from visual defects such as tenseness, nervousness, headaches, digestive disturbances and others.

T A B L E   X L V I I

Percentages of Total Registration Having One or More Failures in School Work

Grade	Boys with Normal Vision	Boys with Defective Vision	Girls with Normal Vision	Girls with Defective Vision
1	16.1	18.2	15.4	7.1
2	32.8	24.4	20.8	30.9
3	36.9	50.0	27.0	40.4
4	26.0	35.0	27.6	36.6
5	44.8	54.3	28.1	32.7
6	43.2	42.0	29.5	35.7
7	37.4	40.0	34.6	30.7
8	35.3	43.5	28.7	40.7
9	39.3	37.5	29.8	20.0
Total	34.3	39.2	25.0	34.2

School lighting and scholarship. The well-known correlations between visual defects and retardation in scholarship naturally suggested the possibility that better lighting in the schoolroom might accelerate the progress made by all the pupils. Such a result has been tentatively confirmed by several investigations. In a recent test [115] in a grade school in Cambridge, Mass., two adjoining and similar rooms were selected for test purposes. One of these rooms was provided with new lighting equipment which was automatically controlled by a photronic cell and relay, and so adjusted that a minimum of 20 footcandles was maintained on all desks. The lighting of the other room, which was left unchanged, provided four to six footcandles upon the desks. It was manually controlled by the teacher according to previous custom. The pupils of the fifth grade were divided into two groups of

[264]

41 pupils each by the Rulon-Croon method [116] by which the chronological, mental and educational ages of the two groups were balanced. Lighting was introduced as the experimental variable on November 1 and the final testing was started on June 1, seven months later. It is recognized that a single test-period of seven months is rather short for revealing the effect of better seeing conditions upon human welfare, efficiency and achievement. However, the results are of value since they are in agreement with both theoretical considerations and the results of various practical tests in schools. At the present time an elaborate and highly controlled test of the effect of better lighting upon scholarship and physical welfare is being made at Joplin, Missouri, under the direction of the Educational Department of the University of Missouri. The results will be available in 1939.

TABLE XLVIII

The Results of Mental Tests Given to Two Balanced Groups of Fifth Grade Pupils. These Values Are Expressed in Months.

Criteria November	(Better Lighted) Room A	(Poorly Lighted) Room B
Chronological age	126.02 ± 1.47	126.15 ± 1.52
Mental age	120.12 ± 1.04	119.37 ± 1.01
Educational age	118.34 ± .64	118.27 ± .79
Reading age	121.61 ± .94	121.10 ± .97
June (7 months later)		
Mental age	128.29 ± 1.46	129.32 ± 1.04
Educational age	129.83 ± .94	128.76 ± 1.01
Reading age	132.76 ± 1.17	130.17 ± 1.21

A summary of the results is presented in Table XLVIII. The gain in educational age of the pupils in the better illuminated room (A) over those in the poorly-lighted room (B) was 1.07 ± 0.71 month, or ten per cent. A probable error of 0.71 indicates that there are 85 chances in 100 that the gain in educational age was caused by some other factor than chance. The gain in the reading age of the pupils in room (A) over those in room (B) was 2.59 ± 1.13 months, or a gain of 28 per cent. A probable error of this magnitude indicates that there are 94 chances in 100 that the gain in reading age was not due to chance.

The task of reading. It seems reasonable to assume from introspective considerations that the amount of material read might depend in the long run upon the ease with which the reading is accomplished. If the visual task is difficult by reason of small type, visual defects or poor lighting, it follows that less reading will be done. Obviously, if the eyes become fatigued and vision blurred, the natural and sensible reaction is to cease reading. This is particularly true in the case of children engaged in reading and study. Furthermore, it should be evident that the efficiency in reading, from the viewpoint of acquiring knowledge, is lowered when the proportion of the total available sense-capacity required for the mere performance of the task is increased. Thus it follows that ease in reading is an important factor in educational progress. This is discussed particularly from the viewpoint of school-children handicapped by very serious visual defects.

The data of Table XLIX give the relative visibilities of 18-point and 24-point type, respectively, as determined by (1) various pupils in sight-saving classes and (2) by adults possessing normal or near-normal vision.[117] These values were obtained with the visibility meter and for an illumination of ten footcandles upon the printed matter. For the cases involving medium myopia, it will be noted that these subjects obtained visibility values nearly as high as did the group of adults possessing normal vision. Thus for them the 24-point type was probably unnecessarily large. It is not likely that any person possessing normal vision would prefer to read a book printed in type of this size. On the other hand, the pupils with cataracts obtained a visibility of only 2.60 and 4.31 when observing 18-point and 24-point type, respectively. By reference to Fig. 76 which relates relative visibility and type-size for normal vision, it is seen that the values of 2.60 and 4.31 correspond to about 6-point and 9-point type, respectively. In other words, 18-point and 24-point types are no more visible to the pupils with cataracts than are 6-point and 9-point types for adults with normal vision. Hence, it follows that these pupils

[266]

need the 24-point type in order to obtain a reasonable degree of visibility. It is emphasized that these conclusions are based upon considerations and measurements of threshold visibility. The conclusion that 18-point type, for example, is as easily read as is 6-point type by persons with normal vision is unwarranted. It is probable that the former need additional assistance since their eyes usually tire rapidly.

Thus, for the pupils of sight-saving classes the factor of size of type determines whether or not they may read at all. For some, mere ability to see the printed characters is the optimum reached by utilizing all aids to seeing. For others, higher levels of illumination and larger sizes of type make the task of reading easier, and hence more material may be read with more attention on perception and understanding and less on vision, *per se*. Admittedly, a discussion based upon the abilities of sight-saving pupils represents the extreme case. On the other hand, the gains from aids to seeing are also extremely significant since they may represent the difference between reading and not reading. Furthermore, the influence of ease of seeing in the acquisition of knowledge is also a factor for those with normal vision.

The data of Table XLIX also quantitatively show the complementary relationship between type-size and footcandles. This phase of the subject is discussed in Chapters VIII and XII.

WORK-WORLD EFFICIENCY

As the complexity of any machine is increased, it follows that the number of factors which may affect its efficiency and output is also increased. Add physiological and mental processes to a complex physical machine and a super-complex mechanism results. Obviously, the efficiency of the human seeing-machine is a function of countless factors. Hence it is not likely that optimum conditions for its operation will be revealed by introspective appraisals of these conditions or by superficial considerations and measurements. For example, the visibility of type increases with increases in size, but the effort of ocular muscles involved in reading a given number of words is also increased. In addition, the recognition and per-

TABLE XLIX

The Individual Values Presented in Columns 3 and 4 Represent the Average of a Series of Ten Measurements of Visibility under a Level of Illumination of Ten Footcandles. The Values Given in Column 6 Indicate the Levels of Illumination Which Are Required in Order to Increase the Visibility of 18-Point Type to Equal That of 24-Point Type under Ten Footcandles.

Diagnosis	Number of Subjects	Visibility			Footcandles on 18-pt.	Probable Errors	
		18-pt.	24-pt.	18/24		18-pt.	24-pt.
Medium myopia (3–6 D.).....	5	7.88	10.16	0.81	15.4	1.8	2.5
High myopia (over 6 D.).....	15	5.71	7.90	.73	18.4	2.2	2.6
Simple myopic astigmatism...	12	4.22	5.68	.75	19.1	2.2	2.6
Compound myopic astigmatism	3	6.60	9.11	.71	30.9	2.7	3.1
High hyperopia (over 6 D.)...	1	6.51	10.33	.63	22.8	1.9	3.1
High hyperopic astigmatism..	4	4.55	6.78	.70	20.9	1.8	2.4
Myopia and nystagmus......	2	3.96	5.10	.78	13.2	1.0	2.0
Myopic astigmatism and nystagmus.................	1	1.84	2.78	.66	19.0	0.9	1.8
Hyperopia and nystagmus....	1	1.65	1.99	.83	28.0	1.6	2.7
Astigmatism and nystagmus..	1	1.86	2.46	.76	24.0	1.5	1.0
Ophthalmic blennorrhea......	1	2.24	4.95	.45	26.7	2.0	1.4
Cataracts.................	2	2.60	4.31	.58	17.0	2.0	3.8
Corneal opacities..........	6	4.16	5.58	.76	16.0	2.0	2.8
Albino and nystagmus.......	3	1.45	2.15	.67	21.7	1.6	2.7
Aphakia.................	1	3.35	4.00	.84	16.6	1.2	0.9
Subluxated lens............	1	3.30	3.82	.87	13.7	1.1	1.7
Choroiditis................	2	3.89	4.90	.78	15.9	1.8	2.4
Ptosis....................	1	2.41	3.27	.74	18.5	1.7	2.0
Divergent strabismus........	1	6.30	8.07	.78	12.5	1.7	2.1
Choroidoretinitis...........	1	1.49	2.16	.69	32.0	2.7	3.4
Secondary retinitis..........	1	5.15	6.43	.80	13.9	1.0	2.5
Old interstitial keratitis......	2	4.48	5.29	.84	14.8	1.4	2.4
Optic atrophy..............	3	2.29	3.16	.72	23.3	2.4	2.2
Choroid retinal scars........	1	4.15	6.92	.60	39.0	2.1	1.7
Pigment degeneration of retina	1	1.84	2.18	.84	21.5	2.3	0.9
Weighted arithmetic mean....	72	4.50	6.15	.74	19.8	2.0	2.1
Group with " normal " vision.	10	8.69	11.68	.75	15.6		

ception of words is a function of the number included in a single fixational-span. Thus it should be evident that the determination of optimum conditions for seeing, using this term in its broadest sense, is difficult even when a single factor, such as type-size, is considered. However, it is particularly noteworthy that the opportunities for improving conditions for seeing are also in proportion to the factors involved. Ease and efficiency in seeing, as in other forms of work, vary in degree although this fact is not universally recognized and appreciated. No one would assume that the quantity and quality of physical work done by a human being are independent of the conditions under which the work is done. Certainly it is equally true that the quantity and quality of visual work depend upon conditions for seeing. However, the simple tacit assumption that seeing is either possible or not is quite commonly made. That this superficial attitude toward seeing is prevalent is revealed in many ways.

Speed and precision. From a restricted viewpoint of physiological optics, it is to be expected that both the speed and precision of visually controlled operations would be augmented by improving conditions for seeing. Laboratory researches and tests in the work-world substantiate this hypothesis. However, it is again emphasized that human activity and behavior are influenced by many psychophysiological factors in addition to those pertaining directly and obviously to the visibility of the object or visual task. For example, some investigations indicate that the lighting or brightness environment influences the quantity and quality of both mental and physical work. For example, it has been noted that on "dull" days the quantity and quality of mental work were inferior to that on brighter days. For obvious reasons, the effect upon physical work was not so decisive. Furthermore, it is possible that differences in temperature between cloudy and clear days are factors affecting the output of physical work.

The data of Fig. 79 indicate the influence upon the precision of visually controlled manual operations of (1) changes in the level of illumination upon the task; and (2) alterations in the quality of the lighting. In this research [118] the task consisted in setting the two black pointers in vertical alignment through the turning of a hand-wheel which moved one of them. Although the pointers possessed a relatively high degree of visibility, in comparison with the threshold size, marked decreases in the error of adjustment were obtained when the brightness of the white background was increased by increasing the level of illumination. It will be noted that the change from dark to light surroundings around the visual task decreased the magnitudes of the errors of alignment. This

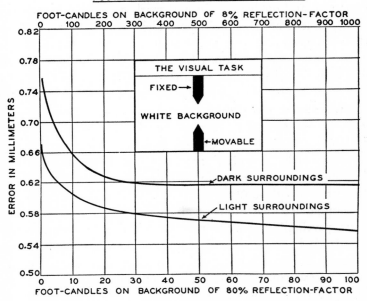

FIG. 79.—Showing the effect of level of illumination upon the precision of performing a mechanical task guided by vision. The insert illustrates the visual task. The term "dark surroundings" means that the visual field except for the small portion shown by the insert was comparatively dark. "Light surroundings" means that the entire visual field was approximately the same brightness as the field immediately about the test-object.

effect would be expected from a consideration of experimental investigations of Cobb [73] pertaining to the effects of bright and dark surroundings upon foveal vision. The results are illustrated in Fig. 51. In addition to the obvious significance of the data of Fig. 79 in many industrial operations, these data are also important in establishing correlations between theoretical and practical investigations. The former usually involve the perception of single and simple test-objects, whereas the latter often involve muscular response to a series of stimuli of various degrees of complexities. Furthermore, objects of high contrast have been commonly used in fundamental researches without including objects of low contrasts. The latter are very common in the world of seeing,

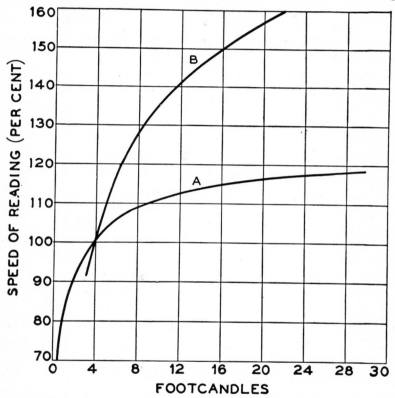

FIG. 80.—The effect of level of illumination on the speed of reading. *A* is for the usual condition of black print on white paper of 80 per cent reflection-factor; and *B* is for black print on a gray background of 23 per cent reflection-factor. The two curves are not comparable quantitatively.

and effects of various factors which influence seeing are generally greater for low contrasts than for high ones.

The relationship between the time required to recognize a single object of elementary geometrical design and level of illumination is shown in Fig. 52. In Fig. 80 is shown the relationship between the speed (reciprocal of time) of reading and level of illumination.[119] On comparing the results with those shown in Fig. 52 it will be noted that the influence of increases in illumination is quite similar in both. This is additional evidence that the effect of a given aid to seeing can be predicted for the complex situations encountered in practice from the fundamental data in the realm of physiological optics. In Fig. 80, Curve A represents the relationship between brightness or level of illumination and the speed of reading black print upon white paper reflecting 80 per cent of the incident light. Curve B represents a similar relationship for reading black print on gray paper having a reflection-factor of 23 per cent. It is obvious that level of illumination corresponding to the optimum speed of reading is a variable which depends upon the difficulty of the task, upon the efficiency of the visual mechanism, and upon other important factors in seeing.

It should be emphasized that optimum speed in reading or in the performance of world-work tasks may be a very misleading criterion for specifying conditions for seeing. Such a criterion does not necessarily include a consideration of optimum ease of seeing. Thus the conditions corresponding to optimum ease of seeing and of performance, respectively, are not always identical as is shown in Fig. 8. We have proved conclusively that the rate of production of useful work is not a true measure of ease of seeing. For example, the maximum rate of reading a stationary page was found to be about the same as it was when the page was vibrating in a manner so annoying that much eyestrain was produced even in relatively short periods.[120] It is strange that lessons learned in other human activities are so often ignored in considerations involving seeing. For example, a runner may still be able to sprint with a burst of speed toward the finish of a gruelling race. He does this at the expense of his own energy. Similarly, the production of a worker may often conceal much of the effort and abuse attendant upon the performance of difficult tasks. Such experiments emphasized the need for new concepts and new considerations of ease of seeing.

Production. Many examples of increased production due to increased illumination, reduced glare, and better lighting could be presented. However, only a few representative ones are necessary for the fundamental purpose of this treatise. Production, both in quality and quantity, is a major objective in the work-world. However, it is only one way of measuring benefits of aids to seeing. Doubtless production is related to ease of seeing, but it is not a safe criterion. In Fig. 81 are presented typical relationships be-

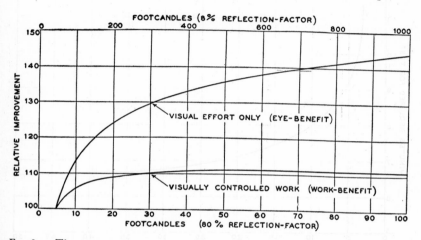

FIG. 81.—The upper curve summarizes the results of several investigations involving only visual recognition of test-objects. The lower curve summarizes the results of several investigations involving the performance of various tasks guided by vision. It is significant that benefit to seeing persists above the level of illumination at which work-benefit ceases to increase.

tween production and brightness, or footcandle-levels, as obtained under highly controlled conditions of the laboratory. Each of these curves is a composite of several researches involving two distinctly different kinds of visual tasks in which the objects were approximately black and were seen against a white background. The lower curve was obtained with manual tasks in which seeing merely guided the manual labor. It is seen that in this kind of task production reaches a practical optimum at about 30 footcandles. This is quite generally true of such tasks. The upper

[273]

curve was obtained for visual tasks in which manual labor was
minimized and visual effort greatly predominated, as in proofreading, inspection, etc. It is seen that the practical maximum rate of
production is not reached at 30 footcandles or even at 100 footcandles. This distinction between various types of visual tasks is
important. It seems reasonable to assume that in the case of tasks

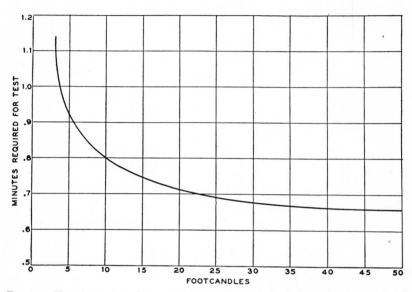

Fig. 82.—The time required to perform the Luckiesh-Moss Visual Test correlated
with level of illumination. One of the patterns or test-objects used in this test is
illustrated in Fig. 22.

merely guided by vision the maximum rate of production is limited by other factors than seeing.

The brightnesses of the white background against which the
objects were seen are expressed by the lower scale of footcandles
upon a surface having a reflection-factor of 80 per cent. If the
background had a reflection-factor of eight per cent, ten times as
many footcandles would be necessary to produce the same brightnesses. In other words, the upper scale of footcandles would
apply. Other factors must be taken into account in a given case,

but it is strictly true that at least the footcandles indicated on the upper scale would be necessary if the background had been the dark gray instead of white. The effect of reflection-factor is obvious in Fig. 80.

Fig. 82 represents the average time required to perform the L-M Demonstration Visual Test [29] under various footcandle-levels. This is a test requiring accurate seeing and some manual effort. It is not entirely a matter of seeing as in the case of proof-reading but it approaches such a task. It is typical of many work-world tasks, but the results shown in Fig. 80 were obtained under perfectly controlled conditions. The speed of performance of this task was found to be measurably decreased by noise and glare.

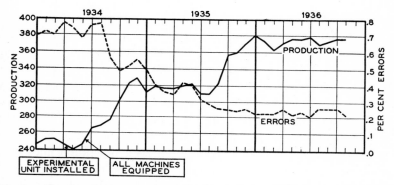

Fig. 83.—Showing the increase in production and the decrease in errors, respectively, which followed the installation of supplementary lighting units upon business machines.

The data of Fig. 83 show the results obtained in a statistical operation known as key-punching due to an increase in the level of illumination upon the work and to changes in the position of the copy with respect to the key-punching machine. The level of illumination on the work was increased from eight footcandles of general illumination to a total of 60 footcandles, chiefly by means of supplementary lighting fixtures designed for this particular use. The posture of the operator was improved by installing an inclined stand to hold the copy in such a position that the latter was well illuminated without any preventable glare and could be read with the eyes in their primary or normal position. This improvement in position relieved the extrinsic ocular muscles to a large extent from unnatural and unnecessary strains. Also, as seen in Fig. 11, increases in level of illumination to at least 100 footcandles reduce fatigue of these eye-muscles from reading black print on white paper. Measurements of convergence reserve were made on these key-punching operators at the beginning and end of each work-day for several consecutive weeks. These results, presented in Table XXXIX, also show a reduction in fatigue of the extrinsic ocular muscles due to the new lighting and higher footcandle-level.

In general, it will be noted from Fig. 82 that production began to increase and errors diminish almost immediately after the installation of the new equipment. However, it is of interest to note that these changes did not reach their optimum values until about 18 months later. In general, these data indicated that the degree of ocular fatigue caused by the day's work, and appraised by the decrement in convergence reserve, was significantly less when the work was done under the 60 footcandles of combined general and supplementary lighting than when done under the eight footcandles of general illumination alone. For years we have advocated this combination system as a practicable means of obtaining higher levels of illumination and also proper lighting of the task. We have good reasons for stating that these striking results would not have been obtained with 60 footcandles obtained by the usual methods of general lighting. Obviously the benefit obtained by the change in posture could be appraised in a similar manner. Although the latter measurements were not included in this investigation, there are very definite reasons for believing that the change to a better posture also reduced the fatiguing effects of this critical and exacting task.

Certain economic advantages of higher levels of illumination are indicated by the summary of a few typical work-world tasks in Table L. Quite aside from the significant consistency of the results of tests relating light and production, it is discouraging to find such low levels of illumination being used in an era which has placed much stress upon industrial efficiency and human welfare. It has been adequately proved that the quality and quantity of productive work can be increased by improvement in seeing conditions due to such factors as light, lighting, backgrounds and surroundings. It may be conservatively estimated that a ten per cent increase in production could be achieved universally by increasing the present average illumination of less than five footcandles in work-places to 25 footcandles. The value of this increased production in this country would amount to many billions of dollars. It appears that this could be achieved at a very small percentage of the cost of materials and labor.[5] In other words, a profit of billions of dollars could be made on the improved lighting alone. Now if some of this were expended for still more light and still better lighting, more contributions would be made to human welfare through conservation of eyesight, health, life and property. These accomplishments would be due to reductions of useless work by the human seeing-machine, wear and tear on human beings, spoilage, and accidents. Here are economic, social and welfare aspects of large magnitude.

TABLE L

Typical Examples of the Increase in Production Resulting from Increased Illumination

Nature of Work	Average Footcandles (Old System)	Average Footcandles (New System)	Per Cent Increase in Production Obtained	Cost of Lighting in Per Cent of Payroll
Pulley finishing	0.2	4.8	35	5
Soft metal bearings	4.6	12.7	15	1.2
Heavy steel machining	3	11.5	10	1.2
Carburetor assembly	2.1	12.3	12	0.9
Electric and gas iron manufacturing	0.7	13.5	12	2.5
Semi-automatic buffing shell-sockets	3.8	11.4	8.5	1.8
Letter sorting	3.6	3.0	4.4	0.6

The results shown in Fig. 83 emphasize the important fact that the ultimate benefits to be derived from improvements in con-

[277]

ditions for seeing are not necessarily revealed immediately after the changes are made. As is seen, two months after the key-punching machines were equipped the increase in production was about ten per cent. Two years later the increase amounted to over 50 per cent. This result cannot be ascribed merely to the fact that the operators were more experienced in the latter case, since all were thoroughly experienced operators before the changes in the equipment were made. Hence these data indicate that the results of laboratory investigations designed to appraise the effects of bet-

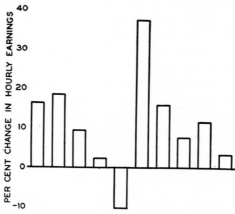

FIG. 84.—Showing the increase (with one exception) of hourly earnings of ten workers following the correction of visual defects with eyeglasses.

ter conditions for seeing are probably conservative, since the appraisals are made immediately after a given change in seeing conditions.

The effect of more light and better lighting upon the production of workers has been emphasized because they are necessary and universally controllable factors. It is also of interest to determine the effect of optical correction of eye-defects upon the production-rate of the worker. Many eyesight specialists and workers in industry will testify to the value of eyeglasses in an economic sense. However, published records of this sort are rare. An analysis [114] of the earnings of ten different workers before and

[278]

after the correction of visual defects by eyeglasses is given in Fig. 84. It will be noted that in each case, excepting one, an increase in the earnings of the worker was obtained after the eyes were corrected. Upon investigation of the case that showed a decrease in earning power, it was found that the worker had been transferred to a new job, and hence this reversal of the general trend is rather meaningless. It will be noted that an average increase in the hourly earnings of over 10 per cent was obtained for the group as a whole as a result of the correction of visual defects. In the light of these data, the cost of uncorrected vision in industry must be enormous, if these data and those of Fig. 73 pertaining to the prevalence of uncorrected vision are typical of the general situation. Many opportunities exist for determining the quality and quantity of work done by workers before and after being fitted with perfect eyeglasses. The professions and industries dealing with eyeglasses should see that authoritative tests of this kind are made. Many obvious effects of uncorrected and corrected vision need quantitative appraisal. In other words, eyeglasses as aids to seeing are of major importance in human efficiency and welfare just as light, lighting and other major factors are.

SAFETY AND SEEING

The influence of quick and certain seeing upon safety should be so obvious that this discussion need only provide a few glimpses of the possibilities of improved seeing conditions. In viewing these, it should be borne in mind that the matter must be viewed statistically and that statistics must be obtained in the everyday world of accidents where it is difficult to control the many factors involved. However, many years of analysis and observation on the part of insurance companies, traffic departments, and lighting experts have established some general facts. These are more exact quantitatively in respect to illumination on the highways than in industrial plants. In the former case there is the daily comparison of accidents in the daytime and after dark. In industrial plants there is no such natural division because the illumination is rather low and of comparable magnitude in the daytime as well as after

dark. Furthermore, the influence of controllable factors of seeing in relation to accidents and their prevention has not been
studied from the modern viewpoint of seeing or to an extent
proportional to its importance. In addition, there are the complexities of human vagaries and deficiencies which introduce uncertainties in seeing, just as the low values of visibility due to physical
external factors do.

Industrial accidents. In the industries of this country the
annual toll of accidents is of the following order of magnitude:

> 17000 workers killed,
> an accident every ten seconds on the average,
> an accidental death every ten minutes on the average,
> 1500000 injured sufficiently to be unable to work for one
>   day or more,
> $1,500,000,000 total material loss.

For years insurance companies have considered poor lighting as a
contributing factor in about 20 per cent of the industrial accidents.[106] From the present viewpoint of the science of seeing it
would appear reasonable to assume that at least in this percentage
poor seeing conditions are a major factor. In fact, it seems reasonable that, where there is no carelessness or mechanical failure, the
inability to see quickly enough or with adequate certainty must
be a major cause. Perhaps the matter can be approached statistically in this manner. The more satisfactory quantitative data
available from streets and highways shed some light on industrial
accidents. The controllable factors in seeing are listed or suggested in Fig. 71.

Accident susceptibility. The studies of Lauer [121] indicate that
three types of individuals are to be found on the highways. The
first group is designated as "accident-free" and consists of 70 to 75
per cent of all drivers. The second, or "accident-liable" group,
consists of some 20 to 25 per cent of the total number. Their
difficulties are perhaps due to either hereditary or environmental
conditions which influence the individual. It is on account of this
group that conditions must be made as safe as possible. The third

group, or "accident-prone" consists of two to five per cent of all the drivers. Usually outstanding defects are found in this group. Among these are lowered visual acuity, restricted visual fields, diplopia, color-blindness, poor coordination, extreme nervousness, etc. According to Lauer, since about one-half of the accidents are caused by seven per cent of the drivers, it follows that special consideration must be given to those so handicapped. In fact, safety measures should be designed for them and not for others less liable to accidents. Although this classification is based upon highway accidents, it does not seem unreasonable to extend it t., other fields of human activity.

Highway accidents. On the highways of this country the annual toll is approximately as follows:

> 35000 persons killed,
> 350000 persons injured,
> 700000 cases of property damage,
> $2,500,000,000 total material loss,
> $100 average annual loss per family.

If the present accident rate is maintained on streets and highways throughout the lifetime of a million children born this year,

> 30000 will be killed,
> 140000 will be seriously injured,
> 900000 highway accidents will befall them.

Analyses of statistics seem to establish certain facts pertaining to traffic and accidents after dark.

> 50 per cent of all highway accidents occur after dark.
> 20 per cent of all highway traffic is after dark.
> 6 times as great as during the day is the accident hazard per vehicle-mile at night.
> 10 times as great are the chances of death at night per vehicle-mile.

On the highway all factors indicated and suggested in Fig. 71 play a part in seeing. All may be utilized by someone. At night the problems of seeing are particularly complex. The combinations of visual factors are commonly such that visibility of important objects is near, or even below, the threshold. The pupils are large and the retina is adapted to low levels of brightness. The conditions are favorable for shock by glaring headlamps and for great reduction in the ability to see. The glare-source which is approaching rapidly is increasing in effectiveness because the foot-

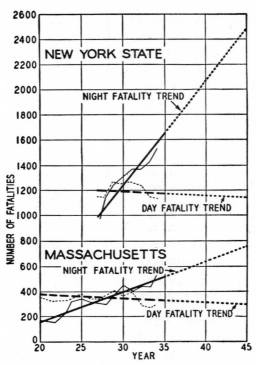

FIG. 85.—Showing the trends of traffic fatalities by day and by night.

candles at the eyes due to it are increasing. Adaptation cannot take place rapidly enough. As a consequence objects of rather low visibility may fall below threshold and one passes the approaching headlamps in a state of blindness. All these and other factors of seeing are sufficient to convince one that safety on highways is to a large extent a matter of great improvements in seeing. This is why there is a movement under way in this country

[282]

to provide lighting on 50000 miles of major highways carrying 75 per cent of the total traffic. Headlamps at their best cannot provide the best seeing conditions. Some of these same considerations can be extended into the realm of industrial safety.

The accident trends for daytime and after dark are shown in Fig. 85 as indicated by an analysis of fatalities in two states. These data should be considered in the light of the fact that only one-fourth of the total traffic on highways in general takes place

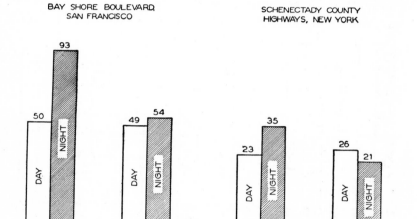

FIG. 86.—Showing the relationship between highway lighting and traffic accidents.

after dark. It is seen that fatalities do not appear to be increasing in the daytime. In fact, the trend is slightly downward. This is probably due to many factors such as education, traffic aids and enforcement. However, the trend of accidents after dark is definitely and even startlingly upward. In fact, at the present time the fatalities for a given number of vehicle-miles are ten times greater at night than in the daytime. Certainly one cannot avoid the conclusion that poor seeing is a major factor in this trend of night accidents.

In Fig. 86 are shown the traffic accidents before and after highway lighting was installed. It will be noted in one case that the number of accidents which occurred at night was reduced from 93 to 54. The fact that the day accident-rate remained substantially the same adds significance to the former values. Somewhat similar results were obtained by highway lighting in the other case illustrated. While these data are too meager to be conclusive in a quantitative sense, they are indicative of the value of better seeing conditions. Besides other statistics of the same sort point to the same conclusions. The recent researches of Reid and Chanon,[122] involving exact measurements of the visibilities of objects seen on the highways under various conditions, show in a

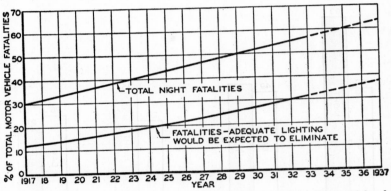

FIG. 87.—Showing the percentage decrease in motor vehicle fatalities which adequate lighting would be expected to eliminate.

very practical manner the value of data pertaining to seeing in the formulation of fundamental principles of highway lighting and in the design of effective lighting equipment. According to present statistics and analyses the accidents which lighting would be expected to eliminate on the highways at night are indicated in Fig. 87. Such potential savings in human life represent a major objective of the application of the science of seeing and its progeny.

Accidents and defective vision. It is axiomatic that a person with good vision would be less likely to have an accident than one not possessing such an advantage. This fact is officially recognized in at least one state by the requirement of a visual acuity of 20/30 in both eyes, or 20/20 in one eye. This regulation ap-

[284]

pears unnecessarily rigid in view of the fact that a 20/30 visual acuity rating corresponds to a *visual* efficiency rating of about 91, as will be noted from Fig. 77. It has been suggested by Weymann [123] that the lower limit of visual acuity be placed at 20/50 in the better eye, with a type of enforcement placing the responsibility for knowing his eligibility upon the driver himself. Such a rating would correspond to a visual efficiency of about 75 per cent. In fact, it would be better to use methods for rating vision which involved other factors than visual acuity. Certainly threshold brightness and brightness-contrast are very important. This is particularly true on the highway at night.

Lauer [124] has presented considerable data relating aspects of vision to various human abilities and limitations involved in accidents. In general, it is indicated that any visual deficiency increases the likelihood of accident. From the results of tests of visual acuity, measured by the Clason device, of many subjects in relation to their performance and ability to see Lauer concludes that

1. The accident index decreased as visual acuity increased.
2. Distance judgment was best for persons with a visual acuity of 70 per cent or better. It decreased gradually as visual acuity decreased from 70 to 40 per cent where it began to decrease rapidly.
3. Performance, as measured by an indoor driving test, improved with visual acuity up to 40 per cent.

Although visual acuity possesses definite advantages as a means for appraising the efficiency of the visual mechanism, it is by no means a complete or adequate one. For example, it has been stated that a loss of 20 to 30 degrees of the peripheral visual field renders the subject liable to bump against pedestrians as he walks along. Obviously, such a person would not be a safe driver. On the other hand, such a person might possess a visual acuity rating of 20/20 or even better. In cases of myopia, for example, these subjects might be safe drivers in the daytime, but at night they may be dangerous due to the reduction of the peripheral field in dim illumination. In this connection, it will be recalled that peripheral vision contributes much toward human safety by detecting motion, or its visual equivalent.

The sensitivity of the eyes to light and brightness-difference is obviously essential in night driving. However, various degrees of night-blindness are not uncommon and these deficiencies would not generally be revealed by visual acuity tests. In such cases, measurements made with our visibility meter would indicate the presence of such defects, under proper conditions of lighting, since the visual threshold is attained by simultaneous changes in both brightness and brightness-contrast. In fact, measurements of visibility which took into account various visibility factors as well as human deficiencies would appear far superior to any other single measurement such as visual acuity.

Reaction-time. The interval of time between the onset of the stimulus and the beginning of an intentional response is obviously an important factor in the prevention of accidents. In general, it has been shown that the reaction-time varies inversely with the intensity of the stimulus.[125] In the case of visual stimuli, increases in brightness, areal extent and duration decrease the time of reaction within certain limits. Apparently the time of reaction does not depend upon the color of the stimulus [126] unless novelty is an appreciable factor. As might be expected, the time of reaction gradually declines with increasing age, although the change does not appear to be as great as that which occurs in other visual functions. The research of Miles [127] indicates that the 12 oldest persons (average age 79 years) in a group of 100 adults registered responses that were from 20 to 30 per cent slower than the general average of the group as a whole. However, one-fourth of the oldest subjects were as quick or quicker than the average for the total group. The researches of Dockeray and Isaacs [128] indicate reaction-times of 0.155 second and 0.197 second to sound and light, respectively. However, it may be said that the relative reaction-time to sound and light stimuli depends upon the magnitude of the stimuli compared, and there is no way of comparing these on an absolute basis. It has also been shown by Todd [129] that the reaction-time to two simultaneous stimuli is less than for either of them presented alone. The practical implications of this fact in increasing human safety should be obvious.

Attention. Generally novelty enhances visibility and is an aid to seeing because it rises above the commonplace and the expected. However, unexpectedness, by itself, is commonly an unfavorable factor in seeing, for the reaction-time may be doubled. The use of novelty or conspicuity in brightness, form, color and location has endless possibilities, and its effectiveness is demonstrated on every hand. A luminous traffic signal involves several

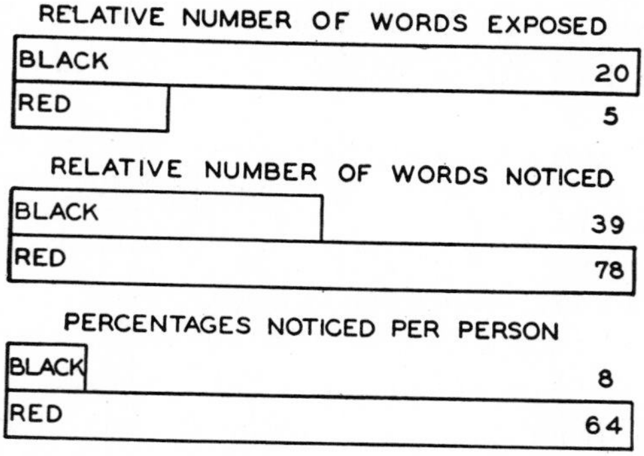

RELATIVE NUMBER OF WORDS EXPOSED

| BLACK | 20 |
| RED | 5 |

RELATIVE NUMBER OF WORDS NOTICED

| BLACK | 39 |
| RED | 78 |

PERCENTAGES NOTICED PER PERSON

| BLACK | 8 |
| RED | 64 |

FIG. 88.—Indicating the effect of novelty in compelling attention. Although there were four times as many words in black as in red, the number of words in red which were recognized was twice as great as the number in black.

factors, but novelty in the sense of conspicuity is almost entirely responsible for its effectiveness. If such a signal is bright enough in the daytime to have high attention-value, this is because of the degree of novelty. This is also true of its color. When its brightness is not conspicuously greater than that of its background, such as the sky in the daytime, there is insufficient novelty. Its degree of novelty or attention-value cannot be properly judged by a person doing nothing else. It must compel the attention of persons not expecting it. This means that its brightness must be much higher than that which makes it noticeable to a person looking at it. We have reason to believe that it should be at least ten times brighter than is apparently necessary to the person who is doing nothing else but look at it.

The value of novelty or conspicuity in compelling attention is so obvious that there is little need for discussion or illustration. One example is presented in Fig. 88. Twenty words were printed in black on a white background and five words printed in red were scattered among them. The entire group was exposed to 24 observers who, immediately after exposure, recorded the words retained in memory. As was to be expected, the attention-value of the words printed in red was much greater than the others. However, this does not mean that red is always more attention-compelling than black. In cases of novelty the results are always relative to the particular competition and situation.

DEMONSTRATIONS OF SEEING

The eyes, the visual sense, and the entire human seeing-machine are necessarily a part of any demonstration of seeing. The inconstancy of these factors makes it necessary to obtain many observations from a representative group of subjects even for careful researches to yield dependable results. The focus of eyes and attention varies from moment to moment and extraneous factors must be under control in researches in seeing. Obviously, these inherent characteristics of the human seeing-machine are serious obstacles in the development of demonstrations of seeing, which are to be really dependable and useful. Inasmuch as it is necessary to resort to the statistical method in establishing the relationship of any factor in seeing to the results of performance of a visual task, one cannot expect much from an observation or two in a quick demonstration. However, within certain limitations demonstrations are possible and practicable with intelligent and skillful use of the various aids to seeing which are noted or suggested in Fig. 71.

Demonstrations pertaining to seeing may be classified according to primary principle involved or realm directly invaded. They differ in many ways, but chiefly in the nearness of their immediate yield to the ultimate benefit which they aim to indicate. Therefore, they differ in effectiveness, which also increases with increasing simplicity and directness of interpretation. Demonstrations in four realms may be briefly described as follows:

1. *The physical realm* of light, brightness, size, contrast, and color, in which the demonstrations involve photometric and other physical measurements and in which vision and the human seeing-machine are incidental. Such measurements are easily obtained and widely used in demonstrating vision, but a wide gap exists between them and the ultimate benefits to human seeing-machines. They can only be interpreted into seeing by means of data available in the science of seeing and several major steps in logic.

2. *The realm of visibility* in which demonstrations involve external physical factors and in which eyes and the visual sense are of primary importance as optical devices. Approximate measurements are readily obtained, but precise measurements require refined apparatus and tedious methods. Many demonstrations can be made with the L-M Visibility Meter with any or many factors. The relation between visibility data and the ultimate benefits to human seeing-machines is still incomplete, but interpretation of the visibility data requires only one major step in logic. This is readily spanned by a correlation between visibility and ease of seeing.

3. *The realm of production of useful work,* in both quality and quantity, in which demonstrations involve the human seeing-machine and its parts as primary factors or devices for performing tasks depending upon seeing. These yield direct results as far as useful work is concerned, but they do not appraise the effects of seeing upon human beings and the drain of resources expended in internal useless work. Increase in the rate of producing useful work can be interpreted as an increase in ease of seeing. Eventually production is limited by other factors and not by seeing, and at this point fails to measure possible further benefits to human beings from further extension of the particular aid to seeing which is being studied. Many simple tasks

can be used for this purpose but those are best which minimize motion and muscular effort and emphasize visual work and effort. The L-M Demonstration Visual Test [10] was developed for such a purpose and the effect of light, lighting, glare, noise, etc., upon performance can be determined quickly.

4. *The realm of psychophysiological effects* of seeing in which demonstrations involve the entire human seeing-machine and yield results directly interpretable into human efficiency, behavior and welfare. These demonstrations, involving the direct effects of expenditure of energy through muscular, neural and mental channels, require elaborate apparatus and tedious statistical methods, owing to the vagaries of human behavior. In addition, they require experience in fields of science remote from physical sciences and measurements. At present, they can scarcely be considered outside the laboratory, or its equivalent. They are the ultimate criteria of the effects of seeing and of seeing factors upon the human seeing-machine. Their results supply the foundation for the interpretation of any demonstration into the ultimate factors of importance to human beings.

Visibility. Demonstrations of the influence of light, lighting and other factors upon visibility of objects are of a basic nature because these factors are readily controllable. They characteristically involve the performance of tasks at or near the visual threshold. Three different fundamental criteria may be used to register the effects of changes in these factors upon visibility. Usually more than one of the factors—size, contrast, brightness and time—are involved in a satisfactory demonstration or measuring device, although one may be of major importance.

1. *Visual acuity,* or the ability of the eyes to perceive small objects. This criterion usually necessitates refined apparatus unless results of a very approximate nature are satisfactory. A hundredfold change in brightness or illumination is frequently required to produce a twofold change in visual acuity. Since the visual size of objects may be

altered significantly by changes in the distance between
the eyes and the object, this factor may be utilized or
be controlled. This type of demonstration often fails
due to the large differences in visual acuity among individuals since an object may be clearly visible to one
person and not recognized by another. In addition, the
necessity for seeing objects of the threshold size is not
usually a requirement of everyday seeing. Nevertheless,
fairly extreme conditions are necessary and therefore
justifiable in demonstrations of seeing.

2. *Contrast sensitivity,* or the ability to distinguish brightness-differences. This criterion is generally the most
favorable one for demonstrating the relationships between
quantity of light and visibility. Variations in the distance
between the eyes and the object are of secondary importance. Variations in vision among individuals are not as
serious a handicap in demonstrations based upon contrast
sensitivity, as is the case in visual acuity tests. This criterion has the advantage of being a fundamental visual
function upon which all seeing depends. Our Demonstration Visual Test and Visibility Indicator are examples
of the use of contrast sensitivity as a major factor. There
are many ways of varying contrast which are available for
demonstration.

3. *Time* required for recognition of objects. This criterion
necessitates refined apparatus or the summation of the
time required for many observations to detect changes
produced by alterations in size, contrast, brightness or level
of illumination. The time factor may be varied by using
sectored disks, photographic shutters, pendulums, springs,
rotating drums, etc. In many cases, such as the operation
of high-speed machinery, a difference in the time required
for the recognition of an object may mean the difference
between seeing and not seeing the object. This type of
demonstration may be strikingly successful. However,
demonstrations which purport to indicate the total time
saved, in the course of a day's work, by adequate lighting
have little practical significance.

In general, relatively large changes in brightness or level of illumination are necessary to compensate for small changes in any of the foregoing factors. The degree of success or the failure of a demonstration depends primarily upon the magnitude of the differentials between the various conditions for seeing. In many cases the differential will be quantity of light, but other factors such as lighting, brightness of surroundings, or glare may be used. If the differential between conditions is too small, the vagaries of human behavior will confuse or conceal the effect to be shown. If the differential is unnecessarily great, the demonstration lacks force due to the obviousness of the outcome of the experiment. The science of seeing offers direct aid in determining the magnitude of the differential between conditions.

It does not seem necessary to describe actual demonstrations because many can be conceived from considerations such as the foregoing. However, the difficulties of achieving striking success are so inherently great that brief descriptions of some successes by the authors may be helpful. The L-M Demonstration Visual Test [10] was based upon the device illustrated in Fig. 22. The breaks in the diagonal lines form a capital letter of the alphabet. The diagonal lines, which greatly contribute to the success of the demonstration, were printed in dark gray ink upon a medium gray background not shown in the illustration. The diffuse reflection-factors of the two grays are 10 and 16 per cent. The development eventually involved very careful printing during which the reflection-factors of the two grays were continually checked by a brightness-meter. The test was printed first as a pack of cards and later, for the sake of preservation, in book form. The latter consists of 17 pages on each of which are four rectangles each containing a different capital letter. This is available with board covers [29] and is also bound as a supplement in an earlier treatise.[1] It has proved very useful in demonstrating the effects of illumination and glare. It has many other uses as a work-task such as determining the influence upon speed and accuracy of work of such factors as fatigue, noise and other hindrances to seeing.

A successful Visibility Indicator [10] was made by having a

page of printed matter printed upon a background properly graded from white to very dark gray as illustrated on the inside cover of this book. Actually these are made on photographic paper, under carefully controlled conditions, by means of a simple device which drew an opaque slide at the proper speed, thus exposing the paper in a manner to produce a proper gradient. Experience in making thousands of these proved the desirability of exposing each individually rather than printing them from a negative. The scale of relative footcandles at the left is for threshold visibility. A test involving many persons with average vision indicates that the lines of printed matter can barely be read at footcandle-levels about one-twentieth of those on the scale. Hence, on the master test-card the top lines can barely be read by a person with normal vision under 0.05 footcandle and the lines near the bottom under 250 footcandles. This has proved to be a successful demonstration involving constant size and variable contrast and brightness. Properly used it is a crude measuring device.

A successful demonstration or visibility indicator was also made in the form of a slide-rule.[10] A transparent glass slide bears a paragraph of black print reduced by photography to a small size. This is moved along a strip which is properly graded from white to nearly black. The slide may be placed first at the white end of the strip, which forms the background for the printed matter on the glass, and the readability of the paragraph is noted as the slide is moved slowly toward the dark end of the background-strip. Eventually, a point is reached at which reading becomes difficult or impossible, due to the low contrast. This point is also noted on the back of the device by means of the glass slide. On the back one scale is graduated in relative footcandles for threshold visibility, and another scale is graduated in per cent contrast between the printed matter and the background strip. The seeing condition is now altered, as, for example, by moving to a place where the level of illumination is at least half or twice as great. The slide is moved until the same low readability is again evident. The point is noted on the scales on the back as in the previous case. Two sizes of type are provided on the glass slide. Anyone will soon acquire a consistent criterion of degree of readability, so that the demonstration can be used as a crude measuring device.

Both these Visibility Indicators are convincing in regard to the effect of the factors involved. A correlation between visibility and ease of seeing makes it possible to obtain an idea of the influence of various visibility factors on ease of seeing.

Production of work. The production of useful work is an obvious as well as often-tried method for demonstrating the benefits of more light or better lighting. Such demonstrations not infrequently produce indifferent or even negative results. The science of seeing enables one to predict the results of such experiments in many cases and to devise methods of demonstration which will prove satisfactory. One or more of the following requirements are usually involved in a successful demonstration:

For demonstrations of short duration,

1. A task involving critical seeing to a major extent
2. A large differential in conditions for seeing
3. A visual task which demands the utmost concentration and effort upon the part of the subject. This requirement is generally in opposition to the inclinations of the average subject. If this condition is not fulfilled, the subject usually takes advantage of the better conditions for seeing in making his task easier rather than in producing more work. This variable expenditure of effort may arise from either physiological or psychological causes. The L-M Demonstration Visual Test fulfills the requirement of controlled effort by taking advantage of severe ocular tasks which are performed by the eyes and which are beyond the conscious control of the subject.

For demonstrations of long duration,

1. Demonstrations involving the production of useful work over periods of weeks or months, such as reading or other work-world visual tasks, obviously necessitate the elimination of extraneous factors.
2. A differential in conditions for seeing equivalent to one

step, and preferably more, in footcandle effectiveness or any other adequate change in seeing conditions.

3. The visual tasks need not be as critical as in the case of shorter demonstrations due to the functioning of physiological and psychological influences.

The average rate of working was assumed in the preceding discussion as a criterion of the effectiveness of illumination or other factors. Other criteria, such as precision and accuracy of working may and have been used. Demonstrations involving precision as the criterion require refined apparatus and tedious techniques. They have the advantage of yielding positive results. If the demonstration is arranged as an accuracy experiment (the performance of the work graded as correct or incorrect), unusually large differentials in conditions for seeing must be provided. Usually, such demonstrations are unsatisfactory. In general, production tests or demonstrations are valueless as indicators of fatigue, strain or waste of human resources through seeing, for the willingness and ability of the worker will maintain the quality and quantity of achievement unless fatigue has progressed nearly to the point of exhaustion. Such demonstrations at one time received much attention but, owing to their limitations, they are now relatively less prominent.

Human behavior and welfare. The complete relationship between seeing and human welfare obviously involves the life-span of the individual and, as such, is not directly subject to demonstration excepting by statistics. Experiments extending over a period of years in which the effects of controllable factors are indicated by the results of periodic examinations may be considered as demonstrations. Eyesight specialists and physicians can do much toward systematic studies of the effects of better seeing conditions upon vision and health in schools, offices, and elsewhere. The ultimate results of their demonstrations will be important milestones in the general attainment of better conditions for seeing.

CHAPTER VIII

Light and Lighting

Many arts necessarily begin as empirical practices and gradually become sciences as knowledge increases and attitude changes. Thus we have practices continually evolving from empiricism to sciences and those intimately involving the welfare of human beings are emphatic examples. They cannot possibly be perfected into sciences in a short time owing to the complexity of human beings, their activities and the purposes and effects of these upon human beings individually and collectively. Many well-established practices could be cited as examples of evolution from empiricism to sciences. The practice of medicine is a good example in any of its aspects, such as the diagnosis of disorders and diseases and the prescription of drugs and treatment. These practices are by no means scientifically complete, but great strides have been made in substituting scientific knowledge and attitude for the inescapable empiricism of earlier years. A glimpse of medical knowledge and practice a century ago reveals empiricism on every hand. This or that drug or treatment was empirically applied over extensive ranges of ailments. Cure-alls flourish in ignorance. For example, bleeding was advocated for many ailments. No medical man need be ashamed of the widespread empirical practices of the past when scientific knowledge and attitude were rare. However, no one can justify the continuance of empiricism in any practice after scientific knowledge is available to use and to build upon. From crude beginnings the medical profession has attained a high standing as a whole. Faith in the sciences underlying medicine, and in the diagnoses and prescriptions, combined with a scientific attitude have established the medical profession in a high place in the services and demands of mankind.

All intimate services to human beings must travel the same

course from empiricism and its lack of public confidence, to scientific soundness and a high place in public respect and demand. Lighting practice and the lighting specialists are analagous to medical practice and the physician and are far behind on the course of evolution from empiricism to a scientific foundation.[7] The diagnosis of seeing conditions and the prescription of light and lighting for human efficiency and welfare are still largely empirical. Only in the last decade or two has the science of seeing begun to supply knowledge, methods and devices upon which to construct a science of lighting and a lighting profession. But science alone cannot achieve the necessary evolution in lighting any more than it could have achieved it in medical practice. The practitioners must absorb the knowledge and spirit of the underlying sciences and put them into practice. Until this is done by lighting specialists on a broad front, empiricism will continue to reign. Socalled cure-alls in lighting will flourish, as general illumination has by itself, without really supplying lighting in its accurate sense. Public confidence and demand will evolve only as empiricism is replaced by practice built upon scientific knowledge and attitude.

Light and lighting are so universally applicable, controllable, and essential in seeing, and they have been so generally neglected from every viewpoint of seeing, that extensive discussions of them are justifiable. Certainly the primary purpose of light and lighting should be to promote seeing. The ideal objectives of light and lighting should be maximum efficiency and welfare of human beings. These are attained when seeing can be done most quickly, most certainly, and most easily. Only recently have these ideals been clearly introduced into lighting considerations as definite objectives toward which lighting progress should point. This introduces the complexity of human factors and human beings into a practice which had been primarily concerned with physical science involving readily understandable material things such as light-sources and lighting equipment. Obviously an extension of knowledge and a change in attitude are necessary if the lighting specialist of the past is to become a seeing specialist skilled in the scientific prescription of light and lighting.

Lighting practice is primarily a chain of three links as illustrated in Fig. 89. They may be briefly described as follows:

1. *Production* of light—a physical science
   Light-sources or illuminants modified or not by inherent parts, such as colored glass bulbs.
2. *Control* of light—a physical science
   The combination of optical principles of reflection, transmission, absorption and diffusion in lighting equipment and installations.

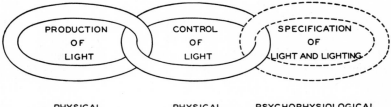

FIG. 89.—Lighting consists of a chain of three links. The science of seeing is forging the third link connecting light and lighting with human needs and welfare.

3. *Specification* of light and lighting—a psychophysiological science
   The effects upon the achievement and welfare of human beings through their influence upon such matters as visibility, vision, seeing, fatigue and attitude.

The interest of lighting specialists has been devoted chiefly to the production and control of light. Therefore, the physical sciences and material aspects of light-sources, equipment and installations have been over-emphasized. Certainly it is self-evident that specifications of light and lighting should be the important objectives of lighting practice. These involve a complex psychophysiological science of seeing which is in the process of development. Its importance in the specification of light and lighting is diagrammatically illustrated in Fig. 90. From this diagram a new science of lighting can be developed and presented comprehensively. At one end of the lighting chain are light-sources.

At the other are human beings. In many respects the picture is an idealistic one. But that is a worthy goal and scientific knowledge leads steadily toward it.

LIGHT VERSUS LIGHTING

There are various ways of separating lighting practice into parts so that considerations may proceed systematically. First it

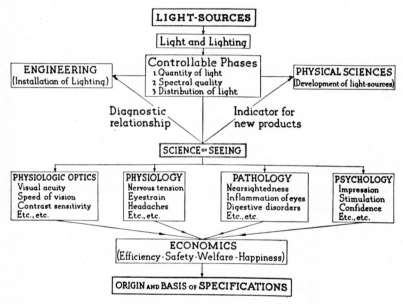

FIG. 90.—The science of seeing is more than a necessary foundation for a science of light utilization. By establishing specifications of light and lighting, it will also influence the choice of illuminants and the design of lighting equipment, and lighting installations.

is desirable to separate *light* from *lighting*. Spectral character is the only inherent characteristic of light. This is treated from the viewpoint of seeing in Chapter XI. After a particular kind of light is chosen, then the amount of light desirable for the specific

visual task or work must be determined. This is variously expressed as intensity of illumination, level of illumination, footcandle-level, and footcandles. Next comes the consideration of
lighting, or distribution of light, upon the work and over the
surroundings. This involves a choice of lighting equipment, kind
of lighting installation and treatment of surroundings. In the
case of three-dimensional objects and polished or glossy surfaces,
the distribution of light upon the work has much to do with the
visibility of the visual objects or tasks. Lighting also plays a
prominent part in the comfort of the human being operating as a
seeing-machine. Such factors as glare, annoying contrasts, confusing shadows which increase discomfort and decrease visibility,
are factors included in lighting rather than in the aspect known
as illumination. Lighting is also responsible for important psychological effects which are seldom given the attention they deserve. By extension, and in connection with reflection-factors of
various surfaces in the visual field, distribution of brightness over
the work and entire visual field is the ultimate result. All such
factors we have found it convenient to include in the term *quality of lighting* [130] which is specifically treated in Chapter X.

From the viewpoint of lighting practice we may separate the
complex matter into three aspects as follows:

1. Quality of light
   Spectral character and color of the illuminant
2. Quantity of light
   Footcandles or level of illumination
3. Quality of lighting
   Distribution of light and brightness upon the visual
   task and over the surroundings.

The choice or modification of the illuminant from the viewpoint
of spectral character or color is a complex matter of economics,
physical control of light, suitability to the visual task, and accepta-
bility to human beings. Excepting in highly specialized uses, no
practical differences among practical illuminants in their effects
upon visibility and comfort have been discovered as yet in quite

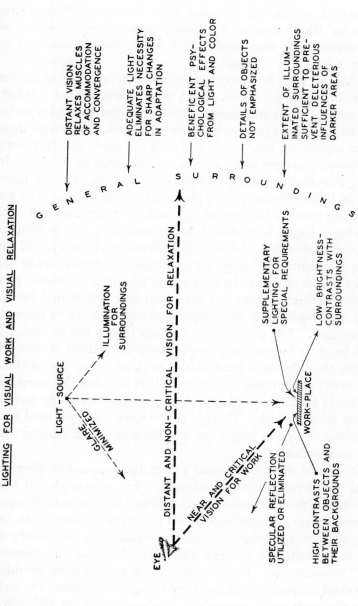

LIGHTING FOR VISUAL WORK AND VISUAL RELAXATION

GENERAL SURROUNDINGS

DISTANT VISION RELAXES MUSCLES OF ACCOMMODATION AND CONVERGENCE

ADEQUATE LIGHT ELIMINATES NECESSITY FOR SHARP CHANGES IN ADAPTATION

BENEFICENT PSYCHOLOGICAL EFFECTS FROM LIGHT AND COLOR

DETAILS OF OBJECTS NOT EMPHASIZED

EXTENT OF ILLUMINATED SURROUNDINGS SUFFICIENT TO PREVENT DELETERIOUS INFLUENCES OF DARKER AREAS

LIGHT-SOURCE

ILLUMINATION FOR SURROUNDINGS

GLARE MINIMIZED

DISTANT AND NON-CRITICAL VISION FOR RELAXATION

SUPPLEMENTARY LIGHTING FOR SPECIAL REQUIREMENTS

LOW BRIGHTNESS-CONTRASTS WITH SURROUNDINGS

WORK-PLACE

NEAR AND CRITICAL VISION FOR WORK

EYE

SPECULAR REFLECTION UTILIZED OR ELIMINATED

HIGH CONTRASTS BETWEEN OBJECTS AND THEIR BACKGROUNDS

FIG. 91.—This is a brief description of light, lighting and seeing in relation to human efficiency and welfare.

a variety of researches. Sodium light is an exception among present-day illuminants in the special cases of seeing objects of high contrast near the threshold of size. This is discussed in Chapter XI.

Adequate light and proper lighting are appropriate objectives of scientific lighting practice. Both affect visibility and comfort. In considering these it is essential to extend the viewpoint to include the surroundings as well as the visual task. Although these complex aspects are extensively analyzed in various chapters, some of the primary aspects and purposes are presented in Fig. 91. In viewing this diagram, note first the locations of the eyes, the light-source or lighting-fixture, work-place and surroundings. The human seeing-machine is engaged in a task of near-vision and critical seeing. Light is provided for illuminating the work-place and the surroundings. Glare in the direction of the eyes of the worker is minimized. Some major physical factors affecting the visibility of the objects to be seen are noted on the diagram. Supplementary direct lighting for the visual task is indicated for obtaining additional light and proper lighting in order to promote high visibility. The general surroundings should not be dark, but should be of an intermediate brightness-level subdued in comparison with the brightness-level of the work-area, but not subdued to the verge of darkness. Some have believed that the surroundings should be dark in order to "rest the eyes" when the worker looks up from his task. There is no evidence that eyes need such an extreme change in brightness and there are good reasons why this is undesirable.

In Fig. 91 some of the chief aspects and purposes of illumination of the surroundings are indicated. The worker should look up from the work occasionally and focus his eyes casually upon the more distant surroundings. This is not done primarily to rest the eyes from the brightness of the visual task, but chiefly to relax the muscles of the eye and also to relieve the "mental strain" momentarily. If the surroundings are too dark, considerable retinal adaptation and pupillary change take place. On looking at the work again, appreciable readjustment must take place.

This is annoying and perhaps fatiguing. If the surroundings are too dark, they are distracting just as a glaring light-source is. Darkness is just as much a reality as brightness. It can be distracting in the peripheral field just as brightness is. Thus dark surroundings can be annoying and fatiguing as a glaring light-source admittedly is. If the surroundings are too bright, unimportant details are emphasized. Under these conditions they are competing for attention they do not deserve. Distraction is the result. Because workers are human, moderate brightness and colorfulness in the surroundings are mildly stimulating and satisfying. Certainly these affect attitude just as cleanliness does. In general, better attention to the visual task and better concentration upon the performance of it are achieved if the brightness of the actual task is somewhat greater than that of the surroundings. These and other important matters of lighting are further discussed in this and succeeding chapters. For the present it is only necessary to bear in mind that the brightness-level of the surroundings is a compromise between that of the work-area and an extremely low level.

LEVEL OF ILLUMINATION

The choice of level of illumination or footcandles is chiefly a complex matter of economics involving the efficiency and welfare of human beings. Various penalties of inadequate light and improper lighting, and rewards of more light and better lighting, are now known. Doubtless, many others still remain hidden in the unexplored realm of psychophysiological effects of seeing. As the science of seeing expands the concepts and reveals new knowledge, one intimately familiar with the known portions of this vast complexity of seeing becomes more and more conscious of the naivete of the past assumptions and empirical practices. To him the human factors become more and more prominent.[120] The old adage—a little knowledge is a dangerous thing—is no better exemplified than in past ideas, and in many current ones, pertaining to what is *enough* light or *proper* lighting.

The science of seeing emphasizes the fact that there are only two cardinal levels of illumination. Briefly expressed they are,

1. Footcandles for barely seeing
2. Footcandles for easiest seeing.

Already a great amount of knowledge of seeing shows that these two levels are far removed from one another. Anyone can determine approximately the level of illumination under which a given object can barely be seen or a given visual task can barely be performed. With some care and simple apparatus this can be determined with considerable exactness. However, the level of illumination for easiest seeing cannot be determined by a simple experiment or even by a single complex one. No single criterion is available for such a determination. We do not know enough about the human being, and particularly the human seeing-machine, to establish such a single criterion. This revealed, more than any other single viewpoint, the need for a science of seeing. And one of the major spheres of activity is the prosecution of researches in seeing which reveal and measure the effects of seeing upon the human seeing-machine. As discussed particularly in Chapters II and VI, useful correlations are being established which eventually will simplify the appraisals and specifications of light and lighting for easiest seeing. They must take into account the three aspects which so vitally influence the ability and welfare of the human seeing-machine. These are (1) the visual task, (2) the visual sense, and (3) light and lighting.

Confronted with just two fundamental levels of illumination, what shall be the choice or ultimate specification? Certainly for prolonged critical seeing no one would specify the level for barely seeing. For many visual tasks less than a footcandle is necessary for barely seeing. All researches which have dealt with ease of seeing, directly or indirectly, indicate that the level for easiest seeing is above 100 footcandles even for the relatively easy task of reading type of large size and contrast. Proceeding by dead-reckoning with physical factors such as size, brightness and contrast, the level of illumination for easiest seeing in the case of small objects of low contrasts and brightnesses is indicated to be in the hundreds and even thousands of footcandles. These foot-candle-levels are impracticable from the viewpoint of present-day wiring and general-illumination methods. All of them are ob-tainable by the more desirable combination of supplementary di-rect lighting with general illumination. However, in cases of extremely high footcandle-levels the problem of attendant heat-ing effect must be solved in some manner. However, this is an engineering matter which in no way influences the fundamental approach to scientific prescription of footcandles,[132] for the pur-pose of obtaining quick, clear and certain seeing.

In the present state of lighting practice and knowledge of the effects of seeing it is necessary in most cases to compromise between the two fundamental footcandle-levels. This interme-diate or temporary level might be termed the *economic level*. The flaw in this is that it carries the implication or assumption that it is possible to measure in monetary units the penalties and rewards of seeing and to strike a balance between costs of seeing and values of accomplishments through seeing. This being utterly impossible, the compromise intermediate footcandle-level might be termed a *practicable level* provided it were understood to be temporary. Agreement in this direction should not be so difficult. In a schoolroom one would recommend all the footcandles which could be obtained on the desktops from a system of indirect light-ing from the available ceiling-outlets, provided there were enough of them to supply reasonably uniform illumination over the work-area. Even the wiring might be rehabilitated. In this case, it has long been known that approximately 50 footcandles would be the upper limit obtainable from such a lighting system without the expanse of ceiling becoming too bright for comfort. Where localized light, such as is obtained from portable lamps or fixed equipment, is practicable, much higher footcandle-levels are pos-sible with lighting equipment now available. This system involves general illumination plus supplementary direct lighting and can be ideal in many places in the work-world as it is in the reading or sewing room of the home.

ILLUMINATION AND BRIGHTNESS

Illumination is *cause* and brightness is *effect*. We do not see radiant energy as it passes from a light-source to objects. Fundamentally we see only the brightnesses and colors of objects. Through interpretations of these all seeing is accomplished. For the present purpose only brightness will be considered. In fact, brightnesses are generally far more important in seeing than colors are. In lighting practice, light and footcandles have been unduly emphasized. Brightness has been considered secondarily, if at all, notwithstanding the fact that it is the useful and ultimate purpose and result of illumination. In researches and analyses of seeing, brightness is one of the four fundamental factors and illumination or footcandle-level is merely a means to an end.

Look at the various papers or magazines spread over the top of a desk, or note the various brightnesses of the pattern of a carpet. All these different areas in each case may be receiving approximately the same illumination, but owing to the differences in reflection-factor (reflectance) they appear of different brightnesses. Thus reflection-factors are more important than footcandles in making them visible. It is misleading and inadequate to think in terms of illumination or footcandles, unless one also keeps in mind reflectances and brightnesses.[5] The socalled black letters on this page are receiving as much light as their background of white paper. Their contrast is high because they reflect only about one-fortieth as much light as the white paper does.

Place a piece of diffusely reflecting black paper by the side of a white one. View them very close to a light-source and then have someone move the white one farther and farther away. Eventually they will be of equal brightness notwithstanding the fact that their reflectances may be two per cent and 80 per cent, respectively. It is only necessary for the black paper to receive 40 times as much light as the white one. By moving the white paper farther away, the point will be reached where by comparison the white paper appears black and the black paper appears white. This is very readily demonstrated by controlling the light on each of two such specimens. This is a simple matter which has been generally ignored in seeing, particularly in lighting practice. To emphasize it further, Table LI is included. In it are presented the footcandles necessary to make diffusely reflecting surfaces of different reflectances of the same brightness, ten footlamberts. The same procedure can be used for any diffusely reflecting surface to make it appear of the same brightness as any other such surface, regardless of their respective reflection-factors.

TABLE LI

Combinations of Reflection-Factors and Footcandles Producing the Same Brightnesses

	Reflection-Factor (Per Cent)	Footcandles
Perfect black	0	∞
Black velvet	1	1000
Black ink	2	500
Gray paper	20	50
White blotting paper	80	12.5
Perfect white	100	10

Now let us carry this point further into the everyday world of seeing. Suppose we have a socalled black cloth and a socalled white one having reflection-factors of two and 80 per cent, respectively. Place them at a distance and hold a black thread in the hand so as to view it silhouetted against the two cloths. In order for the black thread to be as visible against the black cloth as it is against the white cloth, the black background would have to be illuminated with 40 times as much light as the white one. In other words, for the two visual tasks to be identical in contrast and brightness, the black background would have to be supplied with 400 footcandles if the white one had ten footcandles upon it. This is an unassailable fact.[5]

Now suppose a piece of the black thread were laid upon both the black and white cloths. An additional factor must now be taken into account. In the preceding experiment the black thread received a constant illumination regardless of its background. Now it receives the same footcandles as its background.

Suppose 400 footcandles illuminated the black cloth and black thread and ten footcandles illuminated the white cloth and black thread. The two backgrounds will now be of the same brightness. However, the piece of black thread upon the black cloth would be 40 times brighter than the piece of black thread on the white cloth. The contrast in the former case has not changed, notwithstanding an enormous increase in footcandles, which raised its brightness-level to that of the white cloth. The visibility of the black thread on the black cloth has been improved somewhat on account of this increase in brightness-level, but not nearly so much as in the preceding experiment when the brightness of the black thread remained unchanged while that of the black cloth greatly increased. In other words, 400 footcandles on the black thread and black cloth does increase the contrast and does not raise the visibility anywhere near that of the black thread on the white cloth with only ten footcandles illuminating them. This apparently simple point is very generally ignored in lighting and in various considerations of seeing. It is very readily demonstrated and measurements of visibility can be readily determined by means of the L-M Visibility Meter discussed in Chapter V.

Actual measurements of the visibility of dull black thread on dull black and white cloths, respectively, show that the illumination necessary to make them of equal visibility as determined by our visibility meter is as follows:

Black thread on white cloth	1 footcandle
Black thread on black cloth	2100 footcandles

BACKGROUNDS FOR SEEING

Throughout the work-world and other realms of seeing, reflection-factors differ greatly. In many cases the detail to be seen cannot be physically separated from its background. Obviously, in such cases the specification of footcandles inversely as the reflection-factors, or in proportion to the absorption-factors, is a very conservative procedure. In cases where the details to be seen can be silhouetted against a separate controllable background, it is obvious that seeing may be greatly influenced by the brightness of the background. Its reflection-factor may be any value from black to white and by separately controlling the light upon it, its brightness can be altered greatly. The proper beginning is to determine whether the specific object or essential details can best be seen as a bright object against a darker background or as a dark object against a brighter background. It is a matter for study not only with visibility measurements, but also with introspective observations or actual measurements of comfort. As discussed in Chapter VI, the reflex blinking of the eyelids has been developed by use for such a purpose. Obviously, backgrounds of diffusely transmitting glass or other media can be utilized in some cases. With light-sources confined behind such a medium, great control of the brightness (and color) of the background is possible. For a very dark background approximating perfect black, one may use a deep hole lined with black velvet. Such a hole is much blacker than a piece of socalled black velvet.[21]

On every hand in the world of seeing there are opportunities for study and applications of backgrounds as aids to seeing. The factors involved are simple ones even though they are generally ignored. In many cases improvements will be obvious. However, there is no system or certainty in such experiments without measurements of visibility and of other factors if possible. In much assembly work and inspection of objects a background of proper brightness is an essential for best seeing. In watch-repairing the worker sometimes purposely uses sheets of white paper in order to see the minute parts appropriately silhouetted. How much easier it is to thread a needle if it is viewed against a bright sky as a background than against a surface of relatively low brightness and accidental pattern. The general absence of controlled backgrounds for seeing and lack of consideration of them are simple illustrations as well as eloquent testimonials of the general absence of a consciousness and knowledge of the factors which influence seeing.

Colored backgrounds have no particular virtue in promoting visibility excepting in special and relatively rare cases. Where sufficient contrast can be obtained between the objects to be seen and the background without using black or white, color can be considered for esthetic purposes including *esthetic comfort*. Shades of green (olive) and yellow (buff) and light tints of yellow are the more likely colors for such purposes. This matter is also discussed in Chapter XI.

SPECULAR REFLECTION

In the foregoing discussion of footcandles and brightness, diffusely reflecting surfaces were considered. In the case of polished or glossy surfaces we are contending with perfect or imperfect mirrors of various shapes, which reflect perfect or distorted images of bright luminous objects or of bright reflecting surfaces in the surroundings. In specular reflection from such objects the footcandles upon the objects play a minor role. A needle or pin lying upon a carpet owes its brightness largely to the highlight which is a distorted drawn-out image of a light-source, a bright ceiling, a patch of sky or other bright object or surface. In countless cases of everyday seeing, highlights of this character are important. Specular reflection may be an aid or a hindrance to visibility and seeing. Sometimes, as in the case of glossy paper and pavements, it may not only reduce visibility but it may cause discomfort. In the work-world, improvements in seeing may be achieved by controlling the position, area, and brightness of the surface whose reflected images are seen as highlights on polished surfaces. In the realms of inspection and assembly throughout the work-world there are countless examples of specular reflection which can be enhanced or reduced, as the case may be, in order to improve visibility and ease of seeing. These are so varied that only the general principles can be discussed here. This is a fruitful field for the seeing specialist in which to make measurements of visibility and for the lighting specialist to combine his ingenuity in brightness-control with a full knowledge of physical optics in the promotion of certain and easy seeing. Here lighting plays a prominent part along with light or footcandles.

Some threshold visibility measurements were made of common pins lying on black and white cloths and illuminated by direct and indirect lighting. These reveal something of the influence upon visibility of specular highlights and of lighting. The footcandles necessary for equal visibility are presented in Table LII.

TABLE LII

Footcandles for Equal Threshold Visibility as Determined by the L-M Visibility Meter

Direct Lighting	Footcandles
Pins on white cloth, highlights prominent....................	4
Pins on white cloth, no highlights noticeable..............	4
Pins on black cloth, highlights prominent.................	3
Pins on black cloth, no highlights noticeable..............	60
Indirect Lighting	
Pins on white cloth, no prominent highlights..............	10
Pins on black cloth, no prominent highlights..............	5

Under direct lighting the highlights on the pins on white cloth appeared brighter than the white background. When the pins were so located that there were no specular highlights, the pins appeared darker than the white background. By accident the threshold visibilities in the two cases were the same under the constant illumination of four footcandles. When the pins were on the black cloth, highlights accounted for much of the visibility, for when the location was changed so that there were no highlights, the illumination had to be 20 times as great to maintain the same visibility. With indirect lighting the highlights are not prominent and the visibility of the pins was greater on the black than on the white background. It required twice as many footcandles on the white cloth as on the black cloth to make the pins equally visible. In the former case the pins were seen as objects darker than the white cloth. In the other case they were seen as objects lighter than the black cloth. These simple experiments yield measurements which reveal the influence of various factors in the complexity of visibility. Such measurements must be extensively made through the world of seeing if guesswork is to be replaced by specifications based on the science of seeing.

Bright specularly reflected images of light-sources may be

quite noticeable at certain positions of observation of reflecting surfaces under a lighting system which might otherwise be quite satisfactory. In such cases it may be advisable to eliminate or greatly reduce these specular reflections by the addition of diffused illumination. Table LIII contains some data pertaining to specific conditions of lighting in which specular glare from glossy paper was reduced by additional diffuse illumination of the paper or reading matter. The light-source, whose specularly reflected image caused annoying glare and reduced the visibility of the reading matter, consisted of a 16-inch diffusing glass globe. Three tungsten-filament lamps were used in it and, therefore, the globe was of three different brightnesses. It hung at two different heights. These are specified because the footcandles upon the glossy paper decreased inversely as the height, but the brightness of the specularly reflected image is independent of height although the size of the image is not. Under the various conditions the additional footcandles necessary to suppress the specular glare were determined. These are indicated in the last column of Table LIII for each condition. These data are presented as an illustration of the method of promoting visibility by reducing the brightness of the specularly reflected image. This is also suggested as a possible means of rating quality of lighting from one specific viewpoint. It will be noted that the glare effect of specular reflection is suppressed with greater difficulty as (1) the angle of incidence increases (2) as the brightness of the source increases and (3) as the distance of the glare-source from the work increases.

TABLE LIII

Angle of Incidence (Degrees)	Distance of Glare-Source (Feet)	Wattage of Lamp in Fixture	Footcandles on Paper from Glare-Source	Additional Footcandles to Suppress Glare
18	9	150	4	15
18	9	300	14	50
18	9	500	20	60
45	12	150	1.5	15
45	12	300	5	65
45	12	500	7	70

[312]

SHADOWS

Many objects are seen and recognized by the aid of shadows. The modulation in light and shade over an object to be seen gives much information as to its form and other characteristics.[21] Its cast shadow upon another surface is also important in seeing. As in the case of highlights or specular reflection, lighting is generally more important than light or footcandles. By controlling the distribution of light, an extensive control over shadows can be exercised. Here again a study by means of visibility measurements is the only certain approach to knowledge. Mere inspection of the objects as the lighting is varied will reveal changes in visibility, but permanent and recordable knowledge is a matter of measurements in this field as in all others. Certainly throughout the work-world studies of shadows, as of highlights, will reveal much knowledge of seeing and particularly of light, lighting and brightness as aids to seeing three-dimensional objects. Shadows may be darkened, sharpened, softened or even eliminated by controlling light and lighting. It is the function of the lighting and seeing specialist to determine what should be done in order to promote high visibility and easy seeing. These matters are discussed in other chapters.

To illustrate the effect of shadows, small white cyclinders with diffusely reflecting surfaces were placed upon dull black and white cloths, respectively. They were illuminated by direct and indirect lighting. The footcandles necesary to make them of equal threshold visibility in all cases are presented in Table LIV.

TABLE LIV

Footcandles for Equal Threshold Visibility as Determined by the L-M Visibility Meter

	Footcandles
Direct Lighting	
Dull white cylinders on white cloth	7.5
Dull white cylinders on black cloth	3.5
Indirect Lighting	
Dull white cylinders on white cloth	30
Dull white cylinders on black cloth	5

Under direct lighting the shadows were insufficient to compensate for the low contrast when the white cylinders were viewed against the white background. It required about twice the footcandles to make these objects as visible on the white cloth as on the dark cloth. Under indirect lighting the shadows were so subdued that they aided visibility very little. It is of special interest to compare the effects of direct and indirect lighting on the visibility of the dull white cylinders upon the white background. It required 30 footcandles of indirect lighting to make the objects of the same visibility against the white ground as they were under 7.5 footcandles of direct lighting. Likewise, it required more footcandles of indirect lighting than of direct lighting to make the objects of equal visibility when seen against the black cloths.

Only general conclusions can be drawn because direct lighting varies widely in its influence upon the threshold visibility of three-dimensional objects, depending upon the location and brightness of the dominant light-source and of the surface characteristics of the objects to be seen. However, these measurements are quantitative proof of the value of direct light from sources of light of relatively small sizes in enhancing the visibility of objects due to shadows. In this case the direct lighting consisted of an inside-frosted tungsten lamp (200-watt) and very little light reached the objects indirectly by reflection from the surroundings.

REFLECTION OF LIGHT

Reflection-factors of surfaces vary in kind and in magnitude. Perfect specular reflection is approached by silvered mirrors, the surface of polished glass, quiescent water and many other materials. This and other kinds of reflection are illustrated in Fig. 92. The angle of incidence I is always equal to the angle of reflection R. Perfect diffuse reflection is approached by blotting paper, velvet, freshly fallen snow, heavily sand-blasted opal glass, and unpacked dry powders such as flour and pigments. Many glossy or polished surfaces exhibit both kinds of reflection quite perfectly. A simple demonstration can be made by placing a thin

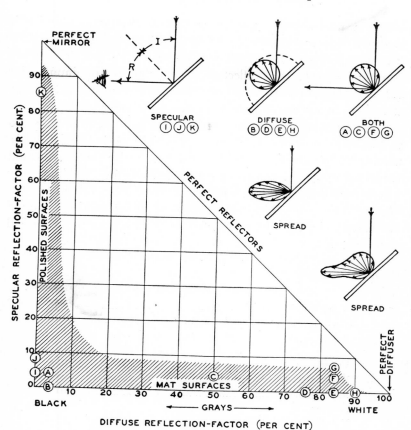

FIG. 92.—Illustrating types of specular and diffuse reflection from surfaces. Combinations of these two kinds of reflection from some materials are plotted on the triangle and indicated on the small diagrams.

(a) Glossy black paint
(b) Mat black paint
(c) Glossy gray paint
(d) White blotting paper
(e) Mat white paint
(f) Glossy white paint
(g) Glazed white porcelain
(h) Powdered zinc oxide
(i) Surface of glass or water
(j) Two surfaces of thin glass
(k) Polished silver

piece of plate glass over white blotting paper. The combined result is also shown. If the white paper is replaced by a black one, the specular reflected images become much more prominent.

There is another kind of reflection, best known as *spread*

[315]

reflection, in which an imperfect or distorted specular reflection is superposed on more or less perfect diffuse reflection. Two characteristic cases are illustrated in Fig. 92. Of these, the upper diagram illustrates the reflection of light from aluminum paint and sand-blasted metal surfaces. The lower diagram is characteristic of the reflection of light from common glossy papers.

Inasmuch as these two types of reflection are commonly exhibited by many surfaces, the triangle in Fig. 92 is helpful in visualizing them. Surfaces exhibiting only specular reflection would be plotted on the vertical side at the left. Those exhibiting only diffuse reflection would be plotted on the horizontal side at the bottom. Others exhibiting both types would generally be found on the shaded area. Those plotted on the diagram are identified in the caption.

TABLE LV

Diffuse Reflection-Factors in Per Cent

Socalled blacks	0–4
Socalled whites	75–95
Common dry powdered pigments	
American vermilion	14
Venetian red	10
Burnt sienna	10
Raw sienna	30
Golden ochre	58
Yellow ochre	50
Chrome yellow, medium	55
Chrome yellow, light	75
Chrome green, medium	14
Cobalt blue	16
Ultramarine blue	7
Common woods	
Curly maple, unfinished	50
Oak, unfinished	35
English oak, finished	17
Walnut, finished	16

A glossy black paint *A* reflects only a few per cent of the incident light both specularly and diffusely. A glossy white paint

F reflects about the same percentage of light specularly but much more light diffusely. This is why F is plotted only the same distance vertically as A is, but much farther out horizontally. Owing to the much higher refractive index of the glaze on porcelain than the varnish of a glossy white paint, the specular reflection-factor of the former may be about twice as great as that of the glossy white paint. That is why G is plotted above F. The other plot is worth studying in connection with the other surfaces in relation to each other. All surfaces whose reflection-factors would be 100 per cent or nearly so would be plotted along the diagonal of the triangle or near it. However, actual surfaces of this kind would plot near the ends of this diagonal.

The reflection-factors of materials vary widely, and it is so difficult to describe the materials and their surfaces that a table of reflection-factors is not very helpful. However, it may be of interest to present in Table LV a few approximate values and ranges of diffuse reflection-factor.

DEFINITIONS AND UNITS

Notwithstanding the universal importance and use of light, familiarity with the simplest terms and units of light, illumination and brightness is by no means universal. An analogous case is the unit of electrical energy—kilowatt-hour—which also is among the most universally used commodities in civilization. It is 1000 watt-hours. By multiplying the watts used by a tungsten-filament lamp, or other electrical appliance, by the hours it is used, the watt-hours are obtained. On dividing by 1000, the kilowatt-hours are obtained. By further multiplying by the cost in cents per kilowatt-hour, the cost of operating a light-source or other electrical appliance is determined.

In the use of light and in the practice of lighting, there is already a sizable array of terms and units and many others are needed in order to complete the relationships of light, brightness, contrast, color, vision and seeing. These are continually being refined and added to. They are described elsewhere.[131] Here it is only necessary to present a few in a readable manner. As is true of all units and terms these are empirical, but they have fundamental value due to their wide acceptance by scientific and technical groups. As knowledge increases, new needs and relationships are revealed and new terms and units are evolved. The unit and scale of visibility originated by us in the development of our visibility meter as described in Chapter V is a recent example of an attempt to fill a great need in the measurement of this highly important factor in seeing. In this case, the unit is a function of many biological variables.

The international *candle* is the unit of luminous intensity and is an arbitrary standard maintained by certain governments. The amount of light emitted by a light-source can be determined in terms of this unit. An ordinary candle about an inch in diameter provides roughly one candlepower in a horizontal direction.

The *lumen* is the unit of light (or luminous) flux emitted in a unit solid-angle (steradian) from a uniform point-source of one international candle. Such a source emits 4π lumens because, as a simple matter of geometry, there are 4π unit solid-angles or steradians surrounding a point. A lumen is the total light flux on a surface of unit area all points of which are at a unit distance from a uniform point-source of one international candle. If the foregoing unit is one foot it is obvious that a footcandle is equivalent to one lumen per square foot.

Lumens per watt expresses the luminous efficiency of an electric light-source.

The *footcandle* is the unit of illumination. The level of illumination upon a surface varies (1) inversely as the square of distance from the light-source of small size relative to the distance; (2) directly with the candlepower of the source in the direction toward the surface; and (3) with the cosine of the angle of incidence of the light upon the surface. The illumination (footcandles) and the diffuse reflection-factor of a surface determine the brightness of a diffusely reflecting surface. A footcandle is approximately the illumination on a small area of vertical surface one foot from an ordinary candle.

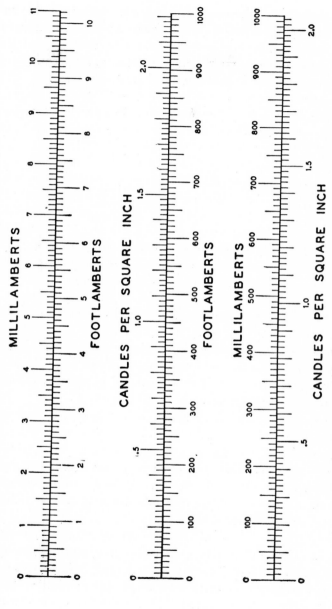

Fig. 93.—Scales for transferring brightness from one unit to another. Obviously these cover the entire range of brightness merely by altering the position of the decimal point.

Brightness is measured in various units. Their fundamental definitions assume perfectly diffuse reflection (or emission) of light

A *lambert* = 1 lumen emitted per sq. cm.
= 1000 millilamberts (ml)
= 929 footlamberts (fl)
= 2.054 candles per sq. in.

A *millilambert* = 0.929 footlambert
= 0.00205 candle per sq. in.

A *candle per square inch* = 452 footlamberts
= 0.487 lambert
= 487 millilamberts

A *footlambert* = 1 lumen emitted per sq. ft.
= 0.00221 candle per sq. in.
= 1.076 millilamberts

Convenient scales for conversion from one brightness unit to another are provided in Fig. 93.

Reflection-factor or *reflectance* is the ratio of the light reflected by a surface to the light incident on the surface. In determining reflectance it is essential to distinguish between diffusely and specularly reflected light.

Transmission-factor or *transmittance* is the ratio of the light transmitted by a transparent or translucent medium to the light incident upon it.

Glare is a term usually applied to a condition of lighting which causes eyestrain or discomfort. It also reduces visibility. It is never entirely absent from lighting, but it can be reduced below the limits of noticeability.

General lighting or *general illumination* is that supplied to a work-area in general without specifically directing the light upon the visual tasks. It is commonly obtained from light-sources symmetrically distributed in respect to the ceiling and floor areas. In *indirect lighting* the light is reflected from large areas such as the ceiling before it reaches the work-area. In *direct lighting* it reaches the work-area directly from such equipment as pendent reflectors.

Color is the general name for the sensation arising from the activity of the visual sense in response to radiant energy. Any color can be completely specified or described in terms of three fundamental attributes.

1. *Hue* is that attribute which indicates the direction of departure of a color from a gray of equal brightness. It

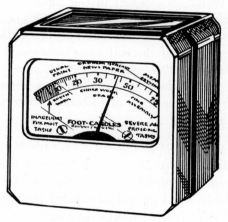

FIG. 94.—A simple meter for measuring footcandles.

permits a color to be described as red, reddish, green, greenish, etc.

2. *Saturation* is that attribute of a color which determines its degree of difference from a gray of the same brightness. It determines tints.

3. *Brightness* is that attribute of a color which permits it to be classed as equivalent to some member of the series of grays (achromatic colors). Relative brightness determines shades. The term, *value,* is used in reference to relative brightness. A value scale is a systematic series of grays covering the range from black to white. See Table III.

MEASUREMENT OF FOOTCANDLES

A great variety of photometers has been developed over the years. These are adequately described in treatises which have dealt predominantly with the physics of light. Recently the development of light-sensitive cells has made it possible to provide very compact light-meters or footcandle-meters because there is no need for batteries. Such devices are now so inexpensive that they should find extensive use. In Fig. 94 is illustrated a compact footcandle-meter representative of those now available. The light-sensitive surface is exposed in the top of the meter. The electric current generated in this cell by radiant energy is indicated by an ammeter whose scale is calibrated in footcandles. Of course, the spectral sensitivity of the cell must correspond to that of the eye in order for the cell to evaluate radiant energy in accordance with the ability to produce light or luminous sensation. The absolute sensitivity of these types of footcandle-meters depends upon the cell and the ammeter.

MEASUREMENT OF BRIGHTNESS

Many devices have been used for measuring brightness. However, no small compact brightness-meter of extensive range has been available which possessed several desirable refinements. In particular it is desirable to focus the image of the object, whose brightness is to be measured, upon a part of the photometric field. To achieve these refinements and to provide a compact brightness-meter which might encourage the measurement of brightness, the instrument illustrated in Fig. 95 was developed by M. Luckiesh and A. H. Taylor.[133] This portable brightness-meter weighing slightly more than two pounds, is designed to measure brightness throughout a great range beginning with the lowest that the visual sense can conveniently measure under practical conditions outdoors at night. Its range is 25,000,000 to 1 between 0.002 and 50,000 footlamberts, or 0.0022 and 53,800 millilamberts, or 0.000005 to 110 candles per square inch.

The meter has two eyepieces at the right-hand end. Through the upper eyepiece the observer views the magnified photometric

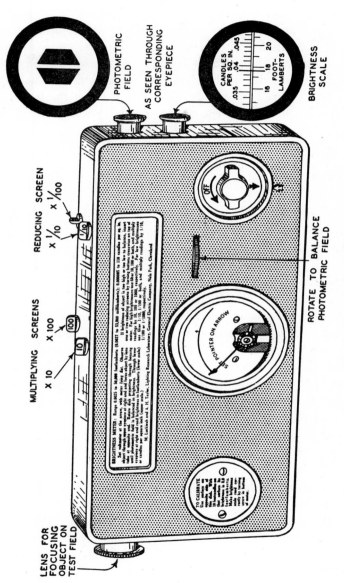

FIG. 95.—The Luckiesh-Taylor Brightness-Meter.

field, consisting of two small silvered trapezoids separated by a narrow clear strip, as shown in the sketch on the photograph. By means of the lens tube at the opposite end of the meter an image of the object to be measured is brought into focus in the plane of the photometric field, in the clear portion between and surrounding the two silvered trapezoids. The latter reflect the image of a diffusing glass in front of the comparison lamp and the brightness of this glass is varied by means of a circular gradient filter. Various filters of constant transmission-factor may also be inserted for extending the range of the instrument. After a photometric balance is obtained, the brightness of the test-object is read from an illuminated scale seen through the lower eyepiece at the right-hand end, as shown on the photograph. The values are given both in candles per square inch and in footlamberts.

The scale in the meter reads from 0.0045 to 0.11 candle per square inch; also 2 to 50 footlamberts. Its range can be extended upwards by two multiplying screens with multiplying factors of 10 and 100, respectively. When these two are used simultaneously, the multiplying factor is 1000. Brightnesses can be extended below the range of the scale in the meter by means of reducing screens with multiplying factors of 0.1 and 0.01 which combined have a reducing factor of 0.001. The range can be further extended downward by lowering the voltage of the comparison lamp. By use of the lower voltage and the reducing screens at the same time a factor of 0.0001 is obtainable. The image of the object to be measured is easily and clearly focused in the photometric field, hence there is no uncertainty as to the object being measured. The optical system is such that the brightness of an object approximately one foot wide can readily be measured at a distance of about 500 feet. When the comparison lamp voltage is set at the higher calibrated value, as it is for all but very low brightnesses, the color of the comparison field is approximately the same as that of the light from high wattage tungsten-filament lamps. This is accomplished by a blue filter fixed in position in the instrument.

Some measurements of brightness made with this meter are given in Table LVI.

[324]

T A B L E   L V I

Brightness of Common Objects, Surfaces, and Light-Sources

	Footlamberts	Candles Per Sq. In.
Outdoors in daytime, clear day in December		
North sky, 10 degrees above horizon	1000	2.21
East sky, 10 degrees above horizon	750	1.7
South sky near sun (hazy)	35000	77.0
West sky, 10 degrees above horizon	850	1.9
Zenith sky	300	0.7
Brick road in sunlight	375	0.8
White cloth in sunlight	4000	8.8
Black cloth in sunlight	250	0.55
Ground in sunlight, very little grass	200	0.45
Fresh snow in sunlight	5000	11.0
Outdoors at night		
Concrete highway, artificial lighting	Less than 1	Less than 0.002
Indoors		
Lighting unit in office, brightest spot of opal glass	1700	3.8
Ditto, darkest spot	280	0.6
Ceiling above unit	140	0.3
Buff wall of same room	8	0.018
Floor of same room	2	0.005
Light-sources		
Candle flame	4300	9.5
Inside-frosted tungsten lamps, brightest spot		
40-watt ....,....................	15000	33
60-watt	16000	35
100-watt	50000	110
200-watt	65000	144
500-watt	95000	210
Filament of 500-watt tungsten lamp	3390000	7500
Cooper-Hewitt mercury tube, maximum	9000	20
400-watt Type H-1 mercury lamp	407000	900
250-watt Type H-2 mercury lamp	294000	650
85-watt capillary tube mercury lamp	5240000	11600
600-watt capillary tube mercury lamp,	129000000	285000
Moon, half-full	350	0.8
Full moon, clear sky	1500	3.3
Sun as observed at earth's surface	450000000	1000000

A simple brightness-meter [135] developed by the authors is illustrated in Fig. 96 for measuring relative brightnesses and relative contrasts. These readings of relative brightness can be converted into absolute brightness by means of measurements made with any convenient footcandle-meter. One tube of the device has a lens D in the end which, in combination with the adjustable eyepiece E, is practically a telescope of universal focus. The instru-

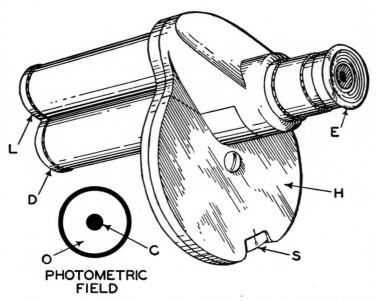

PHOTOMETRIC
FIELD

FIG. 96.—The Luckiesh-Moss Brightness-Meter for measuring relative brightness of adjacent areas. When used with a footcandle-meter, the absolute brightness of any surface can be determined.

ment is so sighted that the image of the object whose brightness C to be measured is seen in the portion of the photometric field surrounded by a mirrored portion O. In the end of the other tube is a perfectly diffusing translucent glass L. Its brightness O is proportional to the footcandles upon L and its brightness is seen in the portion of the photometric field surrounding C. Thus O provides the comparison brightness. The brightness of the object

[326]

focused is varied by means of a circular gradient of extensive range in transmission-factor which is enclosed in the housing H. Thus a setting is made and the relative brightness of the object is read from the scale S.

Suppose the relative brightnesses of the envelope of diffusing glass of a common office-lighting fixture and that of the ceiling surrounding it are to be determined. The foregoing procedure is applied first to the bright portion of the fixture and then to the adjacent ceiling. In both cases the illumination in footcandles upon the diffusing glass L and hence its brightness, remain sensibly the same. Thus O is a constant comparison field for the determination of relative brightnesses of the fixture and ceiling and the brightness-contrast, which is an important factor in visibility and comfort. Inasmuch as the brightness of L depends upon its illumination, a simple measurement of the footcandles received by L provides a means of conversion (with the aid of a predetermined constant for the instrument) of relative into absolute brightness. With the increasing use and availability of inexpensive footcandle-meters such a simple brightness-meter should eventually serve many practical purposes.

MEASUREMENT OF REFLECTION-FACTOR

From the definition of reflection-factor, or reflectance, it is obvious that its measurement involves the determination of the amounts of light incident upon, and reflected from, a surface. Transmission-factors are measured in an analogous manner. Various photometric devices can be used for such determinations. The reflectometer originated by A. H. Taylor [134] is one of the most practicable designed for the specific purpose. With all the usual photometric devices for conveniently measuring reflection-factor the difficulties of comparisons involving color-difference are inherent. One that avoids this difficulty by employing the phenomenon of *induction* has been developed recently by one of the authors. Even in its simplest form its accuracy compares favorably with those devices involving color-difference.

[327]

A reflectance-gauge devised by Luckiesh utilizes the phenomenon of induction. It is illustrated in Fig. 97 in its simplest form. A narrow slot S is bordered by two brightness gradients G which vary gradually and uniformly from black at one end to white at the other. This is placed over the surface R whose diffuse reflection-factor is to be measured. If the eyes are directed back and forth along the slot, it is obvious that at a certain point the brightnesses of the gradients and the slot would appear approximately the same. However, this involves the difficulty of comparing brightnesses differing in color unless the surface to be measured is colorless or gray. Actually one does not equate adjacent

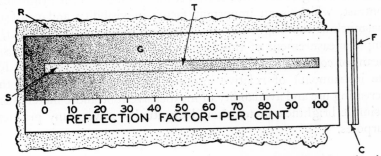

FIG. 97.—The Luckiesh Reflectance-Gauge eliminates the difficulties of color-difference by utilizing the phenomenon of induction.

brightnesses with this device, but uses the phenomenon of induction. Toward the darker end of the gradients the surface viewed through the slot will appear brighter than it actually is. Toward the other (lighter) end of the gradients the surface viewed through the slot will appear darker than it actually is. Therefore, there is a point T somewhere along the slot where there is a transition from the greater *apparent* brightness to the lesser *apparent* brightness, since at this point there is no induction effect on the surface viewed in the slot owing to the absence of brightness-difference between the slot and gradients at this point. Therefore, this point of transition T indicates the diffuse reflection-factor of the surface viewed in the slot which can be read directly from the scale of the gauge.

Inasmuch as the reflection-factor of the bright end of the slot is that of a socalled white which is of the order of 80 per cent, the range of the gauge is readily extended to permit the measurement of reflection-factors approximating 100 per cent. This is accomplished by covering the slot with a light gray transparent filter F of proper absorption-factor. On viewing through this filter the surface to be measured, the brightness of the latter

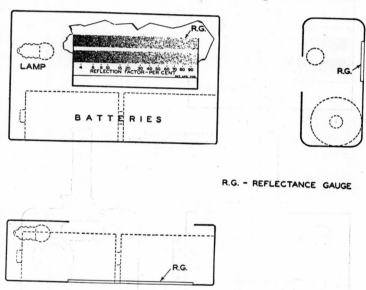

R.G. - REFLECTANCE GAUGE

FIG. 98.—A refined model of the induction Reflectance-Gauge which includes batteries and a light-source enclosed in a housing.

is reduced accordingly. By calibrating the scale of the instrument with this filter F in place it is possible to extend the range to reflection-factors of 100 per cent. The range cannot be conveniently extended to zero at the other end, but is generally limited by the reflection-factor of the black end of the gradient. This can approach four per cent. However, these very low reflection-factors are not of much practical importance. The gradients are protected by a cover-glass C to which they and the filter F are cemented.

The use of the reflectance-gauge has been refined by enclosing it to eliminate the annoyance of specular reflection from the cover-glass, as illustrated in Fig. 98. In this enclosure small batteries and a small lamp are installed as shown. Careful measurements with this device can be as accurate as those made with more elaborate and cumbersome instruments and are well within the ac-

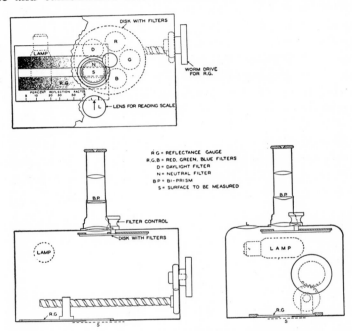

FIG. 99.—A colorimeter using the induction Reflectance-Gauge as a basis. A disk provides the necessary red, green and blue filters, and others. The housing encloses a light-source which is connected to an ordinary lighting circuit.

curacy needed for most work. This device is actually made so that a cover slips over the opening to keep dust out, and the gauge is also readily moved and replaced by a cover and confined in the enclosure for protection when the device is not in use.

This reflectance-gauge has also been used as the basis of a trichromatic colorimeter as illustrated in Fig. 99. Suitable red, green and blue filters *R*, *G*, and *B* are set in a disk. The gauge is viewed through a telescope which includes a biprism. The worm drive moves the reflectance-gauge RG until the transition point is directly under a cross-hair indicated by the arrow. The scale is read through the lens L. Such a reading can be made for each of the three filters, and the color of the surface S to be measured is specified in terms of the R, G, and B components. These filters are placed successively under the eyepiece by rotating the disk by means of the knob designated. A lamp is installed in the enclosure for illuminating the gauge and a plug is available for connecting to an ordinary lighting circuit. Ordinary fluctuations in voltage are of no consequence. The reflection-factor of the surface S can also be measured by means of this device. In fact, the refinements of the cross-hair and biprism result in fairly high accuracy. A daylight filter D is available for determining the reflection-factors for daylight. A neutral filter N is available for reducing the brightness of the surfaces of high reflection-factor because a high level of illumination is provided in order that the low reflection-factors may be determined more readily.

CHAPTER IX

Prescribing Light

The prescription of light and lighting upon a rational basis of visibility [132] has been emphasized in several preceding discussions as a cardinal principle of scientific practice and as an essential step in the evolution of an empirical art into a science. It should be obvious that most levels of illumination in use or recommended are generally arbitrary values because their magnitudes are greater than those required for barely seeing and are usually far less than the indicated optimums for easiest seeing. At the present time intermediate footcandle-levels are generally necessary owing to the limitations of habit, engineering factors and economic considerations. Admittedly such compromises are quite necessary but there is no eventual escape from prescribing footcandles on a rational basis of measurements. Guesswork and empiricism cannot do justice to such universally essential factors as light and lighting in the world of seeing.

A retrospective view of the progress of viewpoint, knowledge and practice reveals four successive eras of footcandle usage.[136] They may be described as follows:

1. Mere light
2. Mere footcandles
3. Production footcandles
4. Humanitarian footcandles.

From the beginning of civilization until the appearance of gas and electric lighting, light-sources were portable flames approximating one candlepower. Placed close to the work, they could supply a footcandle or two upon the visual task. By using a crude reflector and more than one flame, such portable lamps could, and doubtless in some cases did, supply a few footcandles upon the visual task. Inasmuch as these light-sources were not so located as to supply general illumination over a large area, that was an era of *mere light*. It extended from earliest times until the advent of systems of lighting which made possible and even required the distribution of light-sources over a sizable area. This ushered in the era which may be termed that of *mere footcandles* because light was not merely available at the specific task as in the case of portable flames. Areas were illuminated and this general illumination could best be described in footcandles. This era began in earnest about 1880 through the use of gas-mantles and electric lamps.

Early in the present century a scientific and technical interest in lighting practice began. The physical viewpoint of light production and control was extended into the material realm of production, spoilage and safety in the industrial world. The great demand for products of factories during the World War stimulated investigations of the relation of footcandles to the quality and quantity of useful work done by workers. This is now known to be a restricted and inadequate view of the service of light to human beings. Nevertheless, it was a worthy beginning which gave rise to an era of *production footcandles*. This viewpoint and era still persist, but are being submerged by a general acceptance of the dictates of the science of seeing. With the development of adequate concepts and appropriate knowledge of seeing, new vistas and objectives were revealed. The consideration of light and lighting began to include human efficiency in a new and full sense and human welfare as an important ultimate goal. About a decade ago we applied the term *humanitarian footcandles* to the new era definitely in sight.

This brief glimpse provides a helpful background for understanding present habits and practice and for appraising the present trends and future possibilities. It may be additionally helpful to emphasize the footcandles common to the various eras. During the practice of mere light and mere footcandles, the human seeing-machine generally had no more than a footcandle or two available for the visual task. Even at the present time the average level has not increased very much. It averages of the order of two or three footcandles. Even in this era of production footcandles, the average in factories is about three footcandles. In those industries where every advantage is taken to increase the production and to promote the welfare of workers, the average level is perhaps of the order of ten footcandles. From many scientific investigations of quantity of production, it appears that a footcandle-level of 30 footcandles is justifiable even from this narrow viewpoint. When quality of achievement is considered, even higher footcandle-levels seem to be justifiable. Humanitarian footcandles arise from ideals much higher than those dealing with material things. These levels may be conservatively expressed as 100 footcandles and more.

EFFECTIVENESS OF FOOTCANDLES

The footcandle as a physical unit is constant in value; but only as a "glass-case" standard is it invariable. When it is put into service of human seeing-machines, its value or effectiveness varies enormously. This is an unassailable fact which did not permeate far into considerations of lighting and seeing until recently. This is revealed by inspection of lighting codes of the past and most of the researches dealing with light and vision. It is readily demonstrated by adding one footcandle to this page when it is illuminated by one footcandle. The improvement in seeing is obvious. However, if one footcandle is added when the page is already illuminated by 10 or 20 footcandles, no improvement in seeing is noticeable. From many researches dealing with external physical factors, with various aspects of vision, and with the results of seeing, it is thoroughly established that a scale of footcandle effectiveness is approximately a geometric one as illustrated in Fig. 100. In other words, in order to improve visibility by arithmetic steps, footcandles must be increased in geometric steps.

If the ability and performance of the human seeing-machine were constant, small geometric changes would noticeably affect seeing. However, they vary from moment to moment due to involuntary fluctuations of the focus of the eyes and of the attention, and perhaps due to other human vagaries. The length of a rod can be determined with sufficient accuracy for most practical purposes by means of a single measurement with a steel tape. However, this could not be done with an elastic tape. Owing to the "elasticity" of the human seeing-machine as a measuring device, it is necessary to approach the measurement of seeing by the statistical method. Averages, variations and probable errors must be obtained.

Our researches in seeing have provided many opportunities for ascertaining the normal variations. An example is given in Fig. 101 which includes many thousands of observations by so-called normal subjects. Curve *A* represents the average relation-

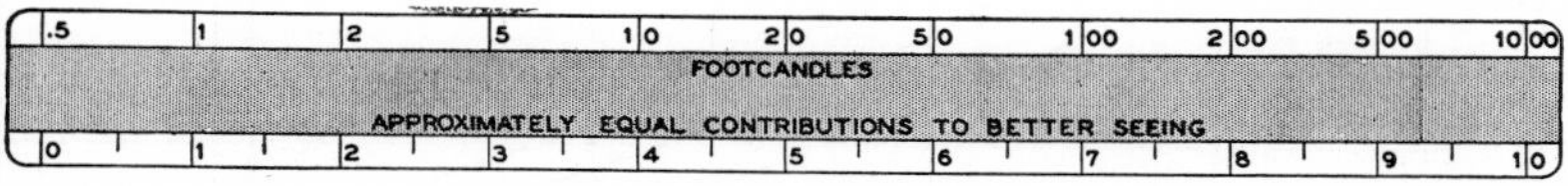

FIG. 100.—The scale of footcandle effectiveness. Numerous and diverse researches have established the fact that the illumination (footcandles) must be doubled to produce equal and significant improvements in seeing.

ship between footcandles and the contrast of a given object with its background necessary for threshold visibility. Curves *B* and *C* represent the average variation from the average performance of this particular visual task but do not include the differences exhibited among various subjects. It is obvious that the average variation, due to variations in human mechanism and behavior, is at least as great as the change in the ability to see due to a 100 per cent change in footcandles. For example, by following any horizontal line in Fig. 101, it will be seen that the distance between the intersections of curves *A* and *B* approximately encompasses a 100 per cent change in footcandles.[1] Thus, even under ideal seeing conditions in the laboratory, it is necessary to double the footcandles before the increase in the effectiveness is comparable with the factor of human variability.

From such data and reasoning we have arrived at the conclusion that, throughout the range of ordinary brightnesses, the *footcandle-level must be doubled to produce an obvious and signifi-cant improvement in seeing.*[7] Thus this becomes a cardinal principle in considerations of footcandles and Fig. 100 is a graphic illustra-tion of it. This does not mean that one footcandle when added to ten footcandles will have no influence. Of course it will; but this influence will be very small and it will not be detectable by

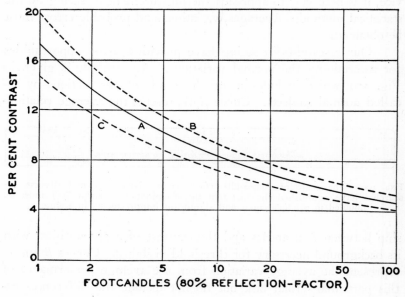

FIG. 101.—Curve *A* represents the average relation between footcandles, or brightness, and the contrast of a given object with its background necessary for threshold visibility. Curves *B* and *C* represent the average variation of observa-tions by normal subjects.

the unaided human seeing-machine. The relationship illustrated in Fig. 100 should be recognized not only throughout lighting practice but in researches in vision and seeing.[137] In the former realm, it eliminates ridiculous recommendations and conclusions and in the latter it clarifies the approach, eliminates useless work and properly extends the range of the research.

Throughout this treatise are presented many glimpses of the effectiveness of footcandles upon various factors which influence

[336]

seeing and the results of seeing. In fact, this aid to seeing has been particularly emphasized because light is always essential and is very generally controllable. Many others could be included which might aid in appraising the value of footcandles in terms of another aid with which much experience has been gained. For example, Fig. 102 illustrates the contribution of illumination or brightness to visual acuity in terms of eyeglasses whose prescriptions are chiefly determined by methods involving visual acuity. Twenty adult subjects who were wearing glasses were selected

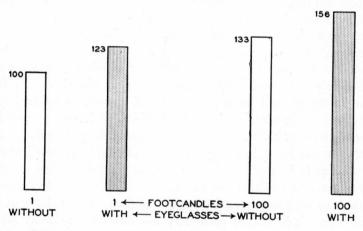

FIG. 102.—Illustrating the average relative improvement in visual acuity due to eyeglasses and illumination for twenty adult subjects.

at random. Their average age was about 30 years. Visual acuity measurements were made by means of apparatus and technique of high accuracy. The refined and variable test-object of high contrast was illuminated by 1 and 100 footcandles, respectively, and under each condition the visual acuity of the subjects was determined with and without their glasses. It is seen that at one footcandle the glasses improved the average visual acuity 23 per cent. At 100 footcandles the average visual acuity was even higher without glasses than it was at one footcandle with the glasses. This strikingly compares the effectiveness of footcandles and eyeglasses in this one respect and shows the combined value

[337]

of both. Of course, it should not be forgotten that eyeglasses are prescribed for other purposes as well as to improve visual acuity. Nevertheless, such data have revealed to the eyesight specialist the value of light. Other criteria than visual acuity reveal similar relationships between these and other aids to seeing.

A STANDARD OF VISIBILITY

Visibility is the basic factor in seeing but we would not contend that all factors and all results of seeing are exactly and completely appraised by determinations of visibility. For example, ease of seeing is not necessarily exactly and completely proportional to visibility, but it appears to be sufficiently so for practical purposes. Visibility and comfort go hand in hand a long way at least, but it need not be contended that comfort is exactly and completely determined by measurements of visibility. In fact, even in the present incomplete stage of the science of seeing, it appears that in certain visual tasks visibility is not a complete measure of the relative difficulty of the task and of the relative cost to the human being in the performance of that task. Still, visibility appears to be the most important basic factor of great practical importance. In fact, no other basis is available.[9] Furthermore, in dealing with matters affecting the efficiency and welfare of human beings it is neither customary nor necessary to delay taking the most important step toward prescribing light on a rational basis until knowledge is complete. If this were done in medicine there would be no medical science now. This is equally true of other sciences and practices involving human beings.

In preceding discussions, visibility has been viewed from many angles from which it has been studied. Particularly in Chapter V the theory and applications of the L-M Visibility Meter [9] have been presented. Therefore, the present discussion will deal with visibility as a basis for footcandle prescriptions in the everyday world. It will be recalled that the basic conditions upon which to specify prescriptions for all other complex tasks of critical seeing were (1) reading matter consisting of 8-point Bodoni Book Monotype, (2) excellently printed with black ink on dull white paper,

[338]

(3) an illumination of ten footcandles, (4) proper lighting without any preventable glare or noticeable discomfort, and (5) a human seeing-machine with average normal abilities. In the light of the present knowledge of seeing, this is a very conservative standard of visibility. Most persons prefer to read larger type, but the size of type commonly used is determined by considerations of space available. This tends toward a compromise between ease of reading and economics of publication.

It is likely that few persons would want less than ten footcandles, even if they were reading 12-point type. In fact, most persons choose nearly 100 footcandles for reading a newspaper having nearly 8-point type. If the standard of visibility were that produced by 10 footcandles on 12-point type, it would be necessary to have about 20 footcandles on 8-point type of the same style. In Table LVII five different standards of visibility are produced by means of different sizes of type of the same style (Bodoni) combined respectively with the proper footcandle-levels. Owing to the ineffectiveness of a few footcandles, the actual footcandle values obtained by measurements of visibility have been rounded off to the nearest convenient number. All of the four combinations in a given horizontal row are of equal visibility. The five different standards of visibility represent equal steps similar to the arithmetic scale in Fig. 100.

TABLE LVII

Five Standards of Visibility Obtained by Different Sizes of Type and Appropriate Footcandles

Footcandles on Printed Matter

12-Pt.	10-Pt.	8-Pt.	6-Pt.
5	7	10	17
10	15	20	35
20	30	40	70
50	70	100	140
100	140	200	340

In Chapter VIII and elsewhere it is emphasized that any footcandle-level between that low one necessary for barely seeing and the high one necessary for easiest seeing is an arbitrary one. Therefore, agreement upon a standard of visibility involves primarily an agreement upon a standard footcandle-level for the standard task. It is assumed that reading matter of a certain size and style of type and excellent paper, ink and printing can be readily agreed

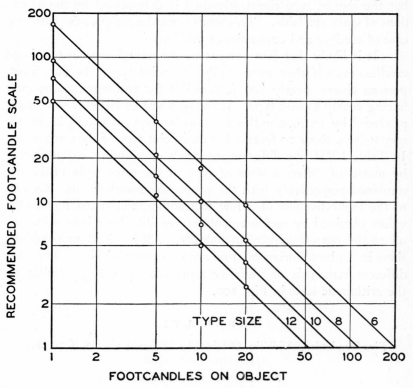

FIG. 103.—Illustrating the effect of various standards of visibility upon the footcandle recommendations for various tasks as obtained by the L-M Visibility Meter.

upon as a standard task. After such an agreement it becomes necessary to agree upon a practicable standard of illumination.

The data presented in Table LVII are graphically shown in Fig. 103 by the small circles representing the averages of the actual measurements. Since the scale of the visibility meter (ordinate values) is calibrated upon the basis of 10 footcandles upon 8-point type, it follows that a scale value of 10 footcandles should be obtained when the 8-point type is illuminated to 10 footcandles. Under this condition, the 12-point type is found to require 5 footcandles. Thus the footcandle values read from the meter scale of *relative footcandles* may be considered as *recommended footcandles* if 10 footcandles upon 8-point type is considered to be a suitable standard. If we assume that 20 footcandles upon the 8-point type is a more satisfactory standard of ease of seeing, then it follows that 10 footcandles should be required upon the 12-point type. It will be noted that this relationship is verified by the experimental results. Since the instrument is calibrated for only a single level of illumination, it should be obvious that the recommended footcandles, for any standard of visibility, may be obtained by altering the illumination upon the objects to be appraised. Thus increasing the standard of visibility from 10 to 20 footcandles upon 8-point type is equivalent to decreasing the illumination upon the objects of appraisal from 10 to 5 footcandles. The same results could be obtained by providing the visibility meter with several scales corresponding to various standards. In the latter case, all measurements would be made under the same level of illumination upon the objects measured.

FOOTCANDLE LEVELS

One of the outstanding problems and objectives of researches in seeing is to establish criteria for determining what the level of illumination should be for various requirements. We have already discussed the results of many researches and analyses approaching the matter from various viewpoints. This appears to be an appropriate place for a brief summary of knowledge bearing upon humanitarian footcandle-levels for persons possessing average normal vision.

Biological adaptation. Human beings are adapted to outdoor environment. Exclusive of clouds, snow, white sands, and some barren soils, the diffuse reflection-factors of major outdoor areas are about five per cent. Under levels of illumination ranging from 1000 footcandles in the shade to 9000 in the sun, the brightnesses of surfaces of five per cent reflection-factor vary from 50 to 450 footlamberts. These brightnesses correspond to those produced by 40 to 360 footcandles on the white paper of this page. It appears that human seeing-machines should be adequately adapted to such brightnesses.

Sensitivity of the visual sense. A general summary of knowledge pertaining to the visual sense indicates that the highest sensitivity or efficiency is reached at brightness-levels somewhere between 100 and 1000 footlamberts. It may be stated conservatively that optimum visual acuity and optimum contrast sensitivity are achieved at brightnesses of white paper illuminated by *more than* 100 footcandles.

Psychophysiological effects. Undesirable effects as measured by such criteria as fatigue, nervous muscular tension, expenditure of energy, blinking and heart-rate are minimized when prolonged critical visual tasks are performed at brightness-levels of more than 100 footlamberts or brightnesses of white paper illuminated by *more than* 100 footcandles.

Visibility of tasks. For the same visibility as easy reading tasks under a few footcandles, difficult reading tasks require brightnesses of more than 100 footlamberts which correspond to brightnesses of white paper illuminated by *more than* 100 footcandles. To produce the same brightnesses of many critical tasks involving low reflection-factors and low contrasts, hundreds and even thousands of footcandles are required.

Production of useful work. In most tasks of the work-world a practical maximum ·of production is reached at about 30 footcandles. However, there is evidence that this is limited by other factors than seeing. Highly controlled researches reveal that even for such relatively easy tasks as reading large print, the rate of reading continues to increase slowly as the brightness is increased to those corresponding to white paper illuminated to more than 100 footcandles. For tasks of greater difficulty and criticalness and chiefly involving visual work, the increase in production beyond brightnesses of 30 footlamberts is more marked. As shown in Chapter VII, the value of the gain in production due to increases from 5 to 20 footcandles is commonly so much more than the increase in the cost of lighting that the net gain can purchase several times more light. In other words, in many places in the work-world humanitarian footcandles can be obtained at no net increase in cost over the average lighting available. Also extensive statistics pertaining to spoilage, accidents and property damage due partially or entirely to poor seeing indicate that humanitarian light and lighting can be paid for by the savings in many cases.[5] However, these economic factors are of incidental interest here even though they are of practical interest in the work-world.

From the foregoing brief analyses it is indicated that the ideal level of illumination for reading even large type excellently printed is above 100 footcandles. Therefore, ten footcandles on 8-point type is a very conservative standard of visibility.

F O O T C A N D L E   P R E S C R I P T I O N S

With the conservative standard of visibility represented by ten footcandles on 8-point type of excellent printing, black ink and dull white paper, let us consider some prescriptions obtained with our visibility meter. Some of these are presented graphically in Fig. 104. It is seen that pencil writing on white paper requires 25 footcandles if it is to be of the standard visibility. Newspaper text matter commonly printed with type slightly less than 8-point requires more than 30 footcandles because of the gray paper and poor printing. The yellow pages in a telephone directory require more than 50 footcandles to be of the standard visibility. Stock quotations involving fractions in small type must have about 80 footcandles if the conservative standard of visibility is to be maintained.

Similar measurements applied to various visual tasks in homes, schools, offices and factories indicate that hundreds and even thousands of footcandles are necessary even to reach the conservative standard of visibility adopted for the present purpose of demonstrating the use of the visibility method of prescribing footcandles on a rational basis. Engraving and sewing required 500 to 3000 footcandles. Inspection operations in a plastics plant required 100,

200, 400 and 1150 footcandles, respectively. Inspection operations
in a rubber plant required from 200 to 800 footcandles. A deli-
cate job on a filing machine used to finish tools and dies required
3000 footcandles. For some of these operations in progressive

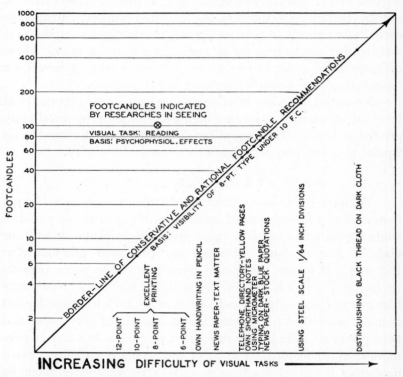

FIG. 104.—Illustrating rational footcandle specifications for various visual tasks.
These are determined by the relative visibility of each visual task and that of a
chosen standard visual task.

factories the footcandle-level actually in use was unusually high
compared with common empirical practice and no one suspected
that 10 or even 100 footcandles could be improved upon. Errors,
spoilage and loss of time were accepted as inevitable. However,
measurements convinced employers and employees that far more
light would still increase the speed, accuracy, and certainty of see-

ing. In many such cases visibility measurements startlingly reveal the influence of lighting; that is, distribution of light.

On every hand there are opportunities for substituting measurements for guesswork. However, the examples given are sufficient to illustrate the principles. It is emphasized that the footcandle prescriptions presented in the foregoing are those necessary to provide the standard visibility which is conservative. Anyone who thinks that thousands of footcandles are too much for some of the common visual tasks involving low contrasts and reflection-factors should try inspecting dark textiles or viewing details such as stitches under 1000 footcandles in the shade outdoors or even under 5000 to 9000 footcandles of direct sunlight. This is also demonstrated by the L-M Visibility Indicator.

Although there is no scientific substitute for the proposed method of specifying the light and lighting on a visibility basis for the particular visual task and human seeing-machine, it is

T A B L E   L V I I I

Conservative Footcandle Recommendations on a Rational Basis of Characteristics of the Visual Task and Requirements of Performance

100 Footcandles or More—For very severe and prolonged tasks, such as fine needlework, fine engraving, fine penwork, fine assembly, sewing on dark goods and discrimination of fine details of low contrast, as in inspection.

50 to 100 Footcandles—For severe and prolonged tasks, such as proofreading, drafting, difficult reading, watch repairing, fine machine-work, average sewing and other needlework.

20 to 50 Footcandles—For moderately critical and prolonged tasks, such as clerical work, ordinary reading, common benchwork and average sewing and other needlework on light goods.

10 to 20 Footcandles—For moderate and prolonged tasks of office and factory and when not prolonged, ordinary reading and sewing on light goods.

5 to 10 Footcandles—For visually controlled work in which seeing is important, but more or less interrupted or casual and does not involve discrimination of fine details or low contrasts.

0 to 5 Footcandles—The danger zone for severe visual tasks, and for quick and certain seeing. Satisfactory for perceiving larger objects and for casual seeing.

helpful to make fairly sweeping recommendations provided they
are based upon the science of seeing. The first attempt of this
kind was made by us several years ago [2] and it is presented in
Table LVIII.

These were based upon experience with a thresholdometer [138]
which we eventually developed into the L-M visibility meter [9]

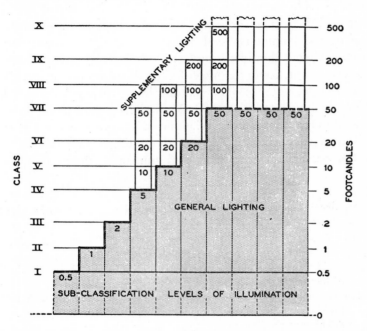

FIG. 105.—Illustrating the principle of supplementing general illumination with
the illumination of the visual task supplied by localized or directed lighting.
The diagram is based upon the footcandle scale of effectiveness. Visual tasks
are divided into ten classes corresponding to the footcandle-levels indicated. The
supplementary illumination does not exceed ten times the general illumination.

and upon new concepts and knowledge of seeing. They were the
first specifications of minimum desirable footcandles which attempted to recognize and to harmonize economic, practical, hygienic and humanitarian aspects. No claims of perfection were or
are made. However, by comparing Table LVIII with any section
of lighting codes existing at that time, it will be seen that it repre-

sents a large step from the realm of guesswork and empiricism toward an adequate scientific basis. Furthermore, in the light of the science of seeing, the recommendations are conservative notwithstanding the fact that when they first appeared they were considered radically and impracticably high in value.

FOOTCANDLES FOR READING

In the foregoing it is seen that footcandles can be prescribed for the particular visual task. In the past, footcandle recommendations have been made for a variety of operations involving seeing. It has seemed to us much more practical to establish ten levels of illumination, for example, in accordance with Fig. 105 and to assign each task to one of these levels or classes. This is discussed later. However, the need for such a system is emphasized when the great range in footcandles for various tasks under the same name is recognized. For example, reading varies greatly in the physical factors such as size, brightness and contrast and in the requirements of performance such as severity, criticalness, continuity, duration, etc. Certainly no general recommendation for reading has any meaning or value.

Let us begin by considering typical dogmatic recommendations of footcandles for reading which have appeared quite recently. These state that 5 or 10 or 15 footcandles are enough for reading; that 10 or 11 footcandles are enough for this individual; that 5 to 20 footcandles are the limits of tolerance of another individual; that 5 footcandles are adequate for reading when obtained by direct lighting; that 10 footcandles are enough when obtained by semi-indirect lighting; and that 15 footcandles are enough when obtained by indirect lighting. Such conclusions do not reveal even a meager conception of the complexity of seeing. They cannot possibly take into account the unassailable fact that mere inspection or introspection cannot determine the proper level of illumination or can draw such fine distinctions between direct and indirect lighting. So many factors are ignored that such statements would not deserve scientific consideration were it not for the fact that they are given consideration by the inexpert.

Even lighting codes of the past contain similar dogmatic, meaningless, inconsistent recommendations. For example, for years ten footcandles were recommended for office lighting and 20 footcandles for sewing on dark goods. Even a casual consideration of reflection-factors would reveal that the latter required many times more footcandles than the former in order to have comparable brightnesses without any consideration of contrast which is a highly important factor in seeing. In addition, a broad recommendation for office lighting ignores the great range of visibilities of the task involved. Some of these are illustrated in Fig. 105.

Returning to the footcandle recommendations for reading, let us begin with the realization that reading involves a variety of tasks having an enormous range in visibility for the same footcandle-level. Shall we assume that children or adults or old persons are doing the reading? It seems reasonable to provide even greater factors of safety for young and old than for average adults. Let us assume ten footcandles upon a page printed with 12-point type, with excellent ink and paper as our temporary standard of visibility. Let us see what the footcandle-levels must be for other reading tasks involving printed matter in order to maintain this standard of visibility. These are summarized briefly in Table LIX from measurements of visibility which already have been

TABLE LIX

Approximate Footcandles Necessary to Maintain a Given Standard of Visibility for Different Reading Tasks

Footcandles

1. For 12-point type of high standard of printing. Minimum size desirable for anyone, particularly young and old 10
2. For 6-point type of high standard of printing. Minimum size commonly used 30
3. For 6-point type of lower standard of printing. A common characteristic of newspapers 100
4. For recognizing individual 6-point letters or numerals. A characteristic of proofreading 200
5. For commonly deficient and defective vision. An additional step in the footcandle scale of effectiveness appears conservative 500

presented. It is not insisted that in taking each step that the same ease of seeing is maintained, but that visibility is maintained the same as the step above in each case.

It does not seem necessary to discuss in detail the steps presented, but a few comments may be helpful in revealing the need for rational footcandle specifications and how to obtain them. Reading is discussed more in detail elsewhere. Beginning with ten footcandles for the standard task consisting of 12-point type and excellent printing, it is necessary to have about 30 footcandles for 6-point type if the standard visibility is to be maintained. This is obvious from Table LVII. In Fig. 104 and elsewhere we have shown that the lowered visibility due to poor printing on relatively low-grade paper requires at least three times as much light to maintain the standard of visibility. Therefore, the illumination must be increased from 30 to about 100 footcandles. On introducing such characteristics of performance as close attention to details as in proofreading, discrimination of stock quotations and the labored reading of children, it has been shown that higher visibility is necessary in order to maintain the performance and degree of ease of seeing. Adding merely one step in the footcandle scale of effectiveness, we reach 200 footcandles.

The foregoing deals with average normal vision but this is not representative of the general public for which footcandle recommendations are made. It is shown elsewhere that refractive errors as small as 0.5 diopter reduce visibility 25 per cent. This requires a large increase in footcandles in order to maintain the assumed standard of visibility. It seems conservative to add approximately one more footcandle step. Thus it is easy to reach 500 footcandles for reading tasks that are difficult in various ways, or for various reasons.

All the foregoing tasks involve printed matter. However, reading includes a variety of tasks of relatively low visibility such as mimeographing and other reproductions, pencil and ink writing such as shorthand notes, various bookkeeping and other office tasks, addresses viewed through window envelopes by the mail-sorter, etc. Besides these there are various characteristics or requirements of performance which add to the difficulty of the task. All this added to the foregoing reveals the folly of making sweeping recommendations not founded upon measurements. An analysis similar to the foregoing may be made using any other standard of visibility including those in Table LVII. An inevitable result of any scientific approach will be a large range of footcandle specifications to cover the variety of reading tasks.

After the foregoing brief glimpses of the variety of reading tasks and the relation of visibility and footcandles to them, it may be interesting to look over Table LVIII again. In respect to reading we recommend

> *50 to 100 footcandles* for severe and prolonged tasks such as proofreading, difficult reading, etc.
>
> *20 to 50 footcandles* for moderately critical and prolonged tasks, such as clerical work, ordinary reading, etc.
>
> *10 to 20 footcandles* for moderate and prolonged tasks of office and factory, and when not prolonged, ordinary reading, etc.

These recommendations have been emphasized because they were first made quite a few years ago and were considered by us to be conservative in the light of the new concepts and knowledge of seeing which were woven into general specifications of footcandles for the first time. It seems unlikely that anyone familiar with the important facts and factors and who actually experimented with these levels of illumination under good lighting conditions would conclude that these recommendations are not conservative. Certainly they are practicable compromises far below the indicated ideal levels.

Attempts to establish different footcandle-levels for reading when obtained by socalled direct, semi-indirect, or indirect systems are also extremely arbitrary, if not ridiculous, without proper measurements and specifications of factors not adequately described by such terms as direct lighting. Also there is no accepted basis for establishing brightness tolerance of normal human beings with such low and narrow ranges as represented by the cases quoted earlier in this section.

INDIVIDUAL SELECTION OF FOOTCANDLE-LEVELS

A brief discussion of the meaning and results of individual selections of footcandles for a given task is desirable for several reasons. However, at the outset it is emphasized that such a procedure has no scientific standing, and at best the results are of limited meaning. Owing to the facts that we first introduced such a demonstration and that it has been used to some extent as a basis of footcandle specifications, it is worth discussing briefly.

For several years we had in the laboratory a large booth containing many light-sources above a diffusing glass. These were so arranged that by means of a series of switches we could obtain the series of footcandle-levels illustrated in Fig. 100. This was a scientific tool for it provided the approximate geometric steps in footcandles corresponding to arithmetic steps of effectiveness. Many uses were made of this booth. It also became a common procedure to have subjects and visitors make their own choice of footcandles for such a task as reading.

Thousands of persons have been tested in this manner under different conditions and the average choice is near 100 footcandles. However, the choice is influenced by the brightness of the surroundings, by the footcandle-levels available, by the visual task, by the manner of approach and in other ways obvious to those familiar with psychological factors. Many years ago when we used such a method and had only a moderate maximum footcandle-level available, we found that subjects usually selected a value somewhat below the maximum regardless of its low value. In recent years our demonstration booth has had a maximum of 1000 footcandles available.

In Fig. 106 are the results [7] obtained with a group of 82 school-teachers with a booth large enough so that its illuminated gray interior filled with the entire visual field. They were asked to select, by actual trial, the footcandles they considered suitable for reading black print on white paper for long periods. The selection was made while reading and solely upon the basis of their own criteria of comfort afforded by the footcandles upon the work and the brightness of the gray surroundings. As shown in Fig. 106 the average illumination selected was about 92 footcandles although the median value was somewhat lower. Owing to the indefiniteness of the criteria and the limitations of the human being as a measuring device, it is not surprising that the maximum and

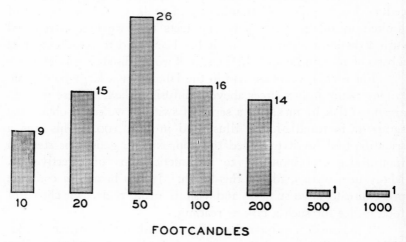

FOOTCANDLES

FIG. 106.—Showing the number of persons of a group of 82 adult subjects who chose various footcandle-levels for reading an ordinary newspaper under a particular condition of lighting.

minimum selections were 1000 and 10 footcandles, respectively. No attempt was made to determine the possible refractive errors of vision or to appraise in any other manner the ability of the subjects as seeing-machines.

Such an experiment is by no means desirable for laying a scientific foundation for footcandle specifications. In fact, it has been adequately proved in many ways that human beings are very poor judges of seeing conditions. They are poor seeing meters. Their ability to see varies continually as illustrated in Fig. 101. However, an experiment of this sort is of some value in a corroborative sense. At least the results show that persons indifferent to the prevalent low levels of one or a few footcandles under which they read at home, for example, commonly choose from 20 to 200 footcandles when they have an opportunity.

Inasmuch as practically everyone will choose a footcandle-level above, and usually far above, that which is commonly available in the artificial world, commercial interests utilized this demonstration. Carelessly it became accepted as having some scientific value. This has not been proved and, therefore, it should not be used as a primary means of specifying footcandles. The idea was also incorporated into convenient apparatus which was sold to eyesight specialists as part of a "light-prescribing technique." As used with a footcandle meter and a variety of visual tasks, it is an excellent demonstration of footcandles as a factor in seeing. However, that is about the extent of its usefulness. If human beings could be depended upon to choose adequate light and proper lighting they would not be so indifferent to the levels of barely seeing in the artificial world where less than a thousandth of Nature's footcandle-levels are commonly found. Countless everyday experiences, and many researches testify to the inability of the human seeing-machine to appraise seeing factors, conditions and results. There is nothing unique about this. The human being unaided by measuring devices founded upon scientific data and significant correlations, is rather helpless as a measuring device in many directions. That is why we have yardsticks, clocks and thermometers for measuring things more readily comprehensible than the complexity of seeing. That is why there should be a widespread usage of meters for measuring footcandles, brightness and visibility.

PRESCRIBING FOR DEFECTIVE VISION

In the foregoing discussions and elsewhere, unless otherwise noted, average normal vision is assumed. This is achieved by eyeglasses of appropriate prescription, if necessary. However, it is likely that the vision of a large percentage of persons is below average normal. Certainly all persons who need eyeglasses do not have them. It is equally certain that all persons who wear glasses do not have the proper prescription because many persons do not have their eyes re-examined often enough. Furthermore, about 30 per cent of the cases of defective vision are "trouble cases" and with such there is doubt as to the ability of present technique and technicians to provide the perfect correction for many of these cases. For these reasons it is safe to assume that average vision is somewhat below average normal vision. If it is below normal by the equivalent of 0.5 diopter, visibility is 75 per cent of normal. This means that the footcandle-level must be approximately doubled to raise the visibility to normal. Some allowance can be readily made for this general deficiency, as described in Table LIX, in the specification of such an essential and universally controllable factor as light. In fact, should not footcandle specifications provide factors of safety which are determined for persons with average low visual efficiency rather than for those with normal vision? Of course, it is best to apply perfect prescriptions of eyeglasses wherever these are necessary and helpful, but nowithstanding increasing consciousness and care of eyesight, there is likely to be an irreducible average deficiency. Also some defects of vision are not correctable by glasses but, as in cases of cataracts and small pupils, are compensated to some degree by light.

Besides the relatively small defects of vision which are very common, there are many persons who have grossly deficient eyesight. Alert eyesight specialists in recent years have aided many to see better by awakening them to the helpfulness of light. In many cases, old persons who have resigned themselves to a conclusion that they are no longer able to see to read have been resurrected, in a sense, by means of high levels of illumination. Sight-saving classes of public schools afford excellent opportunities to investigate the usefulness of light as an aid to seeing, particularly when every possible aid is worth utilizing. Obviously visual efficiency and ease of seeing can be increased through (1) the correction of ocular deficiencies, (2) the provision of more light and better lighting, and (3) the regulation of visual tasks in accordance with the visual ability of the subjects. The discussion which

[354]

follows deals with some aspects of a study of certain controllable factors in sight-saving classes.

Sight-saving classes. Since it is reasonable to assume that reading constitutes the major critical visual task of the classroom, this discussion is restricted to this task. Furthermore, insofar as footcandles can be isolated from intimately interrelated factors, the contribution of illumination will be emphasized. Elsewhere other aspects of vision and seeing among pupils of sight-saving classes are discussed. The textbooks used in sight-saving are commonly printed with 18-point or 24-point type on non-glossy white paper. Thus the physical characteristics of the important visual tasks performed by the pupils are quite definitely describable and, hence, are subject to quantitative analysis. Furthermore, it may be stated that there is no general agreement as to the size of type best suited to the needs of pupils in sight-saving classes. There is no definite agreement as to style or design of the type. This is discussed in Chapter XII which deals with reading.

Doubtless the problem of optimum type-size actually used is complicated by economic considerations. For example, the cost of books in 24-point type is said to be about three times as great as that of books printed in 18-point type. Such an additional cost is economically justifiable if there is a commensurate additional contribution to ease of seeing and human welfare. Obviously ambiguity in the matter of contribution of type of large size beclouds, and even over-emphasizes the additional cost. In general, it is difficult to reach agreement in appraisals of visual and welfare factors in terms of economics. However, the growth of knowledge of the penalties and rewards associated with seeing is the only way that narrow economic viewpoints can be evolved into broad hygienic and social viewpoints.

The results and conclusions presented herewith arise from an investigation [117] of 72 sight-saving pupils in the seventh, eighth and ninth grades located in four different schools in Cleveland. Ten adult subjects possessing normal or near-normal vision were also used in order to permit the appraisal of the results obtained upon an absolute basis as well as upon a relative one. Type-size and the influence of illumination (footcandles) were appraised by visibility determined by the L-M Ophthalmic Sensitometer. Our visibility-meter technique, which has been discussed from various viewpoints of theory and application, was also used.

Some of the experimental data are summarized in Table XLIX along with brief descriptions of the defects of vision involved. The uncorrected vision of some of the subjects was almost nil. Many of these, according to tests with the Snellen chart, were of the order of 6/60. The corrected vision varied chiefly between 6/6 and 6/30. All tests were made with the pupils wearing the glasses prescribed for them. At the bottom of the table it is seen that under a constant illumination of ten footcandles, the average visibility of 18-point type as determined by the 72 sight-saving pupils was 25 per cent less than that of 24-point type illuminated by ten footcandles. Thus it is obvious that the visibility of these particular type-faces is directly proportional to the size of the type expressed in points. At the bottom of the fifth column it will be noted that the ratio of the visibilities of these two sizes of type is the same for both the normal-vision and subnormal-vision groups. The ratios obtained by various individuals vary considerably, but inasmuch as the probable errors of the data were of the order of two per cent, the ratios obtained are reliable from a statistical viewpoint. From the variation in the ratio as obtained by different sight-saving pupils, it is obvious that the same increment in type-size is not equally effective for different individuals. This conclusion is supported, *a fortiori*, by the fact that one subject was unable to read the 18-point type even though the illumination was increased from 10 to 150 footcandles.

Inasmuch as size and brightness are complementary factors of the visual threshold, a decrease of deficiency in one may be compensated by an augmentation in the other, within certain limits. Hence, it becomes important to determine the differential in footcandles which is equivalent to a given differential in type-size. In the sixth column of Table XLIX are shown the levels of illumination required upon the 18-point type to make its visibility the same as that of the 24-point type under the standard illumination of ten footcandles. This value as determined by each individual varies considerably as would be expected for individuals having such marked and different visual defects. The average value is 19.8 footcandles for the sight-saving pupils and 15.6 for the normal group. In general it may be concluded that the difference in size of 18-point and 24-point types can be offset for the average of this sight-saving group by providing twice the footcandles on the former as on the latter.

The footcandle-levels used in this investigation are not to be construed as being recommended by us for sight-saving classes. When pressed for a practical recommendation for such classrooms we have suggested the highest levels of general illumination that can be obtained with comfort by means of indirect lighting. Generally this means 35 to 50 footcandles. When and if it is considered practicable to provide supplementary lighting in addition to general illumination, we do not hesitate to recommend 100 footcandles and even more, provided there are no pathological cases possessing the peculiarity of intolerance to high brightnesses. This advice should also enter the homes of these young people possessing such subnormal vision. Modern portable lamps are available which can provide 100 footcandles upon the visual task and also adequate general illumination so that the lighting effect is quite satisfactory. There appears to be no theoretical reason why 500 footcandles for reading should not be used.

Many interesting facts came to light in this investigation involving sight-saving pupils, but they are more appropriately discussed in connection with reading as a visual task and elsewhere. Here we are limiting the discussion to facts bearing upon the prescription of footcandles. In this connection it is interesting to inquire into the possible aid to seeing that additional footcandles can render specific pupils. With subjects having such marked and different deficiencies it was found that the influence of size of type varied considerably among the group. This was also true of the relation between visibility as determined by the L-M visibility meter and visual efficiency as determined by the method approved by the American Medical Association. Therefore, it is not surprising that the aid to seeing rendered by increasing the footcandles is not the same for all these sight-saving pupils.

HIGH LEVELS OF ILLUMINATION

Inasmuch as the science of seeing reveals the desirability of footcandle-levels very much higher than are commonly in use, it is pertinent to discuss how they may be obtained properly and economically. Because systems of general illumination are so prevalent in the work-world, lighting specialists and others think predominantly in terms of this method of illumination. When 50, 100 or 1000 footcandles are mentioned, the first reaction is to conclude that the cost of footcandles would mount in proportion to the increase in level of illumination. This is by no means true for it is easy to obtain high levels of illumination inexpensively and at the same time provide lighting as well as light. This is done by adding localized directed light by means of supplementary direct lighting to a system of general illumination. This we have termed *general lighting plus*,[138] as discussed in Chapter X, in order that the need for general illumination would not be lost sight of in providing effective footcandles and proper lighting upon specific work-places by means of supplementary lighting.

For the present it is sufficient to note that there is a maximum footcandle-level obtainable with comfort by such a system as indirect lighting. It has long been known that 50 footcandles perhaps represented the upper limit in most cases. Beyond this the ceiling becomes too bright for comfort. Years ago we proposed combinations of general and supplementary lighting as illustrated in Fig. 105. Ten footcandle-levels were established in accordance with the geometric scale of footcandles shown in Fig. 100. A system of general illumination would be suitable for the levels of less than five footcandles because such levels were considered inadequate for critical seeing. Beginning with five footcandles supplementary lighting would be used to supply as much as ten times the five footcandles. General illumination would be increased along with the footcandles of supplementary lighting. We suggested as a safe ratio that the footcandles of general illumination be not less than one-tenth the footcandles from supplementary lighting. In some cases in practice it has been found that a greater percentage of general illumination seems to be desirable. However, this maximum ratio seems to be generally satisfactory as an upper limit.

It should be obvious from Fig. 105 that very high levels of illumination can be obtained by this combined method without increasing the cost of light in proportion to the increase in footcandles. By proper control of the light, it is possible to obtain 500, 1000 and even 3000 footcandles with a light-source of reasonable wattage. It should be borne in mind that the light is not only directed upon the work but the light-source can be close to the work in many cases. Several hundred footcandles can be obtained from a 100-watt lamp in this manner. The desirability of this combination lighting is evident to anyone closely analyzing the lighting, and his reactions to it, obtained from a proper portable lamp in the home. Some light is directed or escapes upward to the ceiling and adjacent surroundings to provide general illumination. Some comes directly to the visual task. The combination is efficient, effective and pleasing. It is natural because it simulates the lighting outdoors on a clear day. Light from the sky provides general illumination. The sun provides direct lighting. On average clear days outdoors about one-fifth of the footcandles reaching the earth come from the sky. On rare clear days about one-tenth come from the sky. This matter of light and lighting is discussed in Chapters VIII and XI.

CHAPTER X

Quality of Lighting

Quality of lighting is a term we have applied [130] to that aspect distinguishing lighting from light as discussed in Chapter VIII. It encompasses chiefly the distribution of brightness within the visual field. This is a simple description of a vast complexity of many factors and effects upon eyes, vision, seeing and human beings. The subject may be subdivided in various ways to facilitate analysis and discussion. However, we cannot escape the difficulties arising from a lack of standardization of units, terminology and definitions. This aspect of lighting has been appraised largely introspectively, chiefly by interpreting feelings of comfort and discomfort. But the distribution of brightness also influences visibility and all the subtle effects and results of various degrees of visibility. These cannot be appraised without measurements as has been adequately demonstrated in other chapters. Some of these ultimate results cannot even be detected without actual measurements. Discomfort, if sufficiently pronounced, is noticeable. In the analysis of quality of lighting, measurements perform the same function as in any other approach to dependable knowledge. At present it is impossible to reduce quality of lighting to exact specifications for lighting practice, but some practical interpretations and conclusions have been formulated from the results of researches and experience. At least the general principles involved are now understood and can guide lighting practice and appraisals provided the prejudices of habit, commercial aims and socalled practical considerations are laid aside.

BASIC CONSIDERATIONS

In the present state of knowledge, quality of lighting cannot be subdivided into discrete phases which completely encompass

[360]

this entire complexity. However, it can be subdivided into predominant phases. An example of this is Fig. 91. The human
seeing-machine is confronted with a visual task in a large visual
field. As viewed by an observer, the lighting of the *central* visual
field (the primary visual task) and that of the *peripheral* visual
field (the surroundings) form natural divisions. Obviously, the
position of the central field varies with the fixation of the eyes or
direction of the visual axis. In general, it will correspond to the
visual task to be performed and is so considered here. A further
subdivision is possible by considering light-sources as a separate
phase of quality of lighting. Although some sources may form
a part of each of the visual fields, their brightnesses are usually of
a different order of magnitude than those of the task and of the
surroundings. Hence they deserve special discussion.

In appraising the quality of the lighting in the central field, the
eventual end-product psychophysiological effects of seeing are of
ultimate importance. For this reason initial and momentary casual
appraisal may not reveal the effects of seeing under the given conditions for a long period of time. Notwithstanding this, the visibility of the objects of regard must be a primary criterion of quality
of lighting, and therefore, the establishment of correlations between
visibility and time-effects of seeing is an important objective. It
appears axiomatic that the conservation of vision and human resources expendable in the process of seeing must depend largely
upon the positive contributions of the lighting within the central
field where critical visual tasks are performed. In general the
measurable influences of the brightnesses of the surrounding fields
are more likely to be negative than positive in this respect. Obviously negative influences, such as preventable glare and "darkness," should be minimized and eliminated if possible.

These conclusions suggest two distinct steps in the design of
lighting:

1. The attainment of maximal visibility within the central
   field without regard to the surroundings.
2. The illumination and control of the brightnesses of the surroundings in such a manner as to produce maximal com-

fort and minimal loss in visibility in the central field whether or not visual fixation alternates between the two fields.

The important positive contribution of the lighting of the surroundings is the creation of conditions which will provide maximal visual and mental relaxation and, in addition, proper conditions for seeing where human safety is involved. Some of the negative or deleterious effects which may result from the lighting of the surroundings are known qualitatively and are recognized when they are particularly offensive. However, the goal of the science of seeing is to provide the refinements of quantitative measurements by means of suitable criteria.

An appraisal of the quality of lighting is adequate only when it is based upon a consideration of seeing as a universal activity of human beings which not only directly influences their efficiency and welfare but also produces far-reaching psychophysiological effects. Numerous examples of lighting practice may be cited wherein the failure to recognize this cardinal principle has resulted in improper lighting and has perpetuated empirical practices and dogmatic criteria. For example, it is a fact that the brightness-difference threshold is a minimum when the brightness of the surrounding field is about equal to that of the central field. But this is only one factor and it applies only to visual fields less than 30 degrees in extent. This single photometric datum is not adequate proof that ideal lighting involves a uniform brightness of the entire visual field. Obviously, such an appraisal does not include possible physiological and psychological factors such as discomfort, fatigue, attention, distraction and relaxation, both visual and mental, which must be taken into account in lighting for human seeing-machines.

Throughout lighting language and practice of the past the prominence of the engineering viewpoint and the general absence of the psychophysiological viewpoint have been apparent. This status must be reversed if lighting is to be practiced for the purpose of seeing. Such descriptions of lighting systems as direct lighting, semi-indirect lighting and indirect lighting may have some meaning from an engineering viewpoint in specific cases if properly described, but are often misleading and grossly inadequate from the viewpoints of lighting effect and of seeing. They may serve as classifications for fixtures, but we have believed that fixtures would be better rated in terms of the components of light emitted below (direct) and above (indirect) the horizontal plane through them as illustrated in Fig. 107. A given socalled semi-

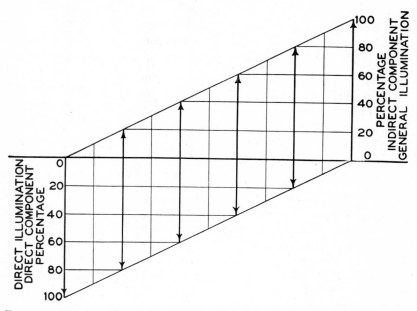

FIG. 107.—Lighting effects from lighting fixtures or lighting installations can be fairly well visualized when one knows the percentages of direct and indirect components or of direct illumination and general illumination.

indirect fixture would be described as direct-indirect, 30-70, indicating that 30 per cent of the total emitted light was in the downward component and 70 per cent was in the upward component. This rating could also be used for lighting systems by describing the relative amounts of illumination achieved by light initially directed upward and downward, respectively, or the relative footcandles provided by directed light and by general illumination, respectively. Certainly, such rating provides in a simple way the

[363]

means for visualizing lighting effects obtainable in a given room in a quantitative manner.

Inasmuch as quality of lighting leads eventually to distribution of brightness and this determines the seeing conditions, such a term as indirect lighting eventually becomes meaningless in this respect when applied to a variety of interiors. In a room of small area with a correspondingly small ceiling, indirect lighting may approach direct lighting in effect. In such a room when the walls have a low reflection-factor, the quality of lighting from a seeing viewpoint differs considerably from that which would result if the walls possessed high reflection-factors. Furthermore, such a system may be quite satisfactory in a small room whose walls possess moderate reflection-factors, but quite unsatisfactory for a large room. In the latter case a great expanse of bright ceiling may be visible some of the time and is always in the consciousness of those in the room. It may seem satisfactory to one who casually or momentarily appraises it. However, working for long periods under such conditions is a different matter. For example, a large area of sky outdoors may not be particularly annoying to the casual appraiser, but actually may become painful to a worker obliged to perform a critical visual task even when the brightness of the central field is not as bright as the sky. The results of a research performed a score of years ago made us wary of purely indirect lighting in large rooms where critical seeing is done. This is discussed in Chapter XI in connection with Fig. 125.

Such facts revealed the dangers of judgments of lighting conditions based upon casual appraisal and not upon measurements of seeing and the effects of long periods of seeing upon human seeing-machines. They also led us to recommend *general lighting plus* [138] supplementary lighting as the ideal goal of lighting for seeing in many cases. Much of our research for years has been directed toward quality of lighting and the evidence continues to accumulate overwhelmingly in favor of an ideal balance between general illumination for surroundings and supplementary lighting for critical visual tasks. Any science must seek out ideal conditions. Actual

[364]

practice is often a compromise, but that compromise should be guided by ideals and adequate knowledge. The science of seeing dictates that lighting should be designed primarily for human beings, individually if possible, but collectively when necessary, and not merely for rooms and other spaces.

Fig. 108 illustrates the central and surrounding field and some of the important factors pertaining to them. It also represents the ideal combination of general illumination and supplementary lighting. Such a combination provides lighting as well

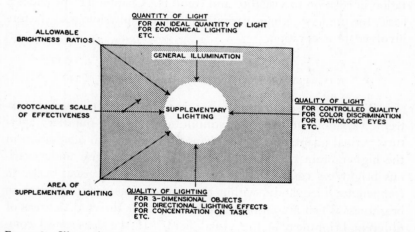

FIG. 108.—Illustrating some of the factors in the central and peripheral visual fields from the viewpoint of combined general illumination over a large area with supplementary lighting confined to the smaller work-place.

as light. This is sometimes true of general illumination but usually only footcandles are supplied and lighting is incidental. However, it can always be true of combined general illumination and supplementary lighting. A study of Fig. 108 will be helpful in visualizing the discussions which follow.

Quality of lighting involves the creation or elimination of specular reflection and shadows which have been discussed from the viewpoint of seeing in Chapter VIII. Specular reflection has been given consideration in connection with lighting practice and this has led to the promotion of indirect lighting where specular glare has been a hindrance to seeing as in reading print on glossy paper. The effectiveness of diffuse illumination in suppressing specular glare is illustrated in Table LIII. On the other hand by controlling light upon the visual task by means of supplementary lighting, specular glare and also shadows can generally be appropriately controlled for the purpose of obtaining high visibility.

In general the most important fundamental approach to the analysis of distribution of brightness, which is the overwhelmingly important aspect of quality of lighting, is through studies of adaptation in relation to visibility and comfort. Chapter III provides a basis for understanding various important physiological factors involved in adaptation.

ADAPTATION AND BRIGHTNESS

The visual sensory processes have evolved to mediate extreme variations in brightness stimuli by changes in pupillary aperture, retinal adaptation and perhaps by neurological adaptation in the higher brain centers. However, difficulties arise under various brightness conditions by the inability of the visual sense to compensate adequately, within the time available, for changes in brightness which are encountered as fixation is directed to areas of different brightness in the visual field. If the eyes could compensate completely, glare from brightness changes would disappear and we would not be temporarily blinded, for example, when going indoors or outdoors at night. Such effects are noticeable because of their magnitude. However, all degrees of such effects are present in lighting. Most of them become "noticeable" only by careful measurement and such measurements are a part of the science of seeing. Hence, the temporal characteristics of the compensatory processes are of fundamental importance in lighting practice. Their significance in seeing depends chiefly upon

1. The differences in absolute brightness
2. The rate and frequency of the changes in brightness
3. The areas and relative locations of the brightnesses
4. The criticalness of the visual tasks to be performed.

[366]

Although adaptation has been extensively investigated, the earlier data are generally useful in practice only in a qualitative sense since the experimental conditions are not easily comparable to those of practice. Certain fundamental conclusions applicable to lighting practice may be drawn from theoretical studies of retinal adaptation. In general, the lag in adaptation is greater and, therefore, more influential in seeing, when the change is from a higher to a lower brightness than it is for the reverse direction when appraised by the criterion of visual efficiency. However, this is not necessarily true when the appraisal is based upon ocular discomfort. Visual efficiency is obviously greatly reduced when one passes from a bright room to a relatively dark one but no particular bodily discomfort is experienced. In passing from a dark room to a relatively bright one, discomfort is often experienced but visual efficiency is quickly recovered. It is shown in Fig. 16 that dark adaptation of the fovea (central portion of the retina) begins immediately with a reduction in brightness and proceeds precipitously during the first 30 seconds reaching a practical state of equilibrium in about 3 minutes.[18] It is emphasized that these data pertain to a change from light to dark adaptation. Hence, it may be concluded that the visual handicap of incomplete foveal adaptation is not generally important after a period of about 30 seconds even for extreme changes in the stimulus. This is true *a fortiori* when the change is from dark to light because the increase in brightness in itself increases visual efficiency. In the reverse case visual efficiency is decreased by the decrease in brightness.

Adaptation phenomena have been recognized in some lighting installations, but there are many opportunities to do so. During the daytime higher intensities of illumination may be desirable in places entered from the street than may be needed at night. Places entered at night may well have low intensities inside near the entrance. Where safety is important, lighting might be provided which increases the brightness in successive steps as a person passes from a darker place, or conversely, which decreases the brightness gradually as a person passes from a brighter place to a darker one.

In the work-world there are many effects of adaptation, most of which are hidden, but are none the less real. If the visual task involves frequent rapid shifts in fixation between areas of different brightnesses, a brief lag in adaptation may be a serious visual handicap even though the difference in brightness is relatively small. This is proved by the results of a research [99] in which the workers

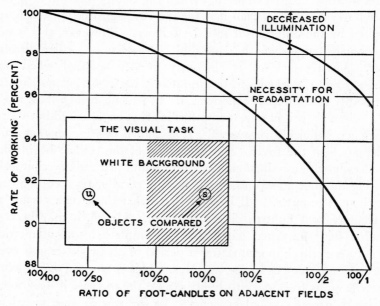

FIG. 109.—Illustrating the effect upon the rate of working when the worker is obliged to alternate fixation between two different brightnesses. The decrease in the rate of working is due partly to decreased average illumination and largely to necessity for repeated readaptation.

were forced to alter fixation between different brightnesses as rapidly as they could recognize the test-object in either field. In this case, a decrease in visual efficiency became measurable when the brightness of one field was only twice that of the other. The average results are presented in Fig. 109. The background consisted of white blotting paper. The footcandles on the two halves could be controlled independently. Thus the two brightnesses could be controlled. Obviously the brightness-ratios are identical with the footcandle ratios. By pressing a button with one hand the letters in the two fields changed quickly and simultaneously. These changes continued as rapidly as the subject could distinguish the two letters. When the two letters were identical, a button was pressed by the other hand. Thousands of combinations were available continuously and the coincidences were known for any range in the series. The rate of working was automatically determined by a counter which recorded the number of pairs of letters scrutinized in a given period of time.

In Fig. 109 it is seen, for example, that the amount of work done was 12 per cent less, when the eyes alternated between two brightnesses one of which was 100 times greater than the other, than the amount of work done when the brightness was uniformly the higher brightness. Such a brightness-ratio is a common result of a combination of diversity in reflection-factors and in footcandles. When one brightness was only 20 times the other, the reduction in work done was five per cent. Such a brightness-ratio commonly results from reflection-factors alone. Some of this decrease in efficiency of the worker was due to decreased illumination, as indicated in Fig. 109, but most of it was due to the necessity for continual re-adaptation. Doubtless undesirable psychological effects also resulted which may be more important than the decrease in work done.

The results of this research emphasize the inadequacy of footcandle measurements and the urgent need for measurements of brightness.[133] Furthermore, conclusions based upon such results extend far beyond lighting into other factors of seeing. For example, one of many reasons for prosecuting this research was the general use of black for finishing office devices such as typewriters and other business-machines. Certainly the contrasts between such "black" areas of low brightness with "white" paper or cards reduce visual efficiency materially when the operator is obliged to look back and forth quickly and continually.

The foregoing facts indicate the importance of determining the course of foveal adaptation under conditions usual in lighting practice by controlled methods. The course of foveal adaptation, corresponding to changes in objective brightness, has been traced by continuous measurements of the brightness-difference threshold. In this investigation fixation was maintained within the central visual field and the brightness of this field was alternately equal to and higher than that of the peripheral field. This procedure is photometrically equivalent to shifting fixation between these two fields except that the brightness changes are practically instantaneous. The subject controlled and automatically recorded the brightness of a small test-field located within the central visual field. Hence the trace of foveal adaptation is a function of the reaction-time characteristics of the subject as well as the state of retinal adaptation. Since the change in brightness is quicker in this experiment than is usual in practice, the lag in recording adaptation phenomena is correspondingly less serious. As the characteristics of the visual task, under levels of illumination usual in practice, are not such as to require critical rod vision, it is not necessary to trace the course of peripheral adaptation. Obviously, this statement is not applicable to the conditions for seeing which are inherent in highway lighting. In fact, owing to the very low brightnesses and visibility and the glare from automobile headlamps, many physiological factors are important in seeing on the highway at night.

The circular central and peripheral fields involved in this research subtended visual angles of 22.5 and 90 degrees, respectively. The brightness of the peripheral field was 1 millilambert in all phases of the investigation.[33] This field corresponds to the general surroundings in the practical situation. The lighting of the central field was arranged to provide brightness-levels of 1, 20 and 100 millilamberts, respectively, or in terms of contrast, brightness-ratios of 20 to 1 and 100 to 1 between the central and peripheral fields. The course of adaptation was traced for brightness changes at intervals of 30 seconds and 2 minutes, respectively. The experimental results indicated that the initial response of the subjects to a change in the stimulus began after a delay of 3 and 1 seconds for the higher and lower brightness-ratios, respectively. Obviously, the significance of these data is also a function of the change in the brightness-difference threshold. It may be concluded that a response delay of 1 second or less, resulting from an occasional change of 20 to 1 in field brightness, is not particularly important. If the change in brightness is from 100 to 1 millilambert, the brightness-difference threshold is altered considerably and a response delay of 3 seconds may be quite important. Obviously, the interval of visual uncertainty, indicated by the response delay, is a most important phase of the course of foveal adaptation. Certainly it is important where quick and certain seeing is desirable or essential.

The interval between the change in the stimulus and the attainment of an approximate state of equilibrium in the adaptation process is a criterion for appraising certain aspects of quality of lighting. Available data indicate that the duration of these intervals is approximately 15 seconds for a brightness change from 100 to 1 millilambert and 10 seconds for a change from 20 to 1 millilambert. It required 20 and 10 seconds, respectively, when the changes in brightness were in the reverse direction. These data include the time required for the motor responses as well as the time consumed in the retinal processes. Obviously, if fixation alternates relatively rapidly between areas of different brightnesses, the lag in adaptation is an important factor. Some results indicated that the effects of changes in the field brightness were more or less accumulative when the changes occurred at intervals of 30 seconds. This integrative effect was not observed for intervals as long as 2 minutes. If only occasional changes are required, the loss in visual efficiency is not considered particularly significant excepting in situations where human safety depends upon quick and certain perception of objects of low visibility. Introspective reports of the subjects in this research indicated that physiological discomfort was not experienced to any appreciable degree directly as a result of these brightness changes. These conclusions pertain only to brief observations and should be interpreted from this viewpoint. Hence such data are valuable in a relative sense rather than as definite standards for lighting practice and for visual situations in which critical seeing is performed for long periods.

[371]

It is probable that the important effects of brightness changes of the order investigated are those which result indirectly from the change in the stimulus. Since the compensating mechanism of the visual processes may mediate brightness changes of perhaps a million to one, it is reasonable to assume that occasional changes of less than a hundred to one do not tax the eyes sufficiently to induce ocular strain or other known undesirable effects. However, experience in performing critical visual tasks, such as reading, establishes the undesirability of high brightness-ratios between the central and peripheral fields. An explanation of this apparently paradoxical situation may be found in the psychological realm. As occasional brightness changes of an order often encountered in practice are a definite handicap to the performance of critical visual work, the reluctance of the subject to experience such changes may be an important factor in seeing and in the effects of seeing upon the human being. Possibly the natural tendency of the subject to relax the ocular muscles from the effort of near-vision may be suppressed to some extent. It is probable that the subject is unaware of such a suppression. Therefore, the annoyance and distraction induced by changes in field brightness may be effective in minimizing the periods of ocular relaxation. This is an example of the subtle psychological influences which are often of considerable importance in seeing. Obviously, such effects are not detectable by casual observation.

Long ago we recommended that, where supplementary was added to general illumination, a brightness-ratio of 10 to 1 between the visual task and its surroundings would be safe and desirable practice. This ratio was extended in lighting practice to illumination instead of brightness with the result that the ratio of brightness of the work-field to that of the surroundings might be 100 to 1. We did not believe that the former was a severe ratio when the surroundings were only fixated occasionally and merely for relaxation. It is seen that our recent researches seem to support this view, but indicate that a brightness-ratio of 100 to 1 may be too great.

Adaptation phenomena of the peripheral retina are of major

importance when the brightness-levels are such that only scotopic (rod) vision operates in the discrimination of objects, as is often the case in exterior lighting at night. For central vision these effects are not important for brightness-levels greater than 0.1 millilambert. This is the practical upper limit of the socalled Purkinje effect (Fig. 12) which is attributable to the rods. It is seen in Fig. 50 that at this brightness-level the cones cease to function and the rods become effective. It is not likely that the rods can be effective in the peripheral retina while the cones are in operation in the foveal region. In general the maximum brightness in the visual field is most important because the state of retinal adaptation is most dependent upon it. Under no circumstances can the Purkinje effect take place in the fovea; that is, in the small area of the field in line with the visual axis. The process of dark adaptation [165] in the peripheral retina, where rods predominate, begins immediately upon a reduction in brightness and proceeds relatively rapidly for the first ten minutes and then more gradually for an hour or more. At the start it is less rapid than cone adaptation. These data pertain to the course of dark adaptation which follows a sudden transition from relatively high brightnesses to darkness. The time required by the process of adaptation is a function of the range in brightness-levels involved. Quantitative data are not now available pertaining to the time required for adaptation from one level to another, but an appreciation of the relative time required for foveal and peripheral adaptation for extreme changes in brightness is helpful in providing factors of safety in seeing.

PUPILLARY CRITERIA

The range of the size of the pupil greatly limits its effectiveness as a protective device, but it is of some help while retinal adaptation is taking place. Its size is of interest from the viewpoint of a possible criterion in appraising brightness conditions and possibly as an indicator of fatigue, discomfort, and other deleterious effects of lighting and seeing conditions. The pupillary light reflex is of particular significance as an aid to seeing when the brightness conditions are of a threshold order, as in scotopic (rod) vision. Under such conditions a small increase in the brightness of the retinal image resulting from a dilation of the pupil may lower the visual threshold sufficiently to permit recognition of certain objects which otherwise would not be seen until retinal adaptation altered the sensibility of the eye. In photopic (cone) vision the temporal characteristics of pupillary action and foveal adaptation are complementary and their effects upon visual efficiency are additive. In comparison, the possible change in foveal sensibility is by far the more important as an aid to seeing.

Apparently the physiological discomfort which may result from an excessive stimulation (innervation) of the iris muscles is the most important pupillary effect of extreme increases in brightnesses. Although fixation may shift rapidly among areas of various brightnesses, the relatively slow rate of pupillary dilation as compared with contraction, as shown in Fig. 25, prevents correspondingly rapid muscular fluctuations which conceivably might result in ocular discomfort. Hence it may be concluded that excessive stimulation from high brightnesses, commonly termed glaring, is the chief cause of strain and fatigue in the iris muscles. The data of Reeves [32] indicate that such brightnesses are of a magnitude comparable with those of primary light-sources.

The pupillary light reflex depends upon temporal as well as intensity characteristics of the stimulus. If the change in field brightness is very gradual, the size of the pupil remains practically constant for a wide range in brightnesses. In a recent experiment the brightness to which the eyes were adapted was gradually decreased during a 30-minute period from 170 to 2 millilamberts without producing an appreciable pupillary dilation. These data emphasize the importance of the factor of time in pupillary phenomena. It has been stated that the socalled "physiological pupil" is obtained at a brightness of about 10 millilamberts and that the pupil will seek this size under a wide variety of conditions if given adequate time. However, the early changes in the pupil size may be a criterion of proper quality of lighting.

In lighting practice it is commonly supposed that the pupils

[374]

of the eyes are larger under totally indirect-lighting systems than they are under direct-lighting systems producing the same illumination on a horizontal plane in the work-area. However, pupillary measurements made under the two systems indicate that this is an erroneous generalization and that the pupils are as likely to be smaller under indirect-lighting as under good direct-lighting. The data of Table LX were obtained from typical direct- and indirect-lighting systems producing the same level of illumination upon

RELATIVE SIZE OF PUPILS OF 16 PERSONS WHEN READING UNDER 10 FOOTCANDLES

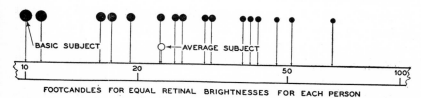

FOOTCANDLES FOR EQUAL RETINAL BRIGHTNESSES FOR EACH PERSON

FIG. 110.—Illustrating the relative size of pupils of 16 adult persons when reading a book printed with black print on white paper and illuminated by ten foot-candles. The lower scale shows the necessary footcandles for equal retinal brightnesses for each person.

the usual horizontal plane of footcandle measurements. The direction of fixation or the visual axis was horizontal in each case.

TABLE LX

Type of Lighting	Illumination	Diameter of Pupils	
		Direct	Indirect
Residential	9 Footcandles	6.07 mm.	5.70 mm.
Industrial	18 Footcandles	4.73 mm.	4.35 mm.

It will be noted from these data that the difference in pupil size under the systems of lighting is not large enough to produce a significant increase in the brightness of retinal images. As indicated later, pupil size may prove to be a criterion of the relative merit of two lighting systems from the viewpoint of comfortable seeing.

The relative sizes of the pupils of 16 subjects, ranging in age from 25 to 35 years, while reading a book printed with black ink on white paper, are drawn to scale in Fig. 110. The illumination

[375]

on the book was 10 footcandles and other brightness conditions were the same for all subjects. It is noted that the size varied considerably. Actually, the area of the largest pupil was over six times that of the smallest one. Obviously the printed page in the case of the smallest pupil had to be illuminated by 65 footcandles to have the retinal image as bright as it would be for the largest pupil when the page was illuminated by 10 footcandles. A scale indicates the footcandles necessary for the pupils of various sizes for equal brightness of the retinal images. This variation in "natural" size of the pupil has much significance in the science of seeing for it may possibly be connected with many factors and effects of seeing.

As discussed in Chapter III, the absolute brightness sensitivity of the retina was determined for various subjects and was found to be a reciprocal relationship to pupil size which reduced the disparity in the efficacy of using light as indicated by the disparity in pupil size. In other words, eyes having naturally smaller pupils had higher absolute retinal sensitivities to brightness. However, retinal sensitivity did not completely compensate for pupil size. In other words, the subjects with naturally large pupils still had an advantage in the matter of efficacious use of brightness and footcandles. Of course, large pupils are likely to unmask refractive errors which might not be significant with small pupils, and poor definition of objects might result. On the other hand, resolving power increases with the size of the pupil.

The pupil is reduced in size by glare, and physical discomfort is believed to be due partly to constriction of the muscles which control the iris or size of the pupil. The subject with the smallest pupil, among the group of 16 subjects, is particularly sensitive to glare discomfort. It may be possible that, the pupil being already quite small, any further efforts to decrease its size as a natural reaction to glare might result in greater discomfort than if the pupil were naturally larger. In the case of the naturally smallest pupil, its size under the ten footcandles of glareless illumination was already close to that of the average pupil under several hundred footcandles.

[376]

INFLUENCE OF SURROUNDINGS

Although situations in which the eyes successively fixate upon areas of various brightnesses are usual in practice, there are occasions when fixation is maintained within a prescribed area for relatively long periods, as in reading. In the latter cases, the mutual influence of the brightnesses of the central and peripheral fields; that is, the brightness-contrast, may be an important factor in visual efficiency. This phase of lighting has been investigated by means of diverse criteria.[73] Experimental results as illustrated in Fig. 51 invariably indicate that excessive brightness-contrasts between the two fields are undesirable and reduce visual efficiency when the central field is smaller than 30 degrees. This is true even though the eyes are continually fixated upon the central field. Visual efficiency is a maximum when the brightness of the central field is equal to that of the surroundings.

In general, a brighter surrounding field reduces visual efficiency more than one which is darker than the central field. In socalled indirect lighting the ceiling is generally much brighter than the central visual field involving the work. This is sometimes true of walls. A practical way to increase visual efficiency in such cases is to provide supplementary lighting for the work so as to make it as bright or brighter than the surroundings or peripheral field. The peripheral field may include ceilings, walls, floors, furniture, machinery, etc. The brighter areas are predominantly influential upon adaptation and therefore upon visual efficiency. Unfortunately much of the fundamental data is of value to lighting practice only in a qualitative sense due to the fact that the experiments usually involve only the extreme conditions. However, extremes reveal the "in-between" effects. These researches also reveal, as a by-product, the unreliableness of introspective appraisals of the influence of the brightness of the surrounding field upon vision within the central field. In such experiments the subjects usually report that they can "see better" when the surrounding field is dark than they can when it is illuminated to the same brightness as the central field. Actually they cannot. These

[377]

subjective data show that the psychological factor of attention or concentration is *apparently* more influential in a superficial appraisal than the physiological effect of brightness-contrast revealed by accurate measurements of visual efficiency. Obviously here we have two important factors which are more or less opposed, and lighting practice must compromise the two and properly weigh their relative importance.

The influence of the brightness and areal extent of the peripheral field upon visual efficiency when fixation is maintained within the central field has been shown [118] by determinations of the precision of performing a mechanical task guided by vision. In this investigation, the test-object appeared at the center of a white field which was illuminated to a brightness of 10 millilamberts and was seen amid comparatively dark surroundings. The results indicated that the dark surroundings appreciably influence the precision of visually controlled work performed in the central field when the latter subtends an angle less than 30 degrees. When the central field is larger than 30 degrees the brightness of the surroundings is unimportant when the brightnesses are within the common range of diffusely reflecting surfaces. These conclusions apply only when fixation is maintained solely in the central field, which in this case was brighter than the surroundings.

Since most critical visual tasks are performed at distances well within arm's reach, it is obvious that a brighter central area subtending an angle of 30 degrees could be obtained from nearly all types of supplementary lighting equipment. Hence, it is concluded that the extent of the brighter central field generally need not be a critical factor in lighting design for conditions in which fixation is within this field. This conclusion is based entirely upon the criterion of visual efficiency. However, it is emphasized that small and sharply defined bright central fields may be objectionable from the standpoint of distraction resulting from the proximity of dark surroundings. If fixation varies, the central visual field will be that encompassed by the several points of frequent fixation. The foveal visual field subtends an angle of about 70 minutes or circular areas 0.29, 1.22, 2.95 inches in diameter at distances of 14 inches, 5 feet, and 10 feet, respectively. It will be noted that the foveal field of view, for a given fixation, is quite restricted.

The conception of quality of lighting as a controllable variable in seeing inherently suggests general illumination plus supplementary lighting illustrated in Figs. 105 and 108, as the method for obtaining maximal satisfactoriness. The important exceptions to this generalization are.

1. The specific situations in which general lighting is more appropriate for the visual tasks involved or more practicable for other sound reasons and
2. Those in which dark adaptation is to be preserved.

Although much has been written upon various systems of lighting, the discussions usually pertain to engineering phases of light distribution and only incidentally to psychophysiological considerations of seeing. The subject of glare is the major exception to this analysis of past lighting practice. Thus lighting techniques have been established largely by empirical rather than by rational methods. The inadequacy of such methods is emphasized in the lighting of the peripheral field since the resultant effects are often indirect and unobvious.

The assumptions are made in the following discussion of the characteristics of the lighting of the surroundings or peripheral field that

1. Seeing within this field is of a casual nature;
2. That fixation does not alternate rapidly between the two fields; and
3. That the extent of the central field is such that the state of retinal adaptation resulting from fixation within this field is not significantly affected by the brightness of the surrounding or peripheral field.

The data presented assist in appraising the particular situation with respect to these specifications. As a result of these restrictions, it may be assumed that ocular, bodily and mental comfort, rather than visibility, is the primary criterion of quality in the lighting of the peripheral field.

Since seeing within the peripheral field is assumed to be casual, the lighting requirements for this purpose are obviously elementary. Hence, the important consideration is to provide conditions which will afford maximal comfort when relaxation is sought from the more or less critical tasks of the central visual field. This relaxation is both muscular and mental when the eyes and the attention are diverted from the work to the surroundings for a momentary respite. After an hour's reading we have found [40] that it requires about ten minutes for the muscles which converge the eyes upon close work to recover from their "fatigue." Since ocular strain and fatigue are considered to result mainly from an over-exertion of the ocular muscles,[135] these muscles should be relaxed during general rest-periods. This is accomplished when the point of fixation is at a distance of fifteen feet or more. However, fixational distances of this order are sometimes impossible indoors. Possibly this spatial difference between exterior and interior conditions for seeing is a fundamental factor contributing to the usual superiority of outdoor conditions for seeing.

The reflex which causes the eyes to turn and fixate an extra-foveal stimulus, as well as the exactness of the fixation, are functions of the visibility of objects in the peripheral field. High brightness-contrasts or objects in motion encourage attention and fixation and, therefore, are undesirable in situations where relaxation of the ocular muscles is desired. This is particularly true for nearby objects. These principles suggest, for example, that the visible parts of shades of desk-lamps should be of a very low brightness. They also indicate that the effects upon muscle tonus resulting from the fixation of bright specularly-reflected images may be far more deleterious than the corresponding effects upon retinal or pupillary adaptation. Obviously, dark surroundings represent the ultimate in the suppression of details within the visual field. In this extreme situation, the necessity for considerable adaptation conflicts with the possible advantage of muscular relaxation. Therefore, it may be concluded that brightnesses somewhat lower than those of the central field are generally most desirable. All experimental evidence indicates that peripheral brightnesses higher than those of the central field are definitely undesirable. These facts have a direct bearing upon the illumination of walls and ceilings. It is emphasized again that these conclusions are based upon the assumption that critical seeing for long periods is the predominant characteristic of the visual activity. Obviously a casual appraisal of lighting conditions neither involves this criterion nor any dependable measurements.

Reflecting and self-luminous backgrounds are properly considered as surroundings and, therefore, as factors in quality of lighting. Although a wide variety of combinations between background and object is possible, it is obvious that only black, white and self-luminous backgrounds can provide conditions of maximal brightness-contrast. In general, the brightnesses of self-luminous backgrounds should be low enough to avoid noticeable inductive effects such as irradiation or diffraction effects such as halos within the eye (entoptic). The outer ring of the latter may extend as much as eight degrees from the light-source under extreme conditions. Uniformity in brightness (and color) is a desirable characteristic of backgrounds and, for revealing minute details, is an essential requirement. Notwithstanding the importance of backgrounds as tools for seeing, they are too generally ignored in the work-world.

PSYCHOLOGICAL EFFECTS

It is not unusual to experience deleterious effects under certain seeing conditions which, for *a priori* reasons, are not necessarily describable as extreme. In such cases, the influences of improper lighting upon easy and comfortable seeing may be of a psychological character. The factors of attention and distraction are of fundamental significance in this respect and must be recognized in lighting notwithstanding the general lack of significance of such phenomena to engineers untrained in the realm of psychology. These are powerful forces in the efficiency and comfort of human beings and in their eventual reactions toward lighting.[1] We cannot escape the effect of subtle or hidden influences whether we recognize them or not. Nor can we "explain away" their effects just because they are termed "psychological." In the mental life of human beings psychological influences are just as real as physical things are in the engineering life of engineers.

Subjective phenomena which arise from voluntary attention to a critical visual task may be appreciated through the performance of a few simple experiments. Brightnesses within the peripheral field which do not seem extreme during casual seeing may be quite annoying when critical seeing is attempted. For example, in the casual viewing of a landscape during the daytime, the brightness of the sky may not seem to be unduly high. However, if fine print is read, the brightness of a large area of sky may become a most annoying factor if a large portion lies in the peripheral field. This lesson is directly transferable to the lighting of large rooms solely by indirect lighting.

There are many reasons for believing that the distribution of brightnesses in Nature is generally quite satisfactory for natural outdoor visual tasks. However, such a distribution is not necessarily ideal for the severe and unnatural visual tasks which are performed indoors. In fact, such a distribution is often undesirable. Outdoors the sky-brightness is usually greater, and often far greater, than that of the object of regard. This is always true in the shade or on overcast days. White paper in direct sunlight may be several times brighter than the sky, but low reflection-factors are the rule in Nature. Indoors and for critical seeing, the ratio in brightness between the peripheral and central visual fields should usually be reversed; that is, the brightness of the object of critical regard should be as great as, or greater than, that of the surroundings. This principle offers an explanation of the lack of complete satisfactoriness of high levels of illumination obtained solely by installations of general lighting and particularly of the indirect type. Certainly in the home where we are concerned with satisfying our "feelings" we generally insist upon a combination of general illumination and supplementary lighting. Although in the work-world we may be more engrossed in our work, that part of us which "feels" is still a part of us.

In addition to the psychological factors of attention and dis-

[382]

traction, which are influenced by the lighting of the peripheral field, there are also the factors of stimulation and impression. The impression which leads to a description of surroundings as "brightly lighted" depends not only upon the absolute brightness but also upon brightness-contrasts within the visual field. This psychological effect is illusory and has no standing in the face of facts, but it explains, partially at least, why higher levels of illumination may be supplied by indirect lighting than by direct lighting, under some common conditions, without creating the impression of being "over-lighted." However, this is not an unmitigated advantage of indirect lighting. Human beings have evolved under natural lighting and the absence of the dominant and directional characteristics of indirect lighting is often considered undesirable. Human beings possess inherent rights to demand what is *natural*. They are children of *Nature*. A compromise which will retain the psychological advantages inherent to both direct and indirect lighting is possible. Certainly it is exemplified in the quality of lighting on sunny days outdoors which are almost universally preferred to overcast days. Of course, this is only a part of the psychological complexity of natural lighting outdoors.[139]

GLARE

Glare is a term generally used in connection with reduced visibility and with certain entoptic and subjective phenomena which are concomitant with extreme brightness stimulation. In this sense the term is particularly applied to a relatively bright light-source or to its specularly reflected image within the visual field. Examples of this kind are,

1. The sun and its image reflected from water, metal, or pavement,
2. An unshaded light-source or bright portion of a lighting fixture and its image reflected from glossy paper, paint and wood, and from polished surfaces such as metal,
3. An automobile headlamp on the highway at night.

If the exposure is of sufficient duration, these extreme brightnesses commonly produce discomfort and, therefore, are particularly no ticeable as glare-sources or conditions for the latter also determine the magnitude and noticeability of the glare. In addition to these high brightnesses, relatively low ones can also be glaring in a broad sense. This emphasizes the importance of conditions contributing to glare such as,

1. The brightness-level to which the retina is adapted,
2. The expanse or areal extent of the brightness such as the sky outdoors in the daytime and illuminated ceilings of large rooms,
3. The performance of critical seeing instead of casual seeing,
4. Relatively low brightness of the work and work-area (central field) compared with that of large areas of surroundings.

A glare-source or condition may directly reduce visibility or indirectly through annoyance or discomfort by,

1. Reducing the size of the pupil and thereby reducing the brightness of the retinal image of the visual object or task,
2. By raising the brightness-level of retinal adaptation thereby reducing the effectiveness of the brightness of the visual object or task or of its retinal image,
3. By reducing or obliterating the visibility of the object by a veiling brightness,
4. By reducing the ability of the human seeing-machine through complexly interwoven physiological and psychological effects such as tenseness, fatigue, distraction, annoyance and discomfort.

Such attributes and effects of glare-sources and conditions have been more or less vaguely and loosely encompassed by the term *glare*. A need has long existed for definitions which separate causes from effects, and also for definitions which distinguish causes from one another and also effects from one another. The factors in the external physical world have been extensively studied and are now fairly well separated. In fact, their relationships are expressible by mathematical equations. However, the biological, physiological and psychological variables make it impossible to describe glare conditions and effects in photometric terms excepting in a relative sense.

The phenomena and effects of glare usually constitute the negative phases of quality of lighting. Since these deleterious effects are generally preventable or greatly reducible, with certain possible and obvious exceptions, they are eventually of secondary importance in the science of seeing which deals primarily with aids to seeing. In other words, a crude art of lighting ignores or tolerates glare conditions, but a science of lighting recognizes and eliminates or reduces them. For this reason the science of seeing is not so much concerned with the precise equations representing the laws and relationships of the factors involved as it is with recognition, reduction and elimination of the conditions which cause the deleterious effects of glare. It begins with a recognition of excessive brightness and brightness-contrast as causes of reduced visibility and of certain entoptic and subjective phenomena concomitant with such extreme brightness stimulation. The latter is a function of the area and brightness of the stimulus and also of the state of retinal stimulation.

The effects of glare may be appraised by various criteria such as visibility,[89] visual efficiency,[141] discomfort,[87] and fatigue. Millar and Gray [142] made an excellent summary of the results of researches pertaining particularly to glare and visibility. In general a given glare condition will appear more serious when appraised by discomfort than by visual efficiency. This conclusion has a rational basis since discomfort involves both physiological and psychological reactions. This is confirmed by extensive researches.[140] These indicate for glare-sources of relatively small size that

1. Discomfort is a function of
   a. the luminous intensity or candlepower of the glare-source in the direction of the observer,
   b. the intrinsic brightness of the glare-source.
2. Reduction of visibility is a function of
   a. the luminous intensity or candlepower of the glare-source in the direction of the observer.

[385]

It is possible that further refinements in the understanding and study of glare and visibility may discover that the intrinsic brightness of the glare-source also plays a part in the reduction of visibility. However, from the extensive work of Holladay,[141] the foregoing statements appear to cover the inherent characteristics of glare-sources of relatively small size. Inasmuch as the luminous intensity or candlepower of a light-source is the product of its area and intrinsic brightness, it may seem that the latter plays a primary part in causing both discomfort and reduced visibility. However, this is not true if, as indicated by Holladay's work, the size of the glare-source is not important when the sizes are relatively small. This can be illustrated by means of two fully exposed tungsten-filament lamps having bulbs of clear and frosted glass, respectively. If they are 100-watt lamps their luminous intensities will be of the order of 100 candlepower toward the observer but the brightness of the bare filament will be of the order of 100 times greater than the brightness of the frosted lamp. Still, in the same location with respect to the observer and visual object, both lamps as glare-sources will reduce visibility of the object about equally. However, the bare filament will cause greater discomfort than the frosted lamp. This also emphasizes the two different viewpoints toward glare. When considering visibility, the visual object or task is the center of attention but when considering discomfort the human being is the center of attention.

Inasmuch as both discomfort and reduced visibility are functions of the candlepower of the glare-source toward the observer, they are also functions of the normal illumination in footcandles at the eyes of the observer due to the glare-source alone. In other words, a characteristic of a glare-source of relatively small size may be specified in terms of the "glare illumination" or "glare footcandles" measured at the eyes of the observer on a plane perpendicular to the line connecting the eyes and the glare-source.

The effect of contrast of the glare-source with its background is intimately associated with the areal and brightness adaptation of the retina. For example, a lighted match, of less than one candlepower and of relatively low intrinsic brightness, may be very glaring outdoors at night as measured by the visibility of objects. On the other hand, a 100-watt tungsten-filament clear-bulb lamp of more than 100 candlepower and of an intrinsic brightness more than 1000 times that of the flame of the burning match, when viewed against the day sky may not be glaring by the criterion of visibility of objects. This emphasizes the im-

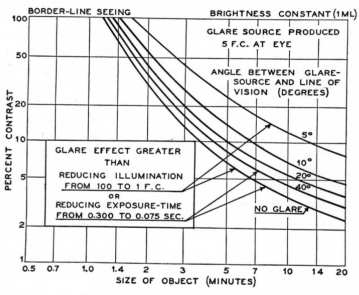

FIG. 111.—Showing the threshold combinations of size and contrast as influenced by a glaring light-source located at various angles above the horizontal line of vision.

portance of retinal adaptation. If a lighting condition involves visible light-sources, a low brightness-ratio between the sources and their backgrounds is desirable in order to minimize,

1. The distraction of the relatively bright sources in the peripheral visual field and
2. The loss in visual efficiency due to the lag in the compensating ocular mechanism with respect to changes in brightness.

The illumination of the background of a visible light-source not only greatly reduces the brightness-ratios between them but also permits the use of sources of lower intrinsic brightness because the illuminated backgrounds supply some of the illumination. This is a cardinal principle of good lighting and seeing which is violated on every hand and in many different ways.

Glare and visibility. Complex mathematical relationships have been developed by a number of investigators [142] of the various factors involved in glare, but they are of less interest here than illustrations of the effects in specific cases. In Fig. 111 are the results of a given glare-source and condition in the reduction of visibility.[89] The glare-source was a 100-watt inside frosted tungsten-filament lamp at a uniform distance from the eyes for all locations studied. It provided a "glare illumination" of 5 footcandles at the eyes. Its effects upon visibility were studied for several locations which were 5, 10, 20 and 40 degrees from the line of vision connecting the eyes and the test-object. The white background of the test-object had a constant brightness of one millilambert. Measurements were also made when the glare-source was "off"; that is, absent from the visual field. In the latter case the relation between size of the test-object and its contrast with the background represents the best that normal eyes can do under conditions of no glare for that particular brightness-level or one millilambert. In Fig. 111 the curve corresponding to this condition is the border-line of threshold visibility. In other words, any combinations of size and contrast which fall below this curve are not visible to persons with average normal vision under the conditions specified.

When the glare-source was 40 degrees above the line of vision, the corresponding curve in Fig. 111 represents the border-line or threshold visibility of combinations of size and contrast. A curve is plotted for each location of the glare-source with respect to the line of vision. It is seen that visibility was greatly reduced when the glare-source was within 5 degrees of the line of vision. In other words, many combinations of size and contrast of the test-object which were visible when there was no preventable glare were invisible, or below threshold visibility, when the glare-

[388]

source was present. As indicated on the diagram, the reduction in visibility due to the glare-source located at 5 degrees from the line of vision was greater than the increase in visibility due to a 100-fold increase in the illumination or brightness of the test-object when no glare was present. The equivalent visibility due to time of exposure of the test-object is also indicated.

The same research was prosecuted for two other brightness-levels; that is, when the brightness of the background of the

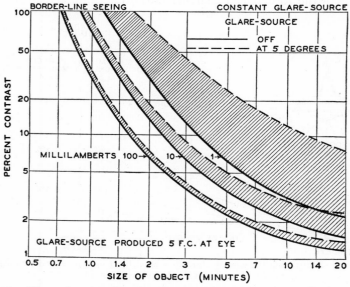

FIG. 112.—Illustrating the effect of glare upon the threshold visibility of objects of various combinations of size and contrast for three different brightness-levels.

test-object was 10 and 100 millilamberts, respectively. The curves showing borderline or threshold visibility, with and without glare, were lower and less separated for the higher brightness-levels. The spread between the curves representing borderline visibility for no glare and for the glare at five degrees from the line of vision, is shown for each of the three brightness-levels in Fig. 112. The shaded areas represent the reduction in visibility due to glare in each case. This diagram is worthy of considerable study for it reveals the enormous range of combinations of size and contrast which fall below the threshold of visibility due to glare and also to various brightness-levels. These data have been discussed more extensively elsewhere.[1]

Although the cost of glare in terms of loss in visibility as illustrated in Figs. 111 and 112 is fundamentally important, it is interesting to view this cost in terms of the equivalent in wasted light. In Fig. 113 a diagrammatic sketch illustrates the results of one of the foregoing researches interpreted into actual practice.

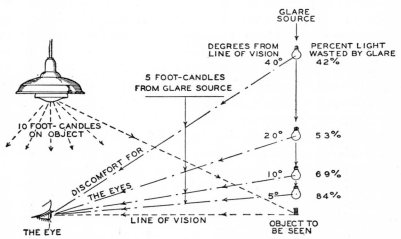

FIG. 113.—Illustrating the cost of glare in wasted light as determined by measurements of visibility with and without glare.

With 10 footcandles on the white background of the object to be seen and 5 footcandles at the eye due to the glare-source, the actual reduction in visibility is expressed in the equivalent waste of light for various locations of the glare-source. For example, when the glare-source was "off" visibility was highest and was that obtainable with 10 footcandles on the test-object. When the glare-source was 5 degrees from the test-object, visibility was only equivalent to what it would have been if there were no glare-source and only 16 per cent of the 10 footcandles (1.6 footcandles) illuminated the test-object. In other words, 84 per cent of the light on the test-object was wasted, as measured by the criterion of visibility, due to the presence of the glare-source. As the glare-source was raised from the horizontal line of vision, it was noted that the waste of light decreases, but 42 per cent is still wasted when the glare-source is 40 degrees above the line of vision.

These two viewpoints of glare and visibility cover the entire realm of human efficiency and welfare. In Fig. 112 are shown the reduction in visibility and visual efficiency due to glare. This means a reduction in human efficiency and in the quality and quantity of achievement which can be translated far and wide into production, comfort, safety, destruction and death. In Fig. 113 this reduction in visibility is presented in equivalents of wasted light due to glare. This can be translated directly into dollars representing the cost of glare merely in wasted light; but hidden wastes of human resources and penalties to human seeing-machines are not included in the evaluation.

Glare and discomfort. The common physical cause of reduced visibility and a feeling of discomfort produce psychophysiological effects in two departments of the consciousness. Visibility can be measured in definite units and expressed clearly in words. This is not true of discomfort. There are no standards of the sensations and feelings involved and no simple units in which they may be measured. A change in the physical glare conditions unquestionably causes a change in the magnitude, and even character, of the sensation or feeling. Holladay and one of the authors [140] devised a tentative scale of 14 steps described in words which aided materially in investigating this effect of glare, but the meanings are not exact to others. Therefore, discomfort cannot be discussed to advantage without understandable units and terms. Only some generalizations will be presented here.

Conditions which produce obvious discomfort should be eliminated or avoided. Being obvious to a person with a consciousness and knowledge of glare does not guarantee that such conditions are obvious to other persons. Everyday observation reveals a need for continual education of the public. Conditions which produce discomfort in lesser degrees are even more wide-

[391]

spread. Being less obvious and far more prevalent than the extreme cases perhaps they need as much attention as the extreme cases. In general, if a person whose sensibility and consciousness are trained by knowledge and experience cannot detect any discomfort from a lighting condition, it is likely that it is fairly satisfactory from the viewpoint of comfort provided that the appraisal is made under the proper conditions. For example, if critical seeing for long periods is being done under the lighting condition, the appraisal must be made while performing the critical seeing over a sufficient period. However, this is a makeshift at best and does not involve appraisal from the viewpoint of visibility. We have proved that the human seeing-machine is a very poor visibility-meter. He can probably be a better comfort-meter. At least the lighting and seeing specialist must perform as a comfort-meter until the science of seeing develops correlations between lighting conditions and comfort which will result in practical methods of measuring comfort or discomfort.

Glare and pupil size. The size of the pupil is generally associated with changes in brightness adaptation, but it is also an indicator of fatigue and discomfort. In fact, the pupil responds decisively to certain glare conditions. For these reasons size is associated with levels of illumination, distribution of brightness, and preventable and unpreventable glare. Since intrinsic brightness and area of both primary and secondary light-sources are complementary factors in the production of a given level of illumination, the relative physiological effects resulting from various combinations of these factors have a direct bearing on lighting practice. Fig. 24 shows the results of a research [33] upon pupil size of combinations of area and brightness of the visual field which always supplied 10 footcandles at the eyes. The pupil size was measured after a few seconds for each combination of area and brightness of the field. The results show that small areas of high brightness and large areas of low brightness, respectively, are the most effective on the basis of admitting light to the retina; that is, the pupils are larger for these brightness conditions. Obviously this fact established by careful measurement may require revision of the prevalent belief that under small and relatively brighter sources the pupil is universally smaller than under socalled indirect lighting. Conversely, it may be concluded that the pupillary light-reflex is least effective as a protecting device for the extreme conditions. The minimal pupil-size was obtained for a luminous area 17 degrees in extent and 500 millilamberts in brightness. The brightness of the largest area (entire visual field) was 36 millilamberts and of the smallest area was 12,900 millilamberts. Pupillary measurements are presented in a preceding section and also in Chapter III.

It may be shown from a theoretical basis that the differences in the size of the pupil are attributable to the fact that the pupillomotor nerves are not distributed uniformly throughout the retina. Also the wide variation in density of both the rod and cone populations in the retina is theoretical evidence indicating that various combinations of area and brightness of light-sources would produce different states of retinal adaptation. Since adaptation phenomena are usually more important than pupillary effects in photopic vision, it is reasonable to assume that quantitative data relating the former with the areal and brightness characteristics of light-sources would be of considerable importance to lighting practice.

Afterimages. In addition to the temporary reduction in visibility due to a lag in adaptation, retinal fatigue must be taken into account in cases of extreme brightness where afterimages are temporarily "blinding" or partially so. The duration of the after-image depends upon the brightness of the stimulus and the duration of exposure to the stimulus. In the cases of bare-filament lamps, the effective duration of the afterimage is often a full minute or more. Even when the stimulus is of relatively low brightness the afterimage may seriously reduce visual efficiency for several seconds. This result of retinal fatigue plays a part in every task of seeing involving continually changing objects such as is the case in reading. However, they are most noticeable in connection with extreme glare as, for example, on the highway at night where automobile headlamps may cause blinding afterimages so intense that safety for a few seconds is jeopardized. The temporary impairment of vision due to afterimages is largely a matter of retinal adaptation as are various other effects of glare.[141]

APPRAISING LIGHTING CONDITIONS

Obvious discomfort and obvious deleterious effects of improper lighting are readily appraised. No rules or methods are needed to recognize them. However, there is a great range from conditions of this sort to the ideal lighting for maximal visibility, comfort, and ease of seeing. No set rules and methods are available for appraisals of lighting conditions throughout this range. However, intelligent use can be made of the data such as presented in this and other chapters and of the generalizations arising from them. As we have often emphasized, the initial appraisal by casual observation may differ greatly from conclusions based upon scientific investigations and exposure to the lighting for a long period of performing the tasks for which the lighting is supplied.

Doubtless researches and correlations will eventually establish relatively simple methods of appraising lighting just as the visibility meter goes a long way toward a complete appraisal of the effectiveness of footcandles not only through the measurement of visibility but through correlations of this with ease of seeing. A promising method for appraising lighting conditions appears to be the rate of blinking which we have investigated, as illustrated in Table XXXIII and Fig. 67, with the hope that it might be used eventually for this and other purposes. Much more work must be done in connection with actual lighting conditions; nevertheless it appears worth while to present briefly the results obtained for three socalled indirect lighting systems. The investigation aimed to compare the quality of lighting of three installations in which no glare from visible primary light-sources was present. Any glare present was due to the brightness and area of the highly illuminated ceilings. An example of poor direct lighting could have been included but it seemed that a more severe test of the criteria would result if only the same types of lighting installations were involved. While the subjects read black print on white paper under the footcandles supplied by the lighting installation, the rate of blinking was obtained by observation without the subjects being aware that blinks were being counted or were even involved in the tests. Pupil sizes were determined with the L-M pupillometer [105] while the subjects were looking at a printed page of a book under the actual conditions of lighting and after the subjects were thoroughly adapted to the conditions.

The results obtained for three subjects in each of the three offices are presented in Table LXI. It will be noted that the average number of blinks occurring on two different days during a five-minute period was 40, 54, and 47 in offices A, B and C, respectively. It is noted that the rate of blinking in B was greater than in A and C notwithstanding the higher level of illumination in B. In Table XXXIII and Fig. 67 it is seen that the rate of blinking during reading black print on white paper is less for high than for low levels of illumination within the range 1 to 100 footcandles.

TABLE LXI

Office	Fixation Point	No. of Blinks in 5 Minutes Subject			
		1	2	3	Average
A	On book (33 fc.)	13	17	91	40
B	On book (39 fc.)	20	24	117	54
C	On book (23 fc.)	14	15	111	47
		Pupil Size (Millimeters)			
A	Below horizontal	3.12	3.64	3.38	3.38
	Horizontal	3.86	4.32	5.58	4.59
	30° above horizontal	3.47	4.25	4.88	4.20
	60° above horizontal	2.37	2.82	3.36	2.85
B	Below horizontal	3.12	2.58	3.24	2.98
	Horizontal	3.78	3.43	3.94	3.72
	30° above horizontal	2.20	2.62	3.46	2.76
	60° above horizontal	1.79	1.96	2.94	2.23
C	Below horizontal	2.96	3.29	3.47	3.24
	Horizontal	3.46	4.26	4.88	4.20
	30° above horizontal	2.72	3.59	4.48	3.60
	60° above horizontal	2.30	2.19	3.42	2.64

In fact, the curve in Fig. 67 shows that under conditions of no glare the rate of blinking while reading decreases markedly as the illumination of the printed page increases from 1 to 100 footcandles. This and other considerations indicate that this criterion must have distinguished between the qualities of lighting, in the three rooms, in their arousal of undesirable effects which cause the rate of blinking to increase. Pertinent data pertaining to the three installations are presented in Table LXII.

Since comparatively few data are involved in the averages presented in Table LXI, some apparent inconsistencies are to be expected. In general, such errors are eliminated by the usual laboratory procedure involving controlled conditions and numerous measurements. However, in view of the fact that this experimental study of quality of lighting was designed for use in practice, it is obvious that the tedious and comprehensive methods of the laboratory would be inappropriate. Notwithstanding the fact that numerous uncontrolled variables were present in this investigation, it will be noted that each subject blinked faster while reading in office B than in either of the other two offices. This indication of less favorable reactions in office B is also supported by the introspective reports of the subject S. The latter indicated that both the brightness of the ceiling and the stroboscopic effects from the mercury light, which was combined with tungsten light, were annoying factors.

The pupillary data indicate that severe constrictions occurred for two of the three subjects when the ceiling of office B was viewed. In the latter case, the pupils were considerably smaller than the average value found by Reeves [32] for subjects viewing a white surface illuminated to 1000 footcandles. In most studies of pupil-size, no preventable glare is present. Apparently the presence of noticeable glare must be taken into account in comparing pupillary data. It is likely that abnormal constrictions of the pupil are undesirable when persisting for long periods. Although the ceiling may be seen directly at rather infrequent intervals, the presence of bright areas within the peripheral field represents a definite psychological handicap since the tendency to fixate a bright parafoveal area is a highly developed and inherent characteristic of the human seeing-machine. Hence the visual situation in office *B* is such that the natural tendencies of orientation and fixation invoke a physiological penalty when they are obeyed. Therefore, it is conceivable that such a situation might result in psychological disturbances and nervous tension resulting in fatigue and various disorders.

TABLE LXII

Office	A	B	C
Floor dimensions in feet ...	19 × 17	6 × 15	17 × 15
Color of walls	Stippled green	Stippled green	Flat buff
Reflection-factor of walls ..	37 per cent	30 per cent	42 per cent
Color of ceiling	White	White	Dirty white
Lighting			
Number of indirect units.	4	2	4
Watts per unit	500 tungsten	500 tungsten	500 tungsten
		250 mercury	
Footcandles on desk	33	65	25
Footcandles at eye			
45° below horizontal	5	11	5
Horizontal	9	23	9
30° above horizontal	14	42	12
60° above horizontal	22	55	16
Footlamberts			
45° below horizontal	18	34	18
Horizontal	0.12*	14	8
30° above horizontal	1.7*	18	8
60° above horizontal	120	200	59

* Subject faced a relatively dark alcove.

In Table LXII some data pertaining to the physical aspects of the installations are presented for those who would examine the results in terms of such data. The ceiling in all rooms was 12 feet above the floor. It will be noted that *A* and *C* were offices of moderate size and *B* was a relatively small one. The reflection-factors of the walls were within the range from which experience seems desirable. With the eyes of the subjects directed horizontally in front and at three different vertical angles with the horizontal, the footcandles at the eyes on a plane normal to the line of sight were measured. The brightnesses seen by the eyes in these positions are also presented. It will be noted particularly that the footcandles at the eye and the brightness directly in the field of view were considerably greater in *B* than in the other two rooms.

This preliminary investigation has been described primarily to demonstrate the need for criteria which will provide some measurements of quality of lighting in terms of relative comfort or discomfort. Therefore, conclusions are drawn sparingly. It appears that the quality of lighting in office *B* is *relatively* less favorable than in the other offices. The constriction of the pupil under certain conditions in this office may be regarded as unfavorable in an *absolute* sense.

In general the human being reacts more obviously to negative factors in lighting and also is apparently a better judge or more conscious of negative factors of lighting than of positive factors such as level of well-diffused illumination. It has been our laboratory experience that subjects will object to glare and other offensive factors or will report dissatisfaction and annoyance when questioned even when these factors do not alter visibility significantly or produce other detectable changes in visual function. On the other hand, they have little realization of the decisive increases in visibility due to large increases of well-diffused illumination upon the visual task. However, in such an investigation as has been described in the foregoing paragraphs there were three different installations of the same type—indirect lighting—which is commonly considered as likely to be the least offensive from the viewpoint of lighting.

Much difference of opinion exists as to the level of illumination which can be supplied by such systems with comfort to the occupants of the rooms. Knowledge has existed for a long time which indicates that the upper limit for comfort is in the neighborhood of 50 footcandles for lighting solely by general illumination even by an indirect system. Harrison [143] recently came to this general conclusion in discussing why ceilings may be too bright in cases of 50-footcandle installations of indirect lighting. He verifies our long-standing conclusion that modifications of this method or additional means are necessary to supply comfortable high-level illumination.[138] The criteria used by us seem to indicate that in office *B* the limit has been passed notwithstanding the fact that the room was quite small. If it had been large, the expanse of bright ceiling would probably have been even more glaring. Some of the footcandles can be obtained with comfort by combining directed light or supplementary lighting with the general illumination. In fact, several times 65 footcandles can be supplied with comfort to workers by the combination of general plus supplementary or directed light. *Balance* of general and directed light is an important factor. This emphasizes the importance of a simple rating of lighting fixtures and lighting systems illustrated in Fig. 107. By providing balance, Nature's lighting is simulated—direct light from the sun and general illumination from the sky. An improvement over Nature may be achieved by having the supplementary or directed light come from a source of much larger size or solid angle than the sun. Also it may be possible by exercising ingenuity to direct light downward upon the workplace from the same fixtures or areas which supply indirect general illumination. These obvious solutions of the problem of obtaining high footcandle-levels have been ignored and even shunned by the lighting specialist until recently. The chief reason seems to have been the desire to promote simplified lighting practice instead of following the dictates of scientific knowledge in the development of a science of lighting for efficient and comfortable seeing.

The L-M visibility meter can be calibrated so as to appraise socalled glare in terms of its effect in reducing visibility. In the absence of a correlation between reduction in visibility and discomfort it cannot appraise the latter. Naturally the distribution of brightness in the visual field affects the amount of light scattered by the slightly diffusing gradients used in our visibility meter. This affects the visibility of objects. Actually this device generally over-emphasizes the effects of preventable glare from the viewpoint of the visibility of objects or tasks. However, it can be so calibrated as to analyze glare in terms of visibility.

CHAPTER XI

Spectral Quality of Light

Spectral quality is the only fundamental characteristic which distinguishes one illuminant from another. This determines the color of the light as seen by looking at the light-source, or preferably at a white or gray paper illuminated by the light. It also determines the appearance of colored objects because the color depends primarily upon the light falling upon the colored object and secondarily upon the selective reflection (or transmission) of the object. Spectral quality of light can only be expressed by a table or graph representing the relative amounts of radiant energy of different wavelengths within the limits of the visible spectrum. These limits, expressed in Ångström units, are approximately λ3900 at the border of the ultraviolet spectrum and λ7600 at the border of the infrared spectrum. The invisible radiant energy—ultraviolet and infrared—which usually accompanies visible energy or light, may or may not be harmful and, as far as is known, is not useful in everyday seeing. Special applications of these can be made in the realm of seeing, but these are not of particular interest here.

The spectral quality of an illuminant may be due to the light-source itself or to a modification of the light by a colored filter placed over the light-source or in front of the eyes. Lights such as those from the sun, blue sky, a bonfire, a candle flame, tungsten filaments, a mercury arc, sodium vapor, and a neon sign differ markedly in spectral quality or distribution of energy throughout the visible spectrum. These represent differences in the fundamental illuminants. However, spectral quality of the useful light is also altered by colored lenses, eyeglasses, papers, and various other means, which in effect is a secondary modification produced by a colored filter. Human beings see these dif-

[400]

ferences in spectral quality usually as a difference or change in color. A difference in color between two illuminants always means a difference in spectral quality. However, the reverse is not necessarily true, for two colors or illuminants may appear of the same hue but may differ markedly in spectral quality. For example, it is easy to make two filters which appear identically yellow under a given illuminant.[53] One is the usual type which transmits green, yellow, orange and red light, but the other transmits no spectral yellow at all. The latter transmits green, orange and red lights, but may appear to be the same yellow as the other filter. This emphasizes the facts that spectral quality is a physical characteristic quite apart from the visual sense and that color is a sensation resulting from the synthesis of the simultaneous stimulation of the visual sense by energy of various wavelengths. Thus in passing from the physical aspects of color to sensations of color, a complex physico-physiological realm is created.

The foregoing indicates that the human being can see the color of an illuminant or colored object, but cannot determine the spectral quality unless aided by physical means such as a spectroscope. To those well acquainted with spectrum analysis the color of light is generally a fair guide to its spectral quality, but there is no substitute for actual physical dispersion of light into its components of various wavelengths for qualitative observation and quantitative measurement. These aspects of color have been adequately treated elsewhere [53] and are touched upon merely to provide a glimpse of the background necessary for understanding color and spectral quality. Here we are interested in the utilization of light by the human being for the purpose of seeing. Owing to certain limitations of the eye as an optical device and of the visual sense as a receiving station, spectral quality of light has some influence upon visibility and the ability to see. Also color has psychological influence through the visual sense as a doorway for impressions which external scenes make upon the internal mental being.[159] However, it may be safely stated that color and spectral quality of light represent realms of seeing in which many incomplete and even false concepts have flourished. In general, it appears that these factors in seeing may be utilized best as refinements in special cases, excepting for general applications which are more safely patterned after Nature than fashioned by man with incomplete knowledge of a vast complexity.

In lighting practice spectral quality of light is one of the three important aspects of every problem. The other two are quantity of light or footcandles and quality of lighting or distribution of light and brightness. Having illuminants available with widely different spectral character such as tungsten-filament light, artificial daylight, mercury light and sodium light, the first question to consider in many current lighting problems is, What kind of light should be used? This is not generally true in lighting the home and in many other places, but it is becoming increasingly important in the work-world and on highways. Of course, the kind of light which is acceptable depends somewhat upon the character of the task of seeing, the environment, the amount of light desired and the requirements as to control of light. Where accurate optical control of light is necessary, the physical size of mercury and sodium lamps at present is sometimes a handicap which may rule them out. If the appearance of the environment is important, the distortion of the appearance of colored objects may also rule out these illuminants with discontinuous spectra. Where efficiency of light production is important, they have an advantage over tungsten-filament light in many cases at the present time. All such factors affect the choice of the illuminant. However, the spectral quality is of primary importance in most cases. The final answers must be based upon the effect of the illuminant upon visibility and upon human seeing-machines.

CHROMATIC ABERRATION AND VISUAL ACUITY

It is well known that the focal length of a simple convex lens is not the same for light of various wavelengths. In other words, a simple lens is not achromatic. In Fig. 114 the results are exaggerated for the purpose of illustration. A prism has long been used to disperse light into its spectrum or components of various wavelengths. A convex lens may be thought of as a prism of revolution with the angle gradually changing to form a convex surface of a lens. Obviously, a perfectly defined image can be produced by a simple convex lens only when monochromatic light illuminates the object. The human eye is, in effect, a simple lens; therefore, it is not achromatic. Early in the nineteenth century Wallaston discovered that it possessed the "defect" known as chromatic aberration. Its magnitude is about two diopters. In

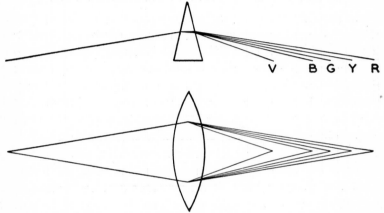

FIG. 114.—Illustrating the cause of chromatic aberration in a simple lens. For a complete spectrum, three-fourths of the aberration is caused by the short-wave half of the spectrum.

other words, it requires a convex lens about two diopters greater in strength to focus upon a given plane the deep red rays, than it does to focus the violet rays from an object at a given distance. Owing to the fact that refrangibility increases as the wavelength decreases, chromatic aberration is about three times greater for the short-wave half of the spectrum than for the long-wave half. In other words, about 1.5 diopters additional is necessary to focus the highly "luminous" energy (yellow or yellow-green) in the same plane as violet light and only about 0.5 diopters additional to focus red light in the same plane as the highly luminous energy. Obviously, the effect of chromatic aberration in the eye is to pro-

[403]

duce a retinal image surrounded by a halo of light which is out
of focus. The effect of chromatic aberration in blurring the retinal
image is greater as the lens is stronger and as the incident rays approach the margin. Chromatic aberration is usually corrected in
optical instruments but not in eyeglasses. In the latter case, the

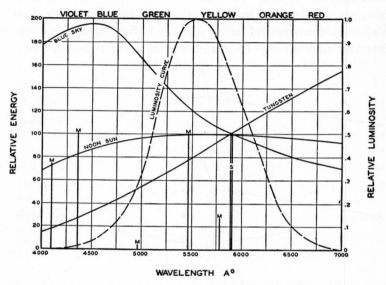

FIG. 115.—The spectral luminosity curve of the eye is in reality the selectivity of
the visual apparatus. It tends to reduce chromatic aberration. Spectral distribution of energy of the several illuminants is shown. One curve shows the
distribution from a tungsten-filament operating at 22 lumens per watt. *M* represents the mercury lines (low-pressure arc) ; *S* represents the sodium doublet.

chromatic defects are usually unimportant since they are seldom
noticeable.

A modifying factor is the selectivity of the visual process. Graphically this is known as the spectral luminosity
curve of the eye. Energy of equal quantities of various wavelengths produces luminosity as shown by the curve in Fig.
115. This is Nature's attempt toward selectivity as man attempts to accomplish it in many instruments such as the
photocell, radio, etc. This *tends* to reduce the extreme effects of

[404]

chromatic aberration, but they are not eliminated as is readily demonstrable in many ways.

The chromatic aberration in the eye can be demonstrated in many ways. Inasmuch as it is impossible to focus blue and red light from a given object in the same plane, a purple object can never appear distinctly in focus. This can be demonstrated by covering a light-source with a purple filter. In railroad yards a purple light is used for short-range visibility on some switches. It cannot be seen sharply outlined. Neither can a blue line on a red background. On looking down a street at night a person may sharply focus the image of a distant neon (orange) sign, but a bluish sign of the same general character will appear fuzzy. If a bright filament of a tungsten lamp is viewed through a dense purple glass, it will be seen to have a red or blue halo depending upon the accommodation of the eyes. The weird effects experienced under purple light are largely due to this kind of fogging. In fact, the eyesight specialist uses red and blue filters to good advantage in testing eyes and prescriptions. This is merely putting into use this inherent limitation of the eye as an optical system. In optical design this defect of a single lens is counteracted by combining one or more lenses in such a manner that chromatic aberration is eliminated for certain wavelengths and is greatly reduced for all wavelengths.

Early in the present century a number of artificial illuminants differing in spectral character were already in use in lighting practice. Naturally those interested in the scientific aspects turned their attention to the possible effect of chromatic aberration. Space does not permit an extended historical presentation of the subject, so we shall begin with Bell's work [144] in which he reported comparative measurements with lights from a tungsten filament and mercury arc, respectively. He assumed he was studying chromatic aberration and visual acuity. Actually his criterion was not visual acuity, which involves the recognition of details at the threshold of size. It had been observed that objects such as printed matter appeared "more distinct" when viewed under mercury light than under tungsten-filament light. In brief, Bell found that it required about two footcandles of the latter to make the printed matter appear of the same degree of distinctness as it did under one footcandle of mercury light. This work was well done, but doubtless owing to the rather primitive stage of knowledge and terminology 25 years ago, he erred in designating this criterion, *visual acuity*. This error has been perpetuated ever since.

Bell actually measured something which might better be described as *apparent distinctness* of the object or objects. He also used other visual tasks, but none at the threshold of size and, therefore, did not measure visual acuity. What did he measure? Is this apparent greater distinctness of some objects under mercury light real or not? Countless illusions [55] cause one to wonder whether this apparent effect of mercury light is an illusion. That some objects appear more distinct under mercury light than under light of an extended spectral character is the testimony of many persons. But the sun and moon appear much larger to everyone when near the horizon than when high in the sky. Actually they are not.

The "strength" of these and of many other illusions can be determined by controlling any influential factor, just as Bell did the footcandles of one of the two illuminants to ascertain how much more tungsten-filament light was required to counteract the effect. We have made unsuccessful attempts to ascertain whether this effect of mercury light is real or not. It cannot be definitely stated at the present time that this apparent effect actually makes seeing quicker, easier, more accurate or more certain, but some results indicate that it does not. If it is real, it should do so at least for certain brightnesses or footcandle-levels. Many users have declared that, for equal footcandles, mercury light is better than light of an extended character. But seeing is such a complex matter that such testimony should have the support of actual measurements from careful scientific research.

Shortly after Bell's work, one of us [145] published the results of researches with truly monochromatic light compared with light of the same hue but of extended spectral character. The green mercury line and the yellow sodium line were used, also special filters and tungsten light. Not only was Bell's criterion of apparent equal distinctness of type used (with practically the same results), but also that of visual acuity by means of the Ives-Cobb acuity test-object illustrated in Fig. 139. Through the elimination of color-difference and the use of purely monochromatic light, the superiority of purely monochromatic light in revealing details of threshold size was proved conclusively. However, the question of visual acuity and mercury light remained open.

TABLE LXIII

Approximate Relative Spectral Distribution of Energy in Four Principal Wavelengths

	$\lambda 4047$	$\lambda 4358$	$\lambda 5461$	$\lambda 5780$
Mercury arcs				
50-inch low pressure	72	102	100	32
250-watt high-intensity	45	99	100	109
400-watt high-intensity	31	77	100	111
Tungsten lamps				
100-watt tungsten-filament	15	27	100	128
200-watt tungsten-filament	16	28	100	126
500-watt tungsten-filament	19	32	100	123

In Table LXIII are presented the approximate relative amounts of energy in four principal wavelengths of mercury light from various present-day lamps. For comparison purposes relative energies from certain tungsten filaments are also presented. It is seen that mercury light contains considerable energy in the violet and blue "lines" and it will be recalled that this short-wave visible energy is most effective in extending the halo around a retinal image when the eye is focused for the most luminous part of the spectrum. Of course, red light also produces a halo of out-of-focus light when the eyes are focused for the most luminous part of the spectrum. However, this halo should be only about one-third as wide as that produced by violet and blue light. In appraising illuminants from the viewpoint of chromatic aberration it is helpful to visualize Fig. 115 with the wavelength scale opened

[407]

out more and more as the wavelength decreases similarly to the prismatic spectrum. The linear distance between λ4000 and λ5700 should be nearly three times as great as that between λ5700 and λ7000. This emphasizes the relatively greater importance of blue light than red light in extending the width of the halo of out-of-focus light surrounding the retinal image. The effect of eliminating the blue light is shown in Fig. 117.

The relative luminosities of the energy of various wavelengths and in the total continuous spectrum emitted by three types of mercury vapor lamps are presented in Table LXIV. The data for the low-pressure arc which has long been in use were obtained by B. T. Barnes[146] and the other data by our colleague, A. H. Taylor.[147] H-1 and H-2 lamps of recent origin are socalled high-pressure mercury lamps with relatively short tubular bulbs. The H-3 lamp consists of a quartz capillary tube and the mercury vapor is under a pressure of many atmospheres. Obviously, the luminosity in the violet and blue regions is so low that it does not seem sufficient to counteract the fair approach to monochromatism in the green and yellow regions. Possibly the explanation of the lack of higher visual acuity in mercury light lies elsewhere in the maze of physiological optics.

T A B L E   L X I V

Relative Luminosity of the Energy in the Various Lines, and in the Continuous Spectrum, in Per Cent of Total

λ	Color	50-in. Low Pressure Tube	400-Watt Lamp Type H-1	250-Watt Lamp Type H-2	100-Watt Lamp Type H-3
4047	Violet	0.03	0.01	0.01	0.01
4358	Blue	1.4	0.65	0.86	0.60
4916	Blue-green	....	0.21	0.14	....
4960	Blue-green	....	0.08	0.07	....
5461	Green	76.2	46.16	47.85	55.94
5769–90	Yellow	22.4	46.17	46.86	23.55
	Continuous spectrum	....	6.72	4.21	19.90
		100.0	100.00	100.00	100.00

C O M M O N   I L L U M I N A N T S

Mercury light has been in use for many years during which certain claims and misconceptions have arisen and have persisted without justification. On the other hand no known deleterious effects upon human beings who have worked for long periods under mercury light have been discovered. This illuminant possesses a discontinuous spectrum. About one-third to one-half of the total visible energy is in the blue and violet regions, $\lambda 4358$ and $\lambda 4047$, as seen in Table LXIII. However, owing to the selectivity of the eye as shown by the luminosity curve in Fig. 115 most of the light or brightness sensation is produced by the green and yellow regions, $\lambda 5461$ and $\lambda 5780$. For this reason mercury light has been considered monochromatic in a practical sense. However, as is seen later, visual acuity measurements do not reveal the expected effect of this socalled monochromatism as in the case of sodium light which is quite monochromatic. Apparently there is enough luminosity produced by the violet and blue energy in mercury light to produce the effect due to chromatic aberration in the eye comparable with that of a continuous-spectrum light.

Certainly mercury light differs markedly from daylight and from the prevalent tungsten-filament light. These other illuminants have continuous spectra. In earlier chapters the importance of Nature's light and lighting as environmental factors has been emphasized. However, the radical difference between the discontinuous spectrum of mercury light and the practically continuous spectrum of daylight has often been emphasized as favoring mercury light by its advocates. Such a stand is untenable until it is certain that the human seeing-machine is not paying any penalties by substituting mercury light for daylight. In the absence of such proof, such a stand means that an unnatural illuminant which just came into use during the present century is an improvement over daylight which has been an environmental factor for eons. Similar unproved claims and superficial concepts are now being made for sodium light which has just come into use. This does not mean

[409]

an intentional dominance of commercialism over the scientific view-point and reasonable philosophy pertaining to Nature, adaptation and environment. It generally means merely superficial consid-erations of seeing and a natural over-emphasis of the superficialities which are comprehended because they are readily accessible.

In Table LXV the color of daylight as determined by A. H. Taylor [148] is presented for sunlight and skylight for various hours of the day and for various seasons of the year. These values are expressed as color-temperature in degrees Kelvin. Also the

TABLE LXV

Color-Temperature in Degrees Kelvin of Light from Various Tungsten Lamps and of Sunlight and Skylight

White Light, from a Black Body, at Approximately........	**6000° K**
Tungsten-filament lamps	
15-watt	2483
50-watt	2719
100-watt	2796
200-watt	2828
500-watt	2925
1000-watt	3012
1000-watt projection	3220
Photoflood	3490
150-watt daylight	3570
300-watt daylight	4035
500-watt daylight	3815
Daylight in Cleveland, Ohio	
Direct sunlight alone, 9 A.M. to 3 P.M.	5400 to 5800
Direct sunlight before 9 and after 3 o'clock	4900 to 5600
Sunlight plus light from clear sky	
9 A.M. to 3 P.M.	6100 to 6500
Before 9 and after 3 o'clock	5700 to 6100
Sunlight plus light from a hazy or slightly overcast sky	5700 to 5900
Sunlight plus light from a 25 to 70 per cent overcast sky	6250 to 6700
Light from a totally overcast sky	6700 to 6950
Light from a hazy or smoky sky	7500 to 8400
Light from clear blue sky	
9 A.M. to 3 P.M.	12000 to 26000
Before 9 and after 3 o'clock	12000 to 27000

color-temperatures of some common illuminants are included for comparison.

Color-temperature of a radiator is the temperature of a perfect radiator (black-body) of the same color. Because the spectral distribution of light from most incandescent solids, such as carbon and tungsten filaments, is approximately the same as that of the theoretical black-body (perfect radiator) such a source is said to have a color-temperature T, if the integral color of the

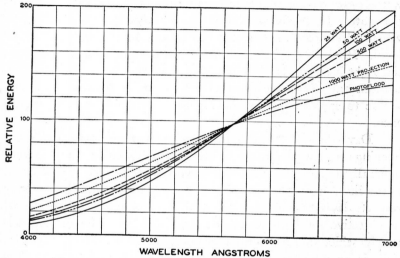

FIG. 116.—The relative spectral distributions of energy from various tungsten-filament (Mazda) lamps.

light is the same as that of a black-body of the actual temperature T. It is expressed in degrees Kelvin. Even light from the sun at different altitudes and from the sky can be approximately described in terms of color-temperature.

Ordinary artificial light from flames and solids such as tungsten filaments also differs from daylight in spectral quality. However, this difference is not as fundamental as in the case of illuminants having large gaps in their discontinuous spectra. As seen graphically in Fig. 115, light from a tungsten filament, for example, has relatively more energy than sunlight in the long-wave

[411]

half of the visible spectrum and less in the short-wave half. This is a difference, but certainly not as fundamental or radical as in the case of the discontinuous spectra of luminous vapors and gases. Actually tungsten-filament light does not differ from average daylight, which is white in color, any more than late afternoon sunlight differs from the light from the blue sky.

In Fig. 116 are plotted the relative energy of various wavelengths emitted by tungsten-filament (Mazda) lamps of different wattages which operated at different luminous efficiencies or lumens per watt. These are so plotted that the spectral qualities of the various illuminants are directly comparable for a given footcandle-level. It might also be emphasized that continuous-spectrum artificial light has been used by mankind since the dawn of civilization without any instinctive rebellion or any deleterious effect, attributable to spectral quality, having been detected by mass experience.

Daylight which enters interiors through windows and other openings is generally white or bluish white in color. This is very generally accepted as ideal for the work-world. Also it is accepted as the illuminant which makes colors appear "natural." In many respects daylight is a fundamental illuminant and is a natural goal or objective for light production and practice. Mercury light is nearly white in color and, therefore, mixes well with daylight. This is an advantage in the work-world. However, it distorts colors which is generally a disadvantage, although in special cases it can become a decided advantage. For example, it emphasizes yellows and, therefore, increases the visibility of minerals of this color in ore when the matrix is gray or of another color. Certainly there are many special applications of such illuminants in the artificial world of countless seeing problems.

Any continuous-spectrum light can be converted by means of a special colored filter to simulate the spectrum of daylight of any quality desired. This has been done in many lamps and fixtures. Even the discontinuous spectrum of mercury light, for example, can produce continuous-spectrum light by fluorescence and phosphorescence. Also, the practice of combining mercury

[412]

light with tungsten-filament light is increasing. Such combinations can produce a white light at high luminous efficiency. Mercury light makes up for the deficiency of tungsten-filament light in the blue and violet regions of the spectrum. Conversely, tungsten light provides an excess of orange and red light to fill the vacancy in the spectrum of mercury light. Of course there are still certain excesses and deficiencies in the spectrum of the combined light, but several desirable improvements are achieved for certain applications.

Sodium light is produced almost entirely by energy of practically one wavelength. Actually the spectrum exhibits the common doublet at approximately $\lambda 5893$. The color of the light is yellow-orange as a gas-flame appears when common salt (sodium chloride) is dropped into it. All objects illuminated by sodium light appear as shades of this hue. Color-contrast entirely disappears and the visual field becomes a yellow monochrome. For this reason this relatively new illuminant is being advocated for highways and other outside areas, such as railroad yards, where color is not an important matter. Although this illuminant is almost strictly monochromatic, tests upon persons working under this light so far have revealed no deleterious effects upon eyesight and human beings. However, it should be emphasized as in the case of mercury light, and even other illuminants differing markedly from daylight, that many possibilities of hidden physiological effects remain to be explored.

Many special applications of sodium light appear attractive owing to the monochromatic characteristic of this light and the higher visual acuity obtainable under lower footcandle-levels than in the case of daylight or tungsten-filament light. However, as already pointed out, visual acuity is greatly over-emphasized in connection with most visual tasks and this advantage is of practically no importance on highways where sodium light seems to have a field of general application. Furthermore, in such an application there scarcely need be any worry over the possible hidden physiological effects because the human seeing-machine is not exposed for hours day after day as in the work-world. Sodium light possesses novelty which may be taken advantage of in some places.

These are glimpses of new illuminants which are new tools for seeing. However, they should not be accepted or applied merely because they are new. Their appraisal should be based upon seeing in its broad sense. Their effect upon visibility, upon the performance of seeing, and upon the human being should be considered. All are subject to measurement. The common error of building an argument upon the narrow viewpoint and incompleteness of knowledge of physiological optics should not be made. This inevitably leads to an entanglement of speculation and controversy because there is no way of knowing how much weight to give to the known details nor how to appraise the unknowns. Therefore, a practical approach is along the detour illustrated in Fig. 6. No better examples of the limitations and pitfalls of physiological optics and the science of vision are to be found than in the arguments and exploitation of spectral quality of light. Many difficulties are eliminated by a scientific approach and attitude.

SEEING IN MERCURY LIGHT

The selection of criteria for appraising an illuminant on the basis of seeing is the primary problem. All the criteria applicable to the study of light or brightness as it influences visibility, seeing and the human seeing-machine are applicable to any illuminant. Already visual acuity has been discussed, but that does not eliminate the need for applying this criterion to mercury light or any other illuminant. It is a factor in seeing although not as important as generally assumed. A diagnosis of visual efficiency under various illuminants by the use of this criterion alone is not a true appraisal of the ability to see. Even less so is visual acuity a suitable basis for specifying light and lighting. The production of contrast or brightness-difference is very important. In Fig. 42 is shown the relation between size and brightness-contrast for threshold visibility. It is seen that for objects less than two minutes (visual angle) in size, contrast is the less important factor.[66]

[414]

The reverse is true for objects larger than two minutes in visual size. One minute visual angle is subtended by 0.004 inch at a distance of 14 inches or by the width of a man at a distance of one mile. Obviously most of our seeing is concerned with much larger objects and in such cases visual acuity ceases to be a dominating factor or adequate criterion. A loose brick at a distance of 100 feet subtends a visual angle of ten minutes. Thus it is inappropriate to emphasize visual acuity universally in the appraisal of mercury light in the work-world. It is quite inadequate in the appraisal of sodium light on the highway.

In the paragraphs which follow various criteria have been used for appraising mercury light as a factor in seeing and in performance dependent upon seeing. Some of these have been condensed from extensive researches.[149] The results of such researches do not reveal *why* something is true, but within their limitations they show *what* is true. All results were obtained under well controlled laboratory conditions.

Visual acuity, under equal levels of illumination from the low-pressure mercury arc and a gas-filled tungsten-filament lamp, was determined for ten adult subjects possessing normal or near-normal vision. The Ives-Cobb acuity object was used and 6000 observations were made under controlled laboratory conditions. The results in terms of visual acuity obtained at three brightnesses, corresponding to three footcandle-levels on white paper, are presented herewith. The slight differences have no significance.

	5 fc.	25 fc.	125 fc.
Mercury-arc light	0.753	0.700	0.687
Tungsten-filament light	0.750	0.717	0.695

The test-object and technique used were capable of measuring very small differences in visual acuity and the number of subjects and observations was adequate for a high order of precision. The conclusion from the results obtained with this particular test-object is that the mercury light was no more monochromatic in effect, from the viewpoint of chromatic aberration, than the continuous-spectrum light from the tungsten-filament lamp.

In order to extend such a comparison of mercury light and tungsten light to lower levels of brightness, a test was made with the brightness of the test-object at 0.1 millilambert. This corresponds to a brightness of an ordinary white paper under approximately 0.1 footcandle. Many brightnesses of this order are found in the work-world due to low reflection-factors and low levels of illumination. The Ives-Cobb acuity object was respec-

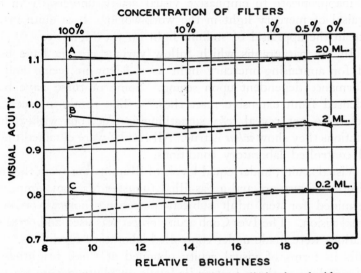

FIG. 117.—Showing the effect upon visual acuity of eliminating the blue end of the visible spectrum by means of various aqueous solutions of potassium bichromate. At the lower brightnesses obtained with the higher concentrations, visual acuity seemed to be maintained notwithstanding the reduced brightness.

tively illuminated by light from a 400-watt high-intensity mercury lamp and from a high wattage tungsten-filament lamp. Visual acuity was found to be the same for both illuminants.

Long ago [150] we found that by eliminating the short-wave visible light from a tungsten-filament lamp by means of yellow filters (various concentrations of potassium bichromate in aqueous solution), visual acuity, as determined by the Ives-Cobb test-object, remained practically constant notwithstanding the reduced amount of light. The results are presented in Fig. 117 for three bright-

[416]

ness-levels corresponding to the brightnesses of the test-object when the filter was pure water. The solid lines represent the averages of the actual determinations of visual acuity. The broken lines indicate what the visual acuity should have been for light unmodified in spectral quality, if it had diminished in accordance with the reductions in brightness due to the absorption of the filters of different percentages of concentration. It appears that absorption of the short-wave visible light roughly compensated for the reduction in visual acuity which takes place when brightness alone is reduced.

Recently we used a filter which entirely absorbed the blue and violet radiation from a 400-watt high-intensity mercury arc and transmitted 83 per cent at λ5461 (yellow-green) and 84.5 per cent at λ5780 (yellow). This filter transmitted 83 per cent of the total mercury light. Visual acuity was determined for six adult subjects having normal vision at two different brightnesses of the Ives-Cobb test-object for tungsten-filament light and for the filtered and unfiltered light from the mercury arc. The results are briefly presented in Table LXVI. The probable error in these averages is less than 0.01. The results may be expressed in another way. For example, the brightness-level of ten millilamberts corresponds to about ten footcandles on white paper. Ten footcandles of tungsten light or ten footcandles of the unfiltered mercury light appear to be about as effective as eight footcandles of the filtered mercury light. Apparently if the blue and violet light could be eliminated from the mercury light without reducing the green and yellow light about 16 per cent, as the filter did in this case, there would be some gain in visual acuity. As it was there is no apparent loss in visual acuity notwithstanding a reduction of 17 per cent in the total light.

T A B L E   L X V I

	Visual Acuity	
	0.1 ml.	10 ml.
Tungsten-filament light	0.90	1.31
Mercury light (unfiltered) ....:....	0.86	1.33
Mercury light (filtered)	0.85	1.31

The visibility of 8-point Bodoni book monotype printed with black ink on white paper was measured by eight subjects by means of the Luckiesh-Moss Visibility Meter. The task was illuminated to ten footcandles by light from a 400-watt high-intensity mercury arc and also from a 100-watt tungsten-filament lamp. The average result obtained by each subject, who made a total of 40 measurements under controlled conditions, is given in Table LXVII as a matter of additional interest. All subjects had so-called normal vision as determined by the present-day technique of the eyesight specialist who corrects refractive errors, but does not measure the ability of the patient to see by means of criteria of more universal significance. No significant difference was found. The criterion in the use of our visibility meter is threshold brightness-difference. It will be noted that the visibility obtained by the various observers differed considerably, but for a given observer was practically the same for both illuminants. In all cases it was equal or slightly higher for the mercury light which may possibly be significant. It seems reasonable to assume that this method should reveal any superiority of mercury light in making objects appear more distinct. However, this assumption may not be entirely tenable.

TABLE LXVII

Subject		Visibility	
		Mercury	Tungsten
1	....	4.1	3.9
2	....	5.0	5.0
3	....	3.8	3.6
4	....	2.9	2.7
5	....	4.9	4.9
6	....	3.8	3.5
7	....	3.4	3.2
8	....	2.9	2.7
Average	....	3.8	3.7

The same technique and illuminants as used in the foregoing case were used with two other test-objects drawn with black ink on white cardboard. They consisted of a circle ten minutes in diameter and a bar 60 minutes long and 1.5 minutes wide. The averages of visibility measurements of these objects, under an illumination of ten footcandles, obtained by six subjects having so-called normal vision are presented herewith.

	Bar	Circle
Mercury light	9.0	10.9
Tungsten light	9.4	11.4

No significance is attached to the differences in the foregoing even though the probable error of these averages is less than 0.2.

The speed of performing the L-M Demonstration Visual Test [1] was determined for mercury light from the 400-watt high-intensity lamp and for light from a 100-watt tungsten-filament lamp. This test consists of letters made by breaks in dark gray diagonal lines upon a lighter gray background. The size of the critical details viewed at 14 inches is 1.5 minutes visual angle. Obviously their size is such that visual acuity is important. However, no significant difference is found in the average speed of performance of ten subjects, possessing socalled normal vision, each of whom repeated the test ten times. The average results are presented herewith.

Tungsten-filament light	0.79 minute
Mercury light	0.80 minute

The probable error in the foregoing results was less than 0.02 minute. In various ways we have shown the limitations of production or rate of performance of work as a criterion for easy seeing. However, it seems reasonable to expect that this particular test involving critical seeing would be favorable to an illuminant if the latter actually caused details to appear "more distinct." Incidentally this Demonstration Visual Test is available in convenient form for scientific research or more practical investigations. Woodside and Reinhardt [151] also obtained similar results by means of this technique. Also using other criteria they found no difference between mercury and tungsten lights in their contribution to seeing.

In the course of the past decade we have systematically permitted persons to choose the footcandles they wished for reading printed matter. As we have pointed out [7] such a test has no scientific standing, but the results are of interest. However, if there is any real difference between mercury light and tungsten-filament light in producing distinctness of fine details, the voluntary choice of footcandles for a given reading task might reveal differences.[5] In Table LXVIII are average choices of four large groups of subjects, each subject making his choice alone and taking as much time as desired. The lighting conditions and surroundings were the same for both illuminants. In the fourth test the paper was dyed gray and had a reflection-factor of 41 per cent. In the other cases the paper was white. In all cases the ink was black and all surfaces were non-glossy. It is obvious that no significant differences were obtained. It is interesting to note that the subject seldom chooses all the light that is available. This reveals a shortcoming of the test which we have not taken seriously as a scientific procedure. However, even with these limitations, it is somewhat significant that no definite preference was revealed for either illuminant.

TABLE LXVIII

Number of Observers	Maximum Footcandles Available	Average Footcandles Chosen	
		Mercury	Tungsten
22	10	6.3	5.3
55	30	14.2	12.7
24	45	16.9	16.1
26*	30	18.0	17.4

* In this case the paper was dyed gray of 41 per cent reflection-factor.

The foregoing represents a variety of researches using different criteria. No significant differences in the effectiveness of mercury and tungsten light were revealed. It is possible that an enormous number of measurements by many subjects would reveal significant differences. However, any possible difference has proved to be very elusive. It is conceivable that other acuity test-objects might reveal differences, but we used a variety of them. It is also conceivable that the apparent greater distinctness of objects under mercury light is real and not an illusion. If so, it is difficult to believe that the effect of this is not detectable by any of the criteria used.

It is emphasized that we do not claim there is no advantage of mercury light over tungsten-filament light as an aid to seeing either in promoting visibility or ease of seeing. Much territory remains to be explored, particularly that which involves prolonged seeing. Various researches which we prosecuted in the realm of ease of seeing and which have revealed the desirability of high footcandle-levels may be performed to ascertain whether illuminants of different spectral character differ in their effects upon the human seeing-machine. It is easy to conceive certain advantages of mercury light over tungsten light due to its greater abundance of blue light, but at the same time the possibility of disadvantages also arises. However, such speculations run deeply into the realm of physiological optics where two persons are likely to choose different byways thereby arriving at different conclusions.

The apparent whiteness of mercury light and the ease with which it mixes with daylight are factors often in its favor. Certainly mixtures of mercury and tungsten light are satisfactorily white in many cases and they reduce or eliminate the distortion of color where this is a factor. In the work-world the colors appropriate for walls and other large areas of the environment are generally the "cool" ones. These can so be chosen as to be satisfactory under mercury light. Certainly there is a complex psychological realm open for whitish light, "cool" colors and even "cool" light to test their acceptance.

Although the specific tests of mercury light described in the preceding paragraphs reveal no significant advantages over tungsten-filament light, it is also worth noting that they revealed no significant disadvantages. These researches reveal no reason why the higher luminous efficiency of mercury light should not be taken advantage of in many places in various fields of lighting. With respect to certain visual tasks where mercury light seems

to be preferred to tungsten light of equal footcandles, it is reasonable to assume that there may be advantages that we do not know
how to measure. Color or spectral character may be the dominant
factor, directly or indirectly, in some of these cases at least. Studies
along this line are desirable. In fact, with a variety of light-
sources becoming available, spectral quality of light becomes an
interesting field for careful observation and sound experimentation.

SEEING IN SODIUM LIGHT

From a practical viewpoint sodium light from present-day
sodium lamps is truly monochromatic light consisting of energy
concentrated approximately at $\lambda 5893$ as indicated in Fig. 115.
Many years ago one of us [145] showed with an improvised sodium
light that it was superior to continuous-spectrum light of the same
hue from the viewpoint of visual acuity. Practicable sodium lamps
have been developed so recently that few investigators have studied
their light from the viewpoint of seeing.

In Fig. 118 are presented the results of an extensive research [152] with nine subjects possessing socalled normal vision. The
brightness range extended from 0.018 to 20 millilamberts owing
to the interest in low brightnesses on illuminated highways, as
well as ordinary brightnesses indoors under artificial light. The
average results as obtained with the Ives-Cobb acuity object show
sodium light is decidedly superior to tungsten-filament light in
revealing detail of threshold size. Incidentally the difference between the two illuminants in this respect is of the same order as
that obtained by one of us 25 years ago [145] with a crude source of
sodium light. This superior revealing power may be utilized in
special cases of seeing in the work-world, but it has little or no
importance when objects far above threshold size are to be seen
as is very generally the case.

Color-contrast under sodium light is entirely obliterated.
Therefore, this aid to seeing is lost under sodium light, although
this is of relatively little importance at very low levels of illumination. Of course, there are many cases where color-contrast is of
no importance excepting from an esthetic or psychological view-

[422]

point. An analysis [153] was made of 595 pairs of colors whose brightness-contrasts were measured under sodium and tungsten lights, respectively. From a purely numerical basis, sodium light enhanced brightness-contrast in more cases than tungsten light did. However, 152 pairs, whose contrasts were greater under tungsten light, had an average contrast lower than the average of the 267 pairs whose contrasts were greater under sodium light. In other words, apparently the tungsten light helped more where visual

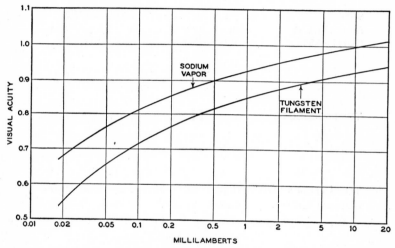

Fig. 118.—Showing the relationship between visual acuity and brightness of the background of the black test-object for sodium light and tungsten-filament light, respectively.

aid was more generally needed; that is, it enhanced the generally lower contrasts which are in a lower range of visibility than higher ones. Conversely it may be said that sodium light enhanced many contrasts which were already high. The conclusion is that these results do not give sodium light any outstanding advantage in enhancing brightness-contrasts. Bouma [155] is inclined to give sodium light some advantage in this respect, but experimental evidence is not particularly decisive. Combining our conclusion with the fact that color-contrast is always obliterated, one can scarcely rate sodium light superior to tungsten light in this respect ex-

[423]

cepting for some special purposes. Probably there are many of these in the work-world particularly involving sorting or inspection. Bouma [155] is inclined to give sodium light some advantage in other respects besides visual acuity.

Speed of retinal impression [153] was studied with two parallel-bar test-objects. One consisted of two black bars separated by one minute visual angle and viewed against a white background having a brightness of one millilambert. Thus the brightness-

	1 MINUTE	10 MINUTES
SIZE:		
BRIGHTNESS:	1 MILLILAMBERT	0.1 MILLILAMBERT
CONTRAST:	98 PERCENT	11 PERCENT
TEST-OBJECTS	▌▌	
TUNGSTEN LIGHT:	0.286 SECOND	0.245 SECOND
SODIUM LIGHT:	0.207 SECOND	0.242 SECOND

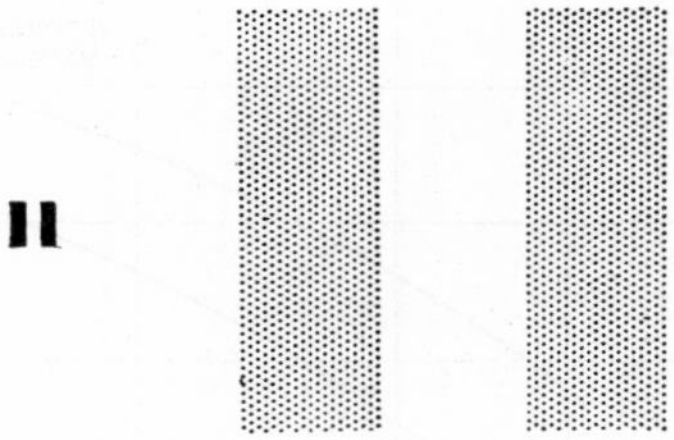

FIG. 119.—Showing the average least time required to recognize each of the two objects indicated under sodium light and tungsten-filament light, respectively. Visual acuity is a primary factor in recognizing the smaller object. Brightness-difference is the primary factor in recognizing the larger object.

contrast was nearly 100 per cent. The other object was ten times larger and consisted of two parallel light gray bars, separated by ten minutes' visual angle, and viewed against a white background having a brightness of 0.1 millilambert. In this case the brightness-contrast was 11 per cent. The average time required by ten subjects to see these objects under sodium and tungsten is shown in Fig. 119. It is seen that the speed of seeing the small object was decidedly greater under sodium light than under tungsten light. Doubtless this is due to the advantage and importance of visual acuity in the case of objects of the order of one minute of visual size. For the larger object the speed of seeing was practically the same under the two illuminants. The latter is a far more important fact for consideration in highway lighting. Therefore, there seems to be no advantage for sodium light, in this respect, on highways where speed of seeing is often involved in safety and where relatively large objects are to be seen.

The size of the pupils of the eyes of eight subjects was accurately measured under the same conditions for brightnesses produced by sodium and tungsten lights. The measurements were made for two different brightness-levels. The averages of pupil size are presented herewith.

	Diameter of Pupil	
	0.1 ml.	1.0 ml.
Sodium light	6.35	5.78
Tungsten light	6.08	5.53

These differences are significant. If they persist under conditions commonly encountered in lighting practice, one would have to conclude that the eye utilizes sodium light slightly more efficiently than it does tungsten light because the brightness of the retinal image is important and this depends, among other factors, upon the size of the pupil.

Glare from sodium and tungsten light was determined [154] both by the criteria of per cent contrast for threshold visibility and by measurement of the apparent angular diameter of the halos surrounding the retinal images of the glare-sources, which were of identical physical size and brightness. The results indicate that the reduction in visibility due to glare is somewhat greater for sodium light than for tungsten light for angles less than five degrees between the glare-source and the line of vision. The difference is insignificant for angles greater than five degrees. Apparently the physiological halos surrounding the images of the glare-sources are responsible for the differences. If the results are appraised by transforming the difference in threshold contrast into additional intensity of illumination to compensate for this deficiency in seeing, sodium light appears at a decided disadvantage compared with tungsten light under the conditions which produce this difference in contrast sensitivity. However, this is a proper interpretation in lighting for seeing.

COLOR-DISCRIMINATION AND COLOR-MATCHING

Color-discrimination is a matter of the appearance of a color by itself; that is, not in comparison with another color. Inasmuch as a given color will have different appearances under different illuminants the choice of the illuminant is important. Usually a color is to be viewed under ordinary artificial light or daylight or both at different times. Color-matching is primarily a matter of color identity; that is, the matching of one color with another which is, in a sense, a standard. Since the visual sense synthesizes sensations or responses to radiant energy of different wavelengths, two colors differing in spectral character may match under one illuminant and not under another. Daylight, particularly that entering a north window, was adopted as a standard illuminant many years ago. This choice was made chiefly because north skylight in this hemisphere is less variable than daylight from other points of the compass. Thus the early attempts to supply a color-matching illuminant aimed at artificial daylight [156] of north skylight quality. On further analysis it appeared that "white" light, such as noon sunlight in midsummer, or average daylight such as that obtained under a thinly overcast sky, was a more fundamental and suitable standard illuminant. As a consequence, daylight of various spectral qualities has been produced by the subtractive method involving a filter of proper spectral characteristics. The exception was luminous carbon dioxide, a forerunner of present neon and similar lamps.

In many industrial applications color-matching involves objects which are known to be substantially the same in spectral reflection, but which may differ slightly in saturation and brightness. Tests made by our colleagues, A. H. Taylor and G. P. Kerr, indicate that in this type of color-matching, light from tungsten filaments may be even better than natural daylight. Neither daylight nor tungsten-filament light alone will reveal differences in color in all cases. Thus there have been cases of spoilage of textiles, for example, due to color-matching under a single light-source. The ideal light-source for color-matching would prevent such spoilage by showing a color-difference when the colors of the materials differ in spectral character.

From theoretical considerations alone it seems probable that a combination of mercury and tungsten lamps would produce a satisfactory color-matching illuminant. Such a combination in-

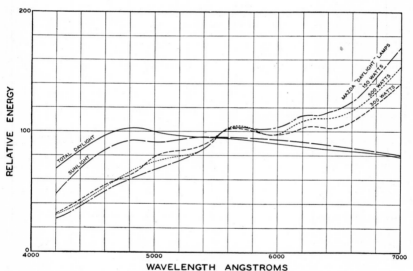

FIG. 120.—The spectral distributions of energy from tungsten-filament (Mazda) daylight lamps compared with total daylight and sunlight during midday.

cludes three strong, widely separated spectral lines and a continuous spectrum relatively strong in the long-wave visible region. It is unlikely that two colored materials having different spectral reflection characteristics, but appearing alike under tungsten light or daylight, would match under this combination illuminant. In order to do so it would apparently be necessary for them to have approximately equal reflection-factors at $\lambda4358$, $\lambda5461$, and $\lambda5780$, the principal mercury spectral "lines."

For many purposes an illuminant roughly approximating day-

[427]

light in spectral character and color is desirable in the work-world in order to blend with daylight. Also, in many color-matching or color-inspection problems, such as the routine examination of colored plastics where color variations of a supposedly uniform product are mainly due to differences in saturation and luminosity, an illuminant differing somewhat from daylight may be quite satisfactory.

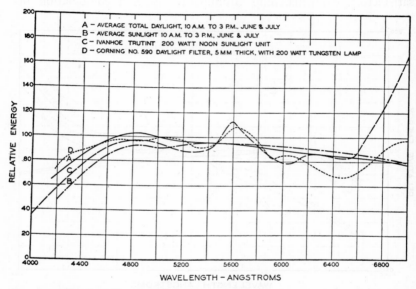

FIG. 121.—Showing the spectral distributions of energy from two "artificial day-light" units compared with that of total daylight and sunlight during midday.

Light from tungsten-filament (Mazda) daylight lamps is intermediate in spectral quality between unmodified tungsten-filament light and daylight, but the integral color of the light appears much nearer to daylight than to ordinary tungsten light. Years ago they were developed by one of the authors [156] to provide a practicable compromise. Fig. 120 shows the spectral energy distribution for three sizes of (Mazda) daylight lamps. It also shows the average spectral energy distribution for sunlight and skylight on a horizontal plane between 10 A.M. and 3 P.M. on several clear days in June and July, also direct sunlight alone, as measured by Taylor and Kerr on the roof of a building in the outskirts of Cleveland. The relative energy curves in this and in succeeding illustrations are based on *equal illumination*. Hence they show the relative energy at each wavelength for *equal footcandles*.

In Fig. 121 the curves for average total daylight and direct

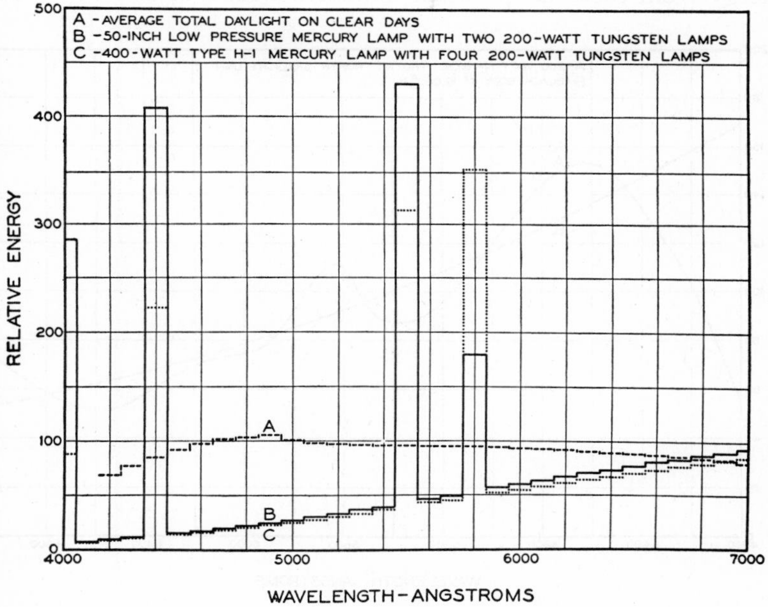

FIG. 122.—The spectral distribution of energy obtained with combinations of mercury lamps and tungsten-filament lamps compared with that of average total daylight on clear days during midday.

sunlight are included as a basis of comparison of the energy distributions from several lighting units employing glass filters developed by one of the authors and by others.[157] The socalled noon-sunlight unit consists of an aluminum reflector, a Trutint glass filter and a 200-watt tungsten-filament lamp. Curve *D* shows the spectral energy distribution of light from a 200-watt tungsten lamp after passing through a Corning No. 590 daylight filter. These curves indicate that when Ivanhoe and Corning daylight glass filters are properly selected and used with tungsten lamps, the resultant light is a satisfactory approximation to daylight from λ4200 to λ6600. Actual use proves this.

The 250- and 400-watt high-pressure mercury lamps (types H-1 and H-2) radiate most of their visible energy in three strong spectral "lines." In order to represent the spectral distribution of energy from these lamps when combined with that of continuous-

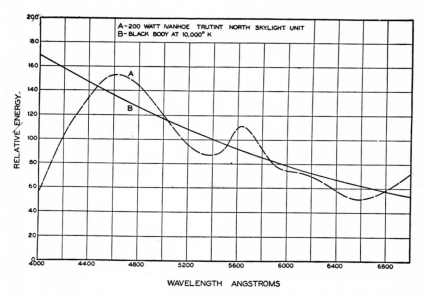

FIG. 123.—Comparing the distribution of energy of an "artificial north-skylight" unit and that of a black-body at 10,000 deg. K.

spectrum tungsten light, it is necessary to divide the energy into bands having certain wavelength limits. In Fig. 122 is shown the spectral energy distribution of light from two types of combination units in which the energy values are shown for wavelength bands 100 Ångströms wide. The curve for average daylight is shown on the same basis. The combination units are radically different from daylight in their energy distribution, and no possible combination ratio of these mercury lamps with tungsten lamps will result in an illuminant which appears exactly the same color as daylight. However, equal lumens from tungsten and the 50-inch low-pressure mercury lamp will produce a light approximating sunlight in appearance where only white or neutral surfaces are concerned. A closer color-match with average daylight is obtained with a lumen ratio of 50 per cent of this mercury light with 40 per cent of light from 200-watt tungsten-filament lamps.

The light-sources discussed in the foregoing are subject to changes due to future improvements. Therefore, this presentation is included chiefly for the purposes of illustrating the principles involved.

Fig. 123 illustrates the spectral energy distribution of visible energy emitted by a theoretical black-body at 10000° K. With it is compared that of an Ivanhoe Trutint North Skylight unit containing a 200-watt tungsten lamp. No generally acceptable spectral energy distribution curve of true north skylight is available, but its color-temperature is approximately 10000° K to 20000° K, depending upon the clearness of the sky. Values higher than these have been observed on exceptionally clear days. Data are available in Table LXV.

The International Commission on Illumination has adopted a system of colorimetry in terms of which any color can be specified. It is essentially a trichromatic stimulus specification using definite red, green and blue stimuli, x, y and z respectively. A clear understanding of these stimuli is conveyed by A. C. Hardy in a recent excellent treatise on colorimetry.[158] Using the I.C.I. tri-stimulus data, the x, y and z values for the light-sources discussed above and others have been computed by Taylor and Kerr and are summarized in Table LXIX. To represent these tri-stimulus values graphically would require a three dimensional plot, which is not practicable. I.C.I. illuminants B and C are combinations of tungsten lamps at 2848° K and liquid color filters. They are intended to represent noon sunlight and average daylight, respectively. Their main advantage is their reproducibility from specifications. Illuminant C is used as the standard white light in the I.C.I. system.

TABLE LXIX

Tri-Stimulus Coordinates for Various Light-Sources, Based on the 1931 I.C.I. Standard Observer and Coordinate System for Colorimetry

Light-Source	Tri-Stimulus Coordinates		
	x	y	z
I.C.I. illuminant B, average noon sunlight	0.348	0.352	0.300
I.C.I. illuminant C, average daylight......................	.310	.316	.374
Direct sunlight in Cleveland, June and July	.346	.364	.290
Average total daylight in Cleveland, June and July....	.329	.344	.327
Tungsten-filament (Mazda) lamps			
100-watt	.454	.408	.138
500-watt	.442	.406	.152
150-watt daylight	.406	.399	.195
300-watt daylight	.387	.398	.215
500-watt daylight	.396	.396	.208
Mercury vapor lamps			
50-inch, low-pressure	.250	.317	.433
Type H-1, 400-watt	.329	.402	.269
Type H-2, 250-watt	.314	.368	.318
Type H-3, 100-watt	.291	.378	.331
Combinations of mercury and tungsten-filament lamps			
50-inch mercury and 2, 200-watt Mazda lamps	.337	.357	.306
50-inch mercury and 4, 75-watt Mazda lamps	.316	.347	.337
Type H-1 mercury and 4, 200-watt Mazda lamps	.384	.405	.211
Type H-2 mercury and 2, 200-watt Mazda lamps	.375	.387	.238
Type H-3 mercury and 1, 100-watt Mazda lamp..	.342	.388	.270
Corning No. 590 daylight glass and 200-watt Mazda lamp	.323	.347	.330
Ivanhoe Trutint 200-watt noon sunlight unit	.336	.355	.309
Ivanhoe Trutint 200-watt north skylight unit	.282	.295	.423
Black-body at 10000° K	.281	.288	.431

COLOR-CONTRAST

Of the four fundamental visibility factors associated with a visual object or task, contrast is very important in seeing. The other three are size, brightness and exposure-time. Brightness-contrast is very generally more important than color-contrast. Also the reverse may be true in specific cases. In the case of colored objects both kinds of contrasts occur simultaneously except-

THE VISIBLE SPECTRUM

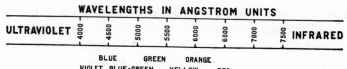

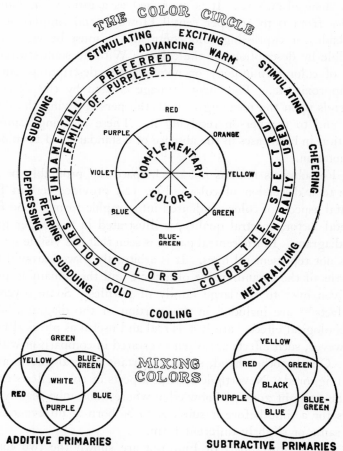

FIG. 124.—Showing various aspects of color—physical, esthetic, psychological, and theoretical color-mixing.

ing in the rare instances where the brightness-contrast is negligible. This may be true in the special case of a red object being seen against a green background. Then only differences in visibility due to color make it possible to see the object. Even a casual study of colored objects seen against colored backgrounds reveals their generally low visibility unless there is an appreciable contrast in brightness. Brightness-contrast can be defined very readily, as has been done elsewhere. It is expressed as a ratio with numerical values from o to 100 per cent. However, no simple means is available for expressing color-contrast. It must be visualized if possible by descriptions of the colors. With no standardized system of color terminology or notation, the descriptions can only be approximate. The mental image created by the description depends upon the meaning to both the person giving the description and to the person receiving it. These meanings cannot be identical in both cases in the absence of a standardized terminology or notation.

For obvious reasons not much space can profitably be given here to a discussion of color. Fig. 124 provides certain fundamental aspects of color condensed into graphic form. The fundamental factor, spectral quality, is illustrated in the upper part of the diagram. In the central part it is seen that the visible spectrum does not represent all hues. It is arbitrarily placed around three-fourths of the circumference of a circle and the remaining portion is given over to the large family of purples. Some psychological facts [159] are included in this portion of the diagram. Many psychological effects [1] are just as real and useful as physical factors. However, such effects are often overrated in comparison with others. On the other hand, some important general effects are too often ignored. Nevertheless, some aspects of color effects are still in the twilight zone of knowledge where buncombe readily flourishes for a time before it subsides to be born again eventually in the same or slightly different form.

In the lower part of Fig. 124 are shown the two common methods of color mixture. When colored lights are mixed they are said to be added. The results of mixtures of two of the socalled primaries are seen where the corresponding circles overlap. These three circles may be considered as spots of light of the primary colors projected upon a diffusing white surface in such a manner that they overlap as shown and with the results indicated. The subtractive method of color-mixture is best exemplified by superposing transparent colored glasses on other media. The same principles are involved in the mixing of transparent solutions of dyes. They are predominant in the mixing of paints, but owing to the opacity and translucency of pigments, the ultimate practical results are modified somewhat from the ideal or perfect results of subtraction illustrated in the diagram. Here it is noted that the result of mixing two socalled primaries is the color which is common to both of them; that is, the color which is transmitted (or reflected) by each of them.

In order to view color-contrast somewhat intimately, the three fundamental characteristics of color should be understood. These are hue, saturation and brightness which are defined in Chapter VIII. There are secondary characteristics such as surface texture which may play a part in visibility, but these should be obvious in any specific case. Hue is that characteristic of color which usually gives it its name such as green, blue, etc. It may be described by the wavelength of a hue in the visible spectrum which matches the dominant hue of the color. Purples do not exist in the spectrum, but the latter furnishes a hue complementary to that of any purple, whether it be lavender, magenta or any other member of the family of purple in the broad sense in which purple is used here. Thus it is seen that color-contrast may involve differences in hue. In other words, hue sensitivity as described in Chapter III is a factor in seeing, but it is generally of secondary importance. However, it may be extremely important in special visual situations.

The next characteristic is saturation. For example, if we begin with a pure blue paint and add more and more pure white paint, the dominant hue may remain fairly constant while a series of tints is produced. Beginning with 100 per cent saturation, the blue becomes less and less saturated. Thus color-contrast may involve differences in saturation. In other words, we may have saturation-contrast as a factor in seeing, but it is generally of secondary importance.

If with the pure blue paint or with any of its tints we mix pure black paint, the brightness or reflection-factor is changed. By adding more and more black, darker and darker shades are produced. In fact, a series of shades is produced beginning with the original color and ending in black. Thus color-contrast can and very generally does involve brightness-contrast. In fact the latter factor is very generally the most important factor in seeing. The brightness of a diffusely reflecting colored surface depends upon its reflection-factor and the quantity of light (footcandles). Usually the brightness of a colored object is considered merely in terms of a theoretical perfectly white object. Then brightness or luminosity, or value in the parlance of the artist, is equal to its diffuse reflection-factor.

Color adds much in the beautification of the external world through the visual sense as a doorway. In fact, this is generally far more important than color as a factor in seeing. Of course, color-contrast generally exists but such factors as size, brightness, and brightness-contrast are generally far more important in the visibility of objects and the ability to see. Color is commonly subdued into tints and shades. Also we have subdued its influence in the process of learning to see. In civilization color is adopted for special purposes for seeing such as in signal lights and traffic aids. Here it is employed largely for its novelty or attention-value. Several conspicuous colors are available, such as red, yellow, green and blue, and some of lesser individuality such as orange, so that codes can be devised for many purposes. Without powerful brightness factors high visibility cannot be obtained in most of these special cases. In the case of color by transmission, as in the case of traffic signals, very high brightnesses can be obtained by using powerful light-sources behind them. In the case of color by reflection the brightness-contrast is inherent in the color. For example, a red traffic light seen against the green foliage of a tree may be very bright by contrast, but a painted red stop-sign seen against the green foliage may not be appreciably different in brightness.

These two different kinds of usage of color for visibility purposes, including novelty and attention-value, are seen to differ greatly in their limitations. In the case of transmitted color, high brightness-contrast can always be obtained. Too commonly in small towns a low-wattage lamp is used, and the traffic signal is barely visible in the daytime. In the great variety of uses of reflected color, as in advertising and traffic signs, attention should be given to the brightness or luminosity component of colors. Red and blue are of low reflection-factor. They can be used when black is also of suitable reflection-factor; that is, with backgrounds of much higher reflection-factor. However, they alone are not of striking visibility because they are commonly too dark. In the case of yellow or yellow-orange, the brightness is relatively high and still there is the novelty of color. It is a suitable color for painting street-cars, trucks and fixed hazards such as safety zones. White is still brighter under the same condition, but it lacks the factor of novelty of color.

Unwarranted claims are sometimes made of greater contrasts under mercury or sodium light than under daylight or tungsten-filament light. This may be true in specific cases, but the reverse may be true in other cases. No generalization of this sort can be made. The proper procedure is to determine the visibility of the particular object or task under the various illuminants. It is unnecessary to limit such tests to common illuminants. Certainly in the inspection of colored objects it may be possible that light of a pronounced color obtained by filter, if necessary, would improve visibility. However, there is always the further question of the human seeing-machine working for long periods under illuminants differing radically from natural light. This is too often ignored.

SELECTIVITY OF THE ATMOSPHERE

That great masses of atmosphere selectively absorb and scatter light is attested by the red sunset and the blue sky. Much of this selectivity is due to dust, smoke and other foreign matter. However, even in the absence of such matter the atmosphere selectively scatters the short-wave visible energy more than the longwave. The blueness of the sky at high altitudes is a testimonial of this fact. Raleigh developed a formula for this scattering based upon theoretical considerations and physical sizes of molecules of atmospheric gases and of various wavelengths of energy. By scattering blue light more than yellow, orange or red light, the sky appears blue and the sun appears yellower than it is outside the earth's atmosphere. In other words, by this selective scattering, sunlight is robbed of more blue light than yellow light. The spectral distributions of energy in average sunlight and blue skylight are shown in Fig. 115.

The effect of selectivity of the atmosphere is readily revealed by measurements of the color-temperature of sunlight at different periods of the day as shown in Table LXV. Without such scattering of light by the atmosphere, the sky would be intolerably black. Shadows outdoors would also be darker and harsher because they would receive no light from the sky. It is a matter of common observation that they get darker at higher altitudes because much of the sky-brightness is left behind. On a very clear day the sky contributes about one-tenth as much light as the sun on a horizontal surface at sea-level. On average days it contributes about one-fifth. At 25000 feet on a clear day, we found [160] that the sky contributed only one twenty-fifth of the total light on a horizontal plane.

These facts are important in the study of lighting effects. The selective scattering and absorption of light by the atmosphere is important only in long-range light signals and signaling. Then the selectivity determines the ranges of illuminants of different spectral quality. In general, range of colored lights of equal candlepower is greater for red light and decreases as the dominant hue of the colored light decreases in wavelength. There are so many variations of atmospheric conditions that no general formulae can be devised for all regions and conditions. The technique of testing the ranges of illuminants is rather simple, but the great distances are troublesome. In general, it may be stated that for reasonably clear atmospheric conditions the range depends primarily upon candlepower or brightness of the source in the direction of the observer, and secondarily upon the color. In very smoky atmosphere, the reverse can be true.

Signaling and other long-range applications of light for seeing are special cases which cannot be treated here. Usually few persons are directly concerned with their visibility. However, for short-range seeing as on the highway, most persons are directly concerned. In these short ranges it is possible to detect a ruddiness in the appearance of light-sources a mile or two away when smoke or exhaust gases from automobiles are present, but this selectivity is of little or no practical importance. Red and yellow are the common danger and caution signals and they penetrate such atmosphere better than other colored lights. The problem is one of having sufficient brightnesses or candlepower so that all such signals or tail-lights are readily visible under unfavorable atmospheric conditions. In some cases novelty should be considered as well as visibility, but the latter is the overwhelmingly important factor.

Much has been said of the selectivity of fog, but the fact is that fog for reasonable distances is not appreciably selective. It affects visibility chiefly by a veiling brightness between the observer and the objects he wishes to see. Notwithstanding the many commercial applications of colored lights, chiefly yellow headlamps or spotlights, many do not have the support of acceptable proof of their efficacy and, therefore, are of doubtful practical value. An illuminated fog is a hindrance to seeing chiefly because it reduces contrast often below threshold. Sometimes one can see better while driving an automobile on a highway in a fog at night without the headlamps turned on. By depressing the beam of the headlamps, the veiling brightness at the eye-level can be somewhat reduced with a corresponding increase in visibility. The best solution is highway lighting. This illuminates the pavement and objects that a driver wishes to see and will tend to increase the contrasts of objects above threshold.

Thus it is seen that color or spectral quality of light is largely of theoretical interest and is generally of secondary importance or of little practical significance in most short-range seeing. Notwithstanding many commercial claims for this or that device, there is no magic in colored light. Seeing still remains a matter of visibility achieved largely by brightness-contrast regardless of the color.

COLORED EYEGLASSES

Colored glasses, properly chosen for specific purposes, have definite applications in promoting visibility and comfort. Here we are not interested in protecting the eyes in industry or in pathological cases. In the daytime outdoors the use of colored glasses is chiefly to reduce brightness. There is plenty of light outdoors, so if some benefit accrues to the human seeing-machine through a reduction in brightness, the net result is worth while. In the case of sunlit snow, any colored glass is better than none, but for the usual everyday condition there is a need for understanding the purpose of this aid to seeing so that one may wisely choose a suitable color from the array being sold.

For the ordinary summer landscapes, when people are outdoors more than at any other season of the year, the sky is generally the most offensive area from the viewpoint of brightness. This brightness is reduced most with the least sacrifice in brightness and color distortion of the earth areas by means of a yellow-green or greenish yellow glass. For such a purpose blue glass is less desirable. There are good optical reasons for choosing a colored glass with a dominant hue near the yellow-green part of the spectrum. This is the region of maximum selectivity of the visual sense. The eyes naturally focus the energy of maximum lumnosity, and in the case of correction by means of refracting lenses, the prescription is based upon this. These and other sound reasons indicate that if a colored glass is to be used, it should have a dominant hue near the middle of the visible spectrum and preferably in the yellow-green or greenish yellow.

In Fig. 125 the effectiveness of a yellow-green glass [53] is illustrated by measurements of visual acuity. The test-object whose details could be quickly altered in size throughout a large range was illuminated by a large expanse of blue sky. Both the test-object and the subject were located in the shade of a building. Visual acuity readings were made continually from the beginning of the test. For three-minute intervals the subject wore clear colorless glasses and yellow-green glasses alternately. The rapid and continuous decrease in visual acuity is noted for both glasses, but it was less for the yellow-green glasses whose transmission-factor was approximately 50 per cent. An important aspect of this

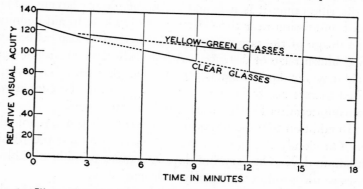

FIG. 125.—Illustrating the decrease in visual acuity during an 18-minute period of measurements with the eyes exposed to a large expanse of sky. The effect of yellow-green glasses in reducing the brightness of the sky is also shown.

test was the discomfort of the observer. While not engaged in critical seeing there was no apparent discomfort. There was none at the beginning of the test, but discomfort soon appeared after the measurements and rapidly increased until at the end of 18 minutes the glare from the large expanse of blue sky became so painful that it was unendurable. On ceasing the work of critical seeing the discomfort immediately diminished and quickly disappeared. The discomfort was markedly less when the yellow glasses were worn.

A lesson may be gleaned from this test which can be used to advantage in appraising lighting effects. An expanse of bright ceiling may appear harmless, when casually appraised. However, if it is a great deal brighter than the visual task, it will effectively compete for attention. The effect of these factors may not be strikingly noticeable unless the observer or appraiser is doing critical seeing over an appreciable period of time.

In such a case as the rifle range, or seeing objects at a great distance, again yellow-green or greenish yellow glasses should be best for normal eyes or eyes properly corrected by means of eye-glasses. From considerations of chromatic aberration, it is well to get rid of the blue and violet rays, which are abundant in daylight, if the consequent distortion of color is not a handicap. On the rifle range it is not, and a pair of glasses having a maximum transmission near the yellow-green is likely to aid definition of the image of the target. Such a colored glass also reduces the veiling bluish haze of distance. Admittedly these are refinements which may not be necessary for average persons. However, if colored glasses are to be worn, they may as well be chosen with some consideration for the facts of vision and seeing.

In addition to these physical aspects there is the psychological one. On cloudy days canary yellow glasses produce the illusion of a sunny day. On very hot days it is quite possible that bluish glasses would produce an equally welcome effect.

The problem of colored glasses is not as serious in the daytime as at night. Particularly on the highway at night, colored glasses can be a real hazard. Visibility at best is of a low order. Colored glasses of whatever color, reduce visibility because they reduce brightness and contrast. This reduction is negligible in the daytime, but at dawn and dusk and particularly after dark no fraction of visibility can be spared without increasing hazards. Even ordinary colorless glasses reduce the brightness of objects eight to ten per cent, and this is sufficient to reduce some brightnesses or brightness-contrasts below the threshold outdoors at night.

Colored glasses of any color will reduce glare in proportion to the reduction of the candlepower or brightness in the direction of the eyes of the observer. We have not been able to detect any difference among colors in their ability to reduce glare.[161]

As yet, colored spotlights and lenses for headlamps have no scientific basis for the claim of special glare reduction. The reduction of visibility due to glare is proportional to the candlepower of the glare-source (such as an approaching automobile headlamp) toward the eye.[140] (See Chapter X.) The reduction of glare by means of colored glasses also reduces the brightnesses of all objects to the wearer of the glasses or the user of the colored headlamp. This means that visibility of certain objects may be reduced so much that hazards are increased through lowered visibility. The problem of glare on the highway should be solved in other ways, such as properly controlled headlamp beams and highway lighting.

Probably colored glasses for use on the highway should be standardized for the daytime and even abolished at night. At any rate, they should be sold and purchased with a full understanding that there is no magic in them and that their effect upon seeing can be readily measured. Obviously, colored glasses should not be of such a high degree of saturation that there is any doubt about the recognition of the colored traffic aids.

Many glasses are recommended and sold by eyesight specialists on the basis of claims having no established scientific foundation. Glasses are sold for protection from ultraviolet energy when there is no energy of this sort present in sufficient amounts to be harmful. Still less excusable is the sale of glasses for protecting eyes from infrared energy, which has not even been proved harmful in quantities from which the exposed face rebels. There may be good uses for colored glasses in pathological cases and in some cases of defective eyes. Such aids are worth trying, but the problems should be approached in a sound scientific manner and not merely through the introspective reports of the patient.

COLORED PAPERS IN PRINTING

The use of colored papers, including those of very light tint, is also associated with weird ideas and unestablished claims of the same category as many of those associated with colored eyeglasses. The principal factors to be considered in the use of nonglossy colored and tinted papers from the viewpoint of seeing are,

1. Visibility
   a. reflection-factor of the paper
   b. spectral quality of the color
   c. reflection-factor of ink and other media
2. Identification by color
3. Esthetic factors
4. Other psychological factors.

High contrast of printed matter and writing depends upon the reflection-factor of the background and of the ink, pencil marks, etc. High reflection-factor for the former and low reflection-factor for the latter produce high visibility, which is usually necessary for easy seeing. Color is useful in identifying records, stationery, and in other ways. However, where a variety of colors is necessary it should be possible to confine the use of color to a portion of the card or sheet, thereby avoiding the use of strong colors or tints as a background for material which must be discriminated accurately or read for long periods. In many cases esthetic considerations are important and, therefore, the result may well give comfort, pleasure and satisfaction to the esthetic sense. Various other psychological factors such as attention-value, distinction, appropriateness may be utilized. Even in advertising and merchandising, copy of low visibility must suffer in effectiveness. Certainly in all cases where seeing is important and the human being is engaged for long periods in performing the task of seeing, visibility should be maintained at a high value. From the viewpoint of chromatic aberration, a yellowish tint should tend to be more desirable but not necessarily measurably so. From the same viewpoint, blue, violet, purple and pink papers are inadvisable. From the viewpoint of eye-comfort and easy seeing opinions are not based upon measurements because no method has been available for this purpose. It appears possible that such criteria as speed of reading and rate of blinking might yield interesting results provided other factors which influence blinking were properly controlled. Results of a study of blinking are presented in Table XXXIII.

We believe that there are esthetic factors involved intricately in judgments of eye-comfort and easy seeing. In fact, much experience with esthetic factors and with persons possessing sensibilities particularly responsive to these has emphasized the need of being alert to them in many analyses involving seeing. Feelings are commonly experienced which might be termed *esthetic comfort* or *esthetic discomfort* and they are as real as physical comfort. For example, a greenish tint might be "easy on the eyes" psychologically but not visually. The cost to the human seeing-machine of an appreciably lower visibility might well be far greater than the value of such a feeling. A yellowish tint may produce a feeling of esthetic comfort, pleasure or satisfaction without paying significantly for it in decreased visibility. Certainly there is no more magic in colored papers than in colored glasses. Mysteries still exist but probably not serious ones. In the absence of more knowledge of ease of seeing and of simple ways of measuring it, there seems to be little justification for departing far from maximal visibility.

The same argument holds for a variety of questions which arise. Advocates of green "blackboards," yellow chalk on black blackboards, and black chalk on white blackboards come and go perennially. These theories are often based upon superficial knowledge and loose reasoning. Possibly blackboards and white chalk are the wrong basis, but practicability gave birth to them. After all, high visibility is desirable and practical considerations must be taken into account. It is possible, but not probable, that printing is on the wrong basis. It has been more practicable to print with black ink on white paper than to reverse the process and to print with white ink on black paper. Certainly books of black paper would scarcely compete with our present ones from an esthetic, or more broadly, a psychological viewpoint. We find that a white object on a black background has about the same visibility as a black object of the same size on a white background. However, there are esthetic and comfort aspects involved which are not readily measurable. Such matters are merely mentioned to illustrate the ramified aspects of seeing.

In the consideration of paper as a background for printing, typing and writing which is to be read extensively, the maintenance of high contrast is so generally desirable that it can be assumed to be essential. This means the use of socalled white or near-white papers. Even the grayish newsprint commonly used in newspapers, catalogues and directories measurably reduces contrast and visibility. A light tint of cream or yellow generally exhibits a reflection-factor only a few per cent lower than it would if it were untinted. With the same ink and character of printing the visibility is not significantly different in the two cases. However, this is not true of other tints such as blue-green and light shades such as buff. These may not appear to be any more "colorful" than the cream or yellow tint, but they generally absorb much more light and, therefore, the reduction in contrast and visibility is appreciable.

As already stated, visibility is not necessarily the entire matter, but generally it is the overwhelmingly important factor. It does not seem that much sacrifice in visibility of printed and reading matter can be justified for the sake of vague and unmeasured socalled benefits. Many persons prefer a slightly tinted paper to one of pure white. Many believe such a paper is "easier on their eyes" than a white paper. Certainly if this percentage of persons is great enough, it would be justifiable to exchange a slight amount of visibility for a good deal of satisfaction or esthetic comfort. The level of illumination can be increased so as to more than compensate for the decrease in contrast. We have recommended such a tinted paper on many occasions upon the basis briefly outlined in the foregoing. Such changes from socalled white paper to a slightly tinted one should not be made without making the proper measurements. Examples of actual cases emphasize this.

A scientific journal made changes from a white paper to one of yellowish tint. The reflection-factors for ordinary artificial light were 74.6 and 72.3 per cent, respectively. The brightness-contrasts between the print and paper were 87.3 and 87.0 per cent before and after the change, respectively. By comparison the two papers appeared quite different in color without there being any significant difference in visibility of the printed matter.

A technical journal replaced a socalled white paper by a sepia-tinted one after analysis showed that the reflection-factors for ordinary artificial light were 76 and 73 per cent, respectively. There was a striking difference in the appearance of the two papers without an appreciable decrease in visibility. Of course, the reflection-factor of paper having a yellowish tint is slightly greater for ordinary (yellowish) artificial light than for daylight with the result that the visibility of the printed matter will be slightly less for the same daylight illumination. However, this difference is not appreciable for the light tints of yellow.

The use of blue and buff papers for typewritten letters is common. When measurements are made it is seen that an appreciable sacrifice in visibility is made without any particular gain in other ways. Typewriting is of much lower contrast against a given white background than black ink is. Therefore, this contrast should not be further reduced by using papers of appreciably lower reflection-factor without obtaining a commensurate gain in some other way. Distinction can be achieved without the use of strong color such as blue over the entire page. Paper of sufficiently low cost can be obtained without resorting to the use of dirty yellowish shades akin to wrapping paper. A specimen of ordinary yellow paper commonly used for carbon copies by typists had a reflection-factor of 66 per cent when one thickness was backed by black paper and four thicknesses had a reflection-factor of 76 per cent. Still it appears a strong yellow color when compared with white paper. This proves that dirty buffs with reflection-factors of 50 or 60 per cent need not be used.

An example of a paper widely promoted as being easy on the eyes will adequately illustrate the dangers of such claims without any basis of measurements. This paper may be described as a greenish gray or a grayish green. It is supplied in various forms with rulings of various colors for bookkeeping and other office records. Data are recorded in pencil and ink. The reflection-factor of the paper is 68 per cent. Socalled white papers have reflection-factors as high as 85 per cent. When pencil and ink are used a lower contrast is obtained on white paper than when printer's ink is used on the same paper. One can scarcely justify an additional reduction in contrast by the use of a paper having a reflection-factor of 68 per cent. Of course, if any appreciable gain in eye-ease is actually proved, it would be possible to increase the visibility by increasing the illumination without increasing the contrast. The visibility of the written material in the case of the special colored rulings is also affected by the maze produced. The visibilities of the rulings themselves are materially less on the greenish gray paper than on white paper and, because they are colored, are much less than black rulings. Certainly such matters are well within the province of the science of seeing.

GLARE AND COLORED LIGHTS

As already emphasized, many claims and applications of colored lights are made without any acceptable proof of their efficacy. Among these claims the reduction and elimination of glare are prominent. We have been unable to find any fundamental difference definitely attributable to the color or spectral character of the light. The case of yellow or greenish glasses in the daytime for reducing the glare due to an expanse of blue sky is quite different from the use of yellow or greenish yellow headlamps and spotlights on automobiles at night. In the former case the brightness of the blue sky is reduced far more than the brightnesses of vegetation, pavement and of most other prominent areas in the landscape because the selective absorption of the yellow or greenish glasses is greater for blue than for other colors. However, when yellow light is emitted by automobile headlamps or spotlights toward an observer at night, it must be proved that yellow light is less glaring per candlepower in the direction of the observer than unmodified light in order to justify even the consideration of yellow lenses.

If this is proved, it is still necessary to prove whether or not the reduction of beam candlepower due to the yellow lenses compared with clear glass is sufficiently great to compensate for the reduction in visibility to the driver behind the headlamps with yellow lenses due to their reduction in the beam candlepower. There is no proof of the existence of such inherent advantages of yellow or greenish yellow light sufficient to justify the reduction in light available to the driver using the light. Of course, any reduction in beam candlepower reduces the glare experienced by an approaching driver or pedestrian, but this cannot be credited to the color of the light. It is necessary to pursue the analysis carefully in order not to arrive at erroneous conclusions. In doing so it is well to separate the two effects of glare—visibility and discomfort. Of these, visibility is by far the more important one.

We and our colleagues, A. H. Taylor and L. L. Holladay, investigated glare from moderately colored lights [161] in comparison with the light from tungsten-filament lamps. The conditions simulated those in the highway at night excepting that the subjects could give their entire attention to the measurement of visibility and the appraisal of glare. The colored glasses used to alter the light from a tungsten-filament lamp had the following transmission-factors:

Clear . . . . 90 per cent
Canary . . . . 79 per cent
Amber . . . . 49 per cent
Light blue . . . . 35 per cent

The light blue glass in front of a tungsten-filament lamp produced approximately white light.

In one test the glare-source was 4.5 degrees to the left of the line of vision. The visual task was the determination of the threshold brightness of a circular test-object for three different constant brightnesses of the background. These were approximately 0.01, 0.03 and 0.07 millilambert. The glare-source and test-object were simultaneously exposed for 9 seconds every 30 seconds. No significant difference in the glare as measured by sensitivity to brightness-contrast was detectable among the four different illuminants for the same beam candlepower toward the observer.

In another test the amber and light blue filters were used and, therefore, the effect of amber light was compared with that of approximately white light. The spots of light were circular in the midst of a dark field consisting of black paper receiving very little light. Concentric with each was a gray ring painted on the black paper about one degree from the periphery of the glare spot. The brightness of the glare-source was adjusted by the observer until the gray ring was barely visible. Eight subjects made observations with each of the two glare-sources on several different days. The brightness of the glare-source or its candlepower to-

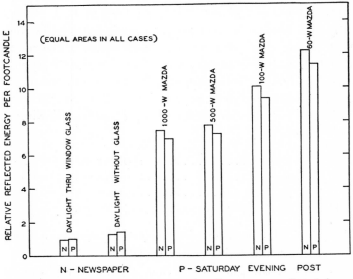

FIG. 126.—Showing the relative amounts of radiant energy reflected from equal areas of two different printed pages when illuminated to the same footcandle-level by daylight and light from various tungsten-filament lamps. Any other artificial light-source can be compared, approximately, by considering its luminous efficiency relative to that of one of the tungsten-filament lamps.

ward the observer was determined for threshold visibility of the concentric gray ring. The results obtained by the different subjects varied from four per cent in favor of the white light to 17 per cent in favor of the amber light. The weighted average indicated that about five per cent more amber light than white light could be emitted toward the observer for threshold visibility of the gray ring. Obviously this slight advantage of visibility of objects only a degree removed from the physical periphery of the glare-source is of no possible practical value particularly when the amber light is obtained at a sacrifice of about 50 per cent of the light which would be available if a clear glass had been used.

A similar test was made with the amber and white glare-sources excepting that the test-object was a small white square of paper about 12 degrees square and located three degrees from the periphery of the glare-source. The black paper surrounding the glare-sources in the preceding case was replaced with a gray paper. The brightnesses of the test-object and background were about 0.25 and 0.2 millilambert, respectively. In this case the average results indicated that the candlepower of the amber glare-source toward the eye could be about 14 per cent greater than that of the white light for threshold visibility of the test-object. This apparent advantage of amber light for viewing objects as close as three degrees to the physical periphery of the glare-source is gained at a loss of about 50 per cent in candlepower of the headlamp. The reduction of visibility of objects on the highway due to a 50 per cent reduction in illumination is a disadvantage in the present state of visibility on the highway which must be taken into account. Therefore, we conclude that at present there is no acceptable proof that the sacrifice of light in obtaining yellow light by the subtractive principle of a color filter is compensated by any inherent advantage of yellow light over ordinary tungsten-filament light.

ULTRAVIOLET AND INFRARED ENERGY

All illuminants are generally accompanied by some invisible ultraviolet and infrared energy. Ultraviolet energy longer than λ3000 is generally considered to be harmless. The spectrum of sunlight at the earth does not extend beyond λ2900 in the ultraviolet region. Certainly ultraviolet energy from the sky and sun is generally harmless outdoors. Only through long exposure or under special conditions of sunlit snow are harmful dosages received. From much experience with "artificial sunlight" we know that erythema [166] can be produced on the skin without harming the eyes. Also, light-sources can be equipped with glasses to cut off the ultraviolet at any point in the spectrum desired. Therefore,

[451]

the ultraviolet aspect is well known and the energy is well under control.

No harmful effects of infrared energy have been established for quantities experienced in ordinary seeing. However, it is worth considering. Years ago we computed the energy density in the eye media [162] for artificial light and daylight. It was thought this might aid in speculations on eye-fatigue and eye-defects. In Fig. 126 are shown the relative amounts of energy reflected from two white papers when illuminated to the same footcandle-level by various illuminants. It is seen that these amounts are considerably greater for tungsten light than for daylight. Any other sources of artificial light can be approximately compared with these by means of their output in lumens per watt, eliminating, of course, the watts used in auxiliary apparatus.

TABLE LXX

Results Obtained With Tungsten-Filament Light With and Without a Water-Filter Which Absorbed 74 Per Cent of the Total Energy

	Without Filter	With Filter
Rate of blinking eyelids	33 per cent	43 per cent
Decrease of convergence reserve	4.2 per cent	5.0 per cent
Diameter of pupil after reading one hour	2.57 mm.	2.50 mm.
Increase in pupil diameter due to one hour's reading	5.0 per cent	5.3 per cent
Rate of reading per hour	29.6 pages	29.9 pages
Time required to perform L-M Demonstration Visual Test	1.15 minutes	1.18 minutes

It will be noted that comparable amounts of total energy are associated with 1000 footcandles of skylight and 100 footcandles of tungsten light, respectively. Certainly one need not be alarmed about the possible effects of infrared energy reflected from objects under artificial light. However, it may produce hidden effects which should be revealed if possible. Therefore, we investigated certain possible effects of reading under 100 footcandles of tungsten-filament light with and without a water-filter which absorbed 74 per cent of the total energy.[163] A number of criteria were used as shown in Table LXX. The investigation was run over the course of three months during which the humidity and temperature could be maintained fairly constant. Five subjects possessing socalled normal vision and health were used. Each subject read an hour under each condition on different days, and repeated each test five different times in the course of the investigation. The probable errors in these averages are omitted for the sake of simplicity. In general, the differences shown in the results with and without the water-filter are not significant.

The rate of blinking was measured during the first five minutes and the last five minutes of the one-hour reading period. The results given in Table LXX are the increases in the rate during the last five minutes in terms of the rate during the first five minutes. We have since established [164] the rate of blinking as a criterion of difficulty or discomfort in seeing as described in Chapter VI.

The decrease of the convergence reserve of certain eye-muscles is taken as a measure of increase in fatigue of those muscles due to reading for one hour. It is seen that they were more fatigued at the end of an hour's reading, but with no significant difference in the effect of the presence or absence of 75 per cent of the total energy.

The diameter of the pupil was measured before and after the hour's reading and the per cent increase in diameter was determined. We know that the pupil increases in size with eye-fatigue and, therefore, is a criterion of fatiguing effect. No significant differences were obtained for the two conditions.

The rate of reading and of performance of the L-M Demonstration Visual Test also revealed no significant differences in the effects of the two conditions.

The foregoing is at least a beginning toward ascertaining the influence, if any, of infrared upon seeing and the effects of seeing.

CHAPTER XII

Reading as a Task

Reading has been selected for detailed discussion and analysis not only because of its universal importance in modern civilization, but also for the reason that it constitutes a critical, uniform and highly controllable visual task. Although the analyses and data presented herein pertain to the specific task of reading, they are significant in a relative sense with respect to innumerable and diversified visual tasks. Therefore, the effectiveness of various aids to seeing, as determined by investigations involving reading as a task, may be considered applicable to countless non-uniform tasks of the work-world, many of which are far more difficult than reading usually is. Obviously, it is impractical to study these from a fundamental viewpoint since the nature of these tasks varies from moment to moment and they cannot be described precisely. However, such tasks are similar to reading in at least two important and fundamental ways for they involve critical seeing of small details and near-vision.

From the viewpoint of this discussion, it is axiomatic that every publisher is first a manufacturer of visual tasks. These tasks are critical in character, and, in common with all near-vision tasks, they are rather abnormal in view of the evolutionary development of the visual mechanism [167] and require the expenditure of considerable human energy in their performance. Reading, *per se,* is not a task from which human beings derive pleasure—one does not "read" words in a language which he does not understand. Such a form of ocular exercise is obviously not analogous to walking for the exercise and exhilaration derivable from muscular activity. We often refrain from reading interesting and instructive material because it is printed in fine type, or because of ocular strain and fatigue due to uncorrected deficiencies in vision. Hence

[454]

the controllable factors by which reading can be made easier are emphasized in this discussion.

TYPOGRAPHY

Visibility and readability. It should be recognized from experience that the characteristics of printed or written material are not completely describable in terms of the visibility of single letters or characters. In ophthalmology, for example, it has long been known that identical visual acuity ratings are not necessarily obtained when single letters and a line of letters of the same size, respectively, are viewed by the patient. In practice, it has been customary to attribute the characteristics of visibility and legibility to printed or written material. We prefer the term readability rather than legibility since (1) it is descriptive of the act of reading; and (2) it is not so likely to be confused with visibility. Obviously, readability is a function of visibility and, in specific cases, the two may be synonymous *for empirical reasons.* In general, the readability of printed or written material may be defined as that characteristic which determines the speed, accuracy and ease with which it may be read. In typography, it depends upon such factors as the size and configuration of type-face, length of line, upper and lower case, lead or the space between lines, and upon the general arrangement of the individual characters. The influence of intellect, experience and education is generally more prominent in readability than in visibility. As this difference decreases readability and visibility tend to become equivalent.

The relative readabilities of different types may be appraised by such criteria as speed [168] and accuracy in reading, physiological effects of reading and by introspection. In general, it may be assumed that the introspective method is of little value, due to its unreliability, for the relative appraisal of modern type-faces. Obviously, such a method may possess some advantage as a means for appraising *esthetic comfort* in reading, although it seems reasonable to assume that this attribute is not one which yields to standardization. Furthermore, laboratory experience indicates that the criteria of performance and ease in reading, while they are undoubtedly applicable for the appraisal of readability, are also tedious in application. Therefore, such criteria are rather impractical for use in appraising numerous combinations of the several fundamental factors in typography.

Since readibility depends to a large extent upon the visibility of the reading material, it follows that the establishment of correlations between visibility and readability offers a basis for the practical appraisal of the latter. Visibility may be measured readily and with precision by our visibility-meter technique. Furthermore, it is conceivable that a technique for measuring visibility may be developed which will yield results comparable with those obtainable by the tedious statistical methods of appraising readability by the methods which have been enumerated. For example, if the reading material is presented to the subject for periods too brief to permit the adjustment of the visibility meter for individual letters, as by placing it on a revolving drum, the characteristics of readability might be revealed by the visibility measurements. In brief, it seems reasonable to assume that the differential between readability and visibility as indicated by typographical factors is a function of the method used for appraising visibility. At the present time, the authors are investigating the possibilities of establishing correlations of this character. We have definitely established such correlations for the factor of illumination in reading.

When the method of measuring visibility involves the recognition of details, it follows *a priori* that single and isolated letters are equally readable when they are equally visible. This conclusion is based upon the assumption that the reader is familiar with the various characters observed. Obviously, Old English and Modern Gothic letters are not equally readable to one who is not familiar with the former. In such a case the mere recognition of the details of design does not signify the perception in consciousness of the character or letter. As an extreme example, it would seem obvious that a monogram is not as readable as one of the letters even though the two are of identical visibility as appraised by threshold measurements involving unlimited time for observation. However, since the present analysis is based upon considerations of ocular hygiene, as the latter is influenced by typographical factors, these extreme cases are of no practical importance. Hence the assumption of familiarity with the characters to be compared is obviously justifiable.

Upon the basis of the foregoing analysis it follows that possible differences between visibility and readability are due to the mutual influence of adjacent letters as well as to other factors such as the boldness of the letters and other configurational characteristics. For example, one investigation [169] indicated that the average visibility of the lower case letters of seven modern typefaces was about 40 per cent higher for isolated than for grouped letters. This value varied from 30 to 56 per cent for the individual type-faces which were measured. Thus one characteristic of readability might be denoted by the ratio between the visibilities of the isolated and the grouped letters. However, such a method is to be regarded as an approximate one which involves certain obvious inadequacies. For example, if adjacent lines of type were sufficiently separated, it follows that the mutual influence between lines could be reduced to zero, although the muscular effort of reading a given number of words might be measurably increased. It is possible that this method of appraising readability would be a useful one in practice regardless of its inherent inadequacy in extreme cases. For the latter, it is probable that introspective appraisals of readability would suffice since practice is seldom concerned with such extremes.

If it is assumed that readability is a function of the "white space" surrounding the letters, then readability might be appraised, at least qualitatively, from measurements of the integrated reflectances of type and background. Thus if two types were equally visible, it seems reasonable to assume that the one which yielded the highest integrated reflectance would be preferred. However, actual measurement of the reflectances of a number of modern types of approximately the same size indicated that the differences among types in this respect are not large.

The value of these approximate and more or less indirect methods for appraising readability will depend upon their correlation with the results obtained by criteria similar to those discussed in Chapter VI. This viewpoint is analogous to that which we have considered in correlating psychophysiological effects of seeing with measurements of visual function. The former criteria are too unwieldy to be used in practice and it is not necessary that they be used, in the event that appropriate correlations can be established. In the past, speed of reading, accuracy in reading and eye-movements have been used as criteria of readability.[39] In general, these criteria are rather insensitive to the differences in readability produced by moderate changes in type-face. However, refinements in technique may still be possible.

Size of type. The data plotted in Fig. 76 show the relationship between type-size and visibility as determined by adult subjects possessing normal or near-normal vision. The measurements were made with our visibility meter and for Bodoni type well printed upon white paper and illuminated to ten footcandles. The fact that the relationship is a linear one is probably largely due to empirical factors involved in the design of this particular series of types and may not be assumed to hold for other type-faces. It will be noted that a visibility rating of approximately unity is indicated for 3-point type. Since unity on this scale of visibility represents the limit of average normal vision, it follows that 3-point type is about the smallest which unaided eyes may resolve, as will be noted from Table LXXI and from Fig. 76. In general, it will be found that few can read 2-point type although the majority of persons with normal or near-normal vision can read 3-point type under otherwise favorable conditions for seeing. Thus these data serve as additional evidence of the rationality of the calibration of our visibility meter.

A standard of visibility. An acceptable standard of type-size is definitely indicated by the characteristics of good typography since these standards have been evolved as a result of mass experience for generations. Furthermore, it seems reasonable to conclude that normal vision has been assumed in the design of type-sizes. Hence the fact that 10-point or 12-point type is used in the better grade of books and magazines may be considered as an indication of the desirability of these sizes. The desirability of type of these sizes is also indicated by the researches discussed in Chapter VI. Furthermore, it may be assumed that 12-point type represents a practical optimum since 14-point type is rarely used for the solid text-matter of books designed for adults. It seems obvious from introspective considerations that larger sizes would not be desired by readers possessing normal vision if the level of illumination were reasonably high.

Let it be assumed, for the moment, that 12-point booktype represents a visual task which is consistent with reasonable ease and comfort in reading if the printing, illumination and lighting are suitable. It will be noted from the data presented in Table LXXI and in Fig. 76 that type of this size has a relative visibility

T A B L E   L X X I

Visibilities of Bodoni Book Monotype of Various Sizes Under Ten Footcandles of Diffuse Illumination. Visibilities of Sizes Not Actually Available Were Determined by Simple Extrapolation.

Size in Points	Relative Visibility	Effective Visibility
3	1.10	1.02
4	1.60	1.10
5	2.11	1.21
6	2.64	1.33
8	3.64	1.62
10	4.65	1.92
12	5.66	2.29
14	6.67	2.75
18	8.67	3.92
24	11.68	6.70

of about 5.7 or a factor of safety of the same value. In other words, this type should be of threshold visibility to a person with a visual efficiency rating of about 44 per cent, as will be noted from Fig. 77. This is less than 20/100 on the Snellen rating. Hence this visual task may be regarded as representative of an "acceptable standard of visibility" for reading and for other tasks of a critical nature which are performed more or less continuously for prolonged periods. It is a standard to be determined and recommended on the basis of ocular hygiene and ease of seeing.

It will be evident from Fig. 75 that such an ideal standard of visibility is far above the average type in newspapers. Perhaps such a standard of visibility, although desirable from the viewpoint of ocular hygiene is not practicable from the publisher's viewpoint. Nevertheless, a consideration of this standard may temper his opinion of the degree of excellence of prevailing typographical practices. Certainly there are many readers who would prefer larger type-sizes even though they were obtained at the expense of the number of words in a given article. Furthermore, it is conceivable that many writers and readers would prefer to accentuate quality rather than quantity. At least one current weekly magazine has demonstrated that relatively few words are not a handicap, but if properly chosen achieve vivid and adequate description.

Type-size and subnormal vision. It is now of interest to examine the results obtained by various individuals of a subnormal-vision group with respect to this standard of visibility. It will be noted from Table XLIX, for example, that the relative visibility obtained by the two subjects with cataracts averaged 2.60 and 4.31 for 18- and 24-point type, respectively. Obviously, these subjects did not receive the visual assistance from the factor of type-size that is demanded by the standard of visibility which has been assumed to be a rational and conservative one. As tasks for normal eyes, these visibility values correspond to 6-point and 9-point type, respectively, as shown in Fig. 76. Furthermore, it will be noted that these equivalent type-sizes are reduced to approximately 3.5-point and 5-point, respectively, for the subjects in the lower ranges of visual efficiency. Therefore, it may be concluded that 18-point type in comparison with 24-point type, cannot be recommended in such cases unless it is possible to augment visibility by some other means.

The data of Table XLIX also indicate that the tentative standard of visibility—that of 12-point type illuminated to 10 foot-candles—may be obtained by certain subjects from either 24-point type under 10 footcandles or from 18-point type under higher levels. For example, the group with simple myopic astigmatism obtained a visibility rating of 5.68 from 24-point type under 10 footcandles and the same rating from 18-point type under 19.1 footcandles. Since the "standard of visibility" is equivalent to a rating of 5.7, it is obvious that the type-size may be reduced, for these subjects, from 24-point to 18-point if the illumination is increased from 10 footcandles to approximately 20 footcandles. However, it will be noted that a rating of 5.7 in visibility is not attainable by many of the subjects even with the 24-point type. Hence an augmentation of the illumination is the only available means for approaching the assumed standard of visibility in these cases. The latter conclusion is based upon the assumption that 24-point type is the largest size practicable.

These generalizations do not imply that the utmost refinement is necessary in regulating visual tasks in accordance with the visual characteristics of the individual. Such a procedure, although ideal from a theoretical viewpoint, is obviously impractical in many situations. However, certain approximations are often possible.

The influence of type-size extends beyond considerations of visual factors. A closely printed page appears formidable and relatively uninviting. On the other hand, large and adequately spaced type is inviting, as is appreciated by publishers of certain magazines and books. Readers like to "turn the page" for this act represents accomplishment, especially when the reading is done for instruction rather than for pleasure. Furthermore, the turning of the page momentarily relaxes the muscular effort of reading and it may furnish a brief respite in mental attention. These psychological factors and others should not be ignored in publishing, and particularly in the field of education.

Type-faces. The degree of visibility, for a given type-size, is also a function of the pattern or configuration of the type-face, but deficiencies in visibility due to design are obviously not justifiable on the basis of cost, for this is not involved. This conclusion is particularly significant in cases where small types of relatively low visibilities are used, as is frequently the case, for appreciable portions of text-matter. As an outstanding example of the importance of type-face, the prevalence of myopia among school-children decreased significantly in Sweden when the complicated characters of Old Gothic print and script were abandoned for simpler ones. This suggests a possible correlation between the prevalence of defective vision in Japan and the visual difficulty of their reading tasks. Recently, many American newspapers have increased the size of type in the interest of ease of seeing for the reader. In one very prominent case, unfortunately, this change involved an unnecessary decrease in boldness of the type-face with the result that the new and larger type was no more visible than the older and smaller type. This reveals the need of measurements and the inadequacy of mere inspection and introspection. In this case there appeared to be a net gain in readability due to the greater separation between letters. However, gains in both visibility and readability could have been secured if the selection of the new type had been based upon measurements. On the other hand, other newspapers have secured higher visibility through changes only in the configuration of the type-face.

In Table LXXII are presented the relative visibilities of a series of 20 different 8-point type-faces as determined with the visibility meter.[170] It is emphasized that these values relate only to the visibility of the printed characters and not to their respective "attention" values. For example, it will be noted that the Caslon Light Italic is less visible than the Caslon Light although it is obvious that a few words printed in the italics and inserted in a body of the latter possess considerable attention-value. Novelty has its place in printing, but not in large portions of text-matter unless it is obtained without significant sacrifices in ease of seeing and reading. It is also obvious that the visibility method of appraising type-faces does not include esthetic considerations of the appearance of the printed matter. However, visibility is generally of major importance and is the predominant factor in exacting penalties in eyestrain, eye-fatigue, nervous tension, wasted energy and other effects upon the human seeing-machine.

The data in Table LXXII possess a high degree of re-

[462]

TABLE LXXII

THE RELATIVE VISIBILITY OF VARIOUS 8-POINT MACHINE SET MONOTYPES*

These data were obtained with the Luckiesh-Moss Visibility Meter and represent the averages of 5 series of 5 measurements each made by 5 different observers, experienced in the use of the instrument. Each style of type was well-printed with black ink upon a good grade of non-glossy white paper. The latter was illuminated to 10 footcandles in all cases. The measurements of visibility pertain to the lower case letters. *(The names of the various type-faces are actually printed in the type-face designated. This caption is printed in 8-point Bodoni Book Monotype.)

Type-Face (8-point)	Relative Visibility	Per Cent Prob. Error	Per Cent Visibility	For Equal Visibility Size in Points	For Equal Visibility Footcandles Required
Bodoni Book.......	3.65	1.0	100.0	8.0	20
Bodoni Book Italic...	*3.50*	*1.2*	*96.0*	*8.3*	*22*
Bodoni Bold......	**3.95**	**1.3**	**108.3**	**7.4**	**17**
Caslon Light........	3.51	1.2	96.2	8.3	22
Caslon Light Italic....	*2.96*	*0.7*	*81.1*	*9.4*	*36*
Caslon Bold.......	**3.89**	**0.8**	**106.5**	**7.5**	**17**
Sans Serif Light......	3.54	0.9	97.1	8.2	22
Sans Serif Medium...	3.86	1.1	105.7	7.6	17
Sans Serif Bold......	**3.81**	**0.7**	**104.3**	**7.7**	**18**
Cheltenham Wide...	3.67	1.2	100.5	8.0	20
Cheltenham Bold.	**3.96**	**1.2**	**108.5**	**7.4**	**17**
Cheltenham Bold Condensed...........	**3.40**	**1.4**	**93.2**	**8.5**	**25**
LIGHT COPPERPLATE GOTHIC**..	3.58	1.0	98.1	8.1	21
HEAVY COPPERPLATE GOTHIC**..	3.74	1.2	102.5	7.8	19
Goudy Light.......	3.43	1.3	94.0	8.4	24
Goudy Antique....	3.88	1.7	106.2	7.5	17
Goudy Bold.......	**3.82**	**1.5**	**104.8**	**7.7**	**18**
Cochin Light.......	3.73	1.5	102.3	7.8	19
Cochin Bold.......	**4.12**	**1.4**	**112.6**	**7.1**	**15**
Garamond Bold....	**4.33**	**1.5**	**118.7**	**6.6**	**14**

* From same manufacturer.
** Equivalent in size to 8-point Bodoni Book type.

liability, from the statistical viewpoint, since their corresponding probable errors are of the order of 1.5 per cent or less. In computing these probable errors the systematic differences among observers were eliminated. The statistical significance of the differences in visibility of the various type-faces is indicated by comparing these data with their corresponding probable errors. For example, the difference between Bodoni Book and Bodoni Bold is statistically real since it is approximately seven times as great as the probable error of the difference. On the other hand, since the difference in visibility between Caslon Light and Sans Serif Light is of the same order of magnitude as the probable error of the difference, these two type-faces may be regarded as approximately equal in visibility.

The differences in visibility among the various type-faces may also be expressed in terms of *type-size* of a particular type-face. Thus the comparisons may be expressed in *points* of type-size rather than in *minutes visual angle* of an arbitrary test-object of a simple geometric pattern. Bodoni Book Monotype was selected as a basis for such comparisons by reason of its wide usage in typography. This relationship is given in the fifth column of Table LXXII. The interpretation of these data is illustrated by the following:

1. The maximum difference in visibility among the various type-faces is obtained for Caslon Light Italic and Garamond Bold and is equivalent to 2.8 points in type-size on the scale developed for the Bodoni Book Monotype. Obviously, a difference in visibility equivalent to nearly three points between two socalled 8-point types is an important one.

2. The difference between Caslon Light Italic and Bodoni Italic is 0.54 in relative visibility or slightly more than one point in equivalent type-size. Thus it is possible to gain the attention-value of italics without a serious loss in visibility as in the case of Bodoni type.

3. The increase in visibility gained by the use of bold-face rather than light-face Cochin type is about three-fourths of

a point.   Approximately the same relationship is obtained for the Caslon and Goudy type-faces.   However, it will be noted that Sans Serif Bold is somewhat less visible than the Sans Serif Medium, and that Heavy Copperplate Gothic is only slightly more visible than Light Copperplate Gothic.

Since illumination is a fundamental variable of the visual threshold, it is obvious that the differences in visibility among various type-faces may also be expressed in terms of this variable. The values given in the sixth column of Table LXXII were computed from the visibility ratings of the various type-faces and the relationship between visibility and level of illumination for 8-point Bodoni Book Monotype.   These values are based upon a degree of visibility and ease of seeing provided by 20 footcandles on 8-point Bodoni Book Monotype assuming the same excellence of paper, ink and printing.   Under this illumination 8-point Bodoni type possesses a visibility rating of about 5, as will be noted from Fig. 76. · Thus this type so illuminated would be barely visible to a person with a visual efficiency rating of about 50 per cent.   It will be noted that Caslon Light Italic illuminated to 36 footcandles is equivalent in visibility to Garamond Bold illuminated to only 14 footcandles.   In general, it may be concluded that the variations in visibility, expressed in terms of illumination, are quite significant in most of the cases.

The influence of esthetic considerations in appraising the readability of material printed in various type-faces and with different degrees of leading may be revealed by the data plotted in Fig. 60. It will be noted that type sample 13 received only a few votes from a total of several hundred, notwithstanding its relatively high degree of visibility.   In general, the readers favored the types with the higher degrees of visibility as will be noted for samples 2, 5, 9 and 11, respectively.   Hence the exception in the case of sample 13 is particularly interesting.   These data are also of interest as evidence of the unreliability of introspective methods of appraising typographical factors.   Although the majority

[465]

of the readers chose the types of highest visibility, it will also be noted that some of the readers selected the types of least visibility as the most desirable on the basis of introspective considerations of ease and comfort in reading.

Length of line. In summarizing the literature concerning the optimum length of line, Vernon[39] concludes the consensus indicates that it should not be longer than ten centimeters. Dearborn has stated that the return movements from the end of one line to the beginning of the next are likely to be more inaccurate for the longer lines of type. However, there is little evidence to show that such inaccuracy is significantly decreased with lines less than nine or ten centimeters. Upon the basis of speed of reading, Tinker and Patterson[171] concluded that the optimum length of line was from 7.5 to 9 centimeters. These lengths of line are somewhat shorter than those generally used in the printing of books. Since the length of line is a controllable factor in seeing, it would seem to warrant further study. Even if only a slight advantage can be shown for a particular length of line, this contribution towards easier seeing would accrue to many individuals during many years of reading. However, practical considerations are bound to influence the adoption of refinements.

Leading. Much remains uncertain as to the importance of leading or interlinage. It has been stated by some investigators that leading should not be used at the expense of body-size of type; that is, the size of the type should not be reduced in order to increase the leading. On the other hand, Bentley[172] has shown that leading is a definite advantage with small types, and also desirable for larger types. Using speed of reading as a criterion, Bentley found that the optimum interlinage was:

Approximately 1/10 inch for 12-point type
"   1/14   "   "   9-   "   "
"   1/17   "   "   6-   "   "

In general, it seems inadvisable to present detailed data regarding this and other similar typographical factors until an acceptable criterion for appraising readability has been developed. It is possible that the influence of these factors may be appraisable from electromyograms taken under various conditions. A few typical records of the activities of the ocular muscles while reading are discussed elsewhere in this chapter.

ILLUMINATION

The complementary relationships between type-size and illumination are shown in Table LXXIII. Each value is the average of 90 observations by ten adult subjects possessing normal or near-normal vision. In each horizontal line are presented the footcandles required for equal threshold visibility of the four sizes of Bodoni Book Monotype, respectively, when paper, ink and printing were of the same excellent quality. It will be noted, for example, that five footcandles on 12-point type produce the same visibility as 17 footcandles upon 6-point type. Furthermore, the footcandles presented in each horizontal line may be considered as the levels of illumination required for different standards of visibility. Thus if the visibility of the 12-point type illuminated by ten footcandles is selected as a standard, it follows that the 6-point type should be illuminated to at least 36 footcandles. Since both type-size and illumination are complementary and controllable factors in seeing, there is little technical justification for the existence of unfavorable conditions for reading. In view of these facts, we believe that the footcandle recommendations for reading which are presented in Chapter IX are conservative.

TABLE LXXIII

Footcandles Necessary for Various Sizes of Type to Equal a Given Standard of Visibility

| Standard of Visibility | Footcandles on Printed Matter | | | |
	12-Point	10-Point	8-Point	6-Point
5 footcandles on 12-point type....	5	7	10	17
10 footcandles on 12-point type....	10	15	21	36
20 footcandles on 12-point type....	20	28	42	68
50 footcandles on 12-point type....	50	71	93	167

The relationship between illumination and the relative visibility of 8-point Bodoni Book Monotype is shown in Fig. 127. It will be recalled that the values of relative visibility denote that the object of regard, 8-point type in this case, is equivalent in visibility to the standard parallel-bar object of corresponding size in minutes visual angle. Thus 8-point type under ten footcandles is equivalent in visibility to a standard test-object whose critical detail subtends an angle of about 3.7 minutes; similarly,

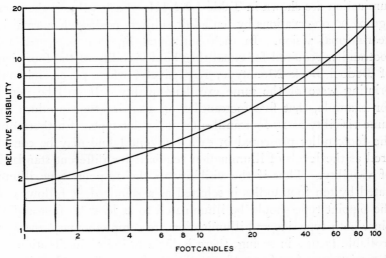

FIG. 127.—The relative visibility of 8-point Bodoni Book Monotype under various levels of illumination as determined by subjects possessing average normal vision.

the same type under 100 footcandles is equivalent in visibility to a standard object of about 17 minutes. In all cases, the standard parallel-bar test-object was illuminated to an intensity of ten footcandles. The conspicuous characteristic of these data is the effectiveness of illumination or brightness of the background in enhancing the visibility of print. Thus the data of Fig. 38 indicate, on a quantitative basis, the benefit which many persons derive when they take a telephone directory to a window in order to read it with certainty. When this is done, the illumination on the directory is often increased a hundredfold.

[468]

READING DISTANCE AND POSTURE

It might be assumed, from theoretical considerations of accommodation and convergence, that reading would be easiest for distance-vision providing that the characters to be read were correspondingly expanded in physical size. However, it is probable that such a condition would not be entirely satisfactory for psychological reasons. The factors of size, distance and visibility are unconsciously compared, and it is likely that the relationships thus established by habit would be distorted by the very thought of reading at unusual distances. On the other hand, if the reading matter were placed at the near-point, it would be possible to read only when the maximum effort of accommodation or convergence was exerted. Adults usually compromise on a distance of 14 to 16 inches. This socalled natural reading distance is generally that which results when the arms are bent at approximately a right angle. Thus the usual reading distance is determined largely by skeletal musculature. In general, the average reading distance appears to be less for women than for men and for children; its value depends upon their physical size. If the arms of the child are bent at angles less than a right angle while holding a book, it is likely that the reading distance is too short since such a position is not one conducive to physical comfort. Obviously, the head may also be bent towards the book thus decreasing the reading distance. In this case, an abnormally short reading distance may be revealed by the rather awkward posture assumed. In either case, eyestrain is indicated. The latter may result from a number of causes such as defective vision, faulty lighting, inadequate light or other physical conditions unfavorable for seeing.

Reading in a recumbent posture is usually undesirable since it is difficult to hold a book at a favorable angle. As a result, abnormal strains are placed upon the extrinsic muscles. Furthermore, as stated by Posey,[173] reading or close work should not be continued when drowsy or physically tired. The ocular muscles tend to relax under such conditions and are only stimulated into activity by a conscious effort of the will and the expenditure of abnormal energy.

EYE-MOVEMENTS

The efficiency of the visual mechanism in reading depends very largely upon the character of the eye-movements. In the normal case, these are more or less rhythmical and the point of fixation progresses along the line of type with few regressions or backward movements. Since each of the many movements which occur during the reading of a single line involves the coordination of the activity of the six extrinsic muscles of each eye and an extremely close coordination of the movements of both eyes, as well as minor changes in other ocular muscles, it is obvious that even slight muscular anomalies impose severe handicaps in reading. Thus the efficiency with which these movements are accomplished is influenced by muscular imbalances, fatigue, refractive errors and numerous other variables of the visual situation. Some of these deficiencies may be overcome by proper ophthalmic corrections and minimized by careful training exercises.[174]

It will be noted from Fig. 128 that about seven fixational-pauses of an average duration of 0.25 second may occur while reading a single line of fiction. In this case, the frequency of regressions averages about 1.4 per line. These data were obtained by Judd and Buswell[175] and are for children of about 15 years of age. It will also be noted that all of these factors vary with the kind of material read. Among the kinds of reading material designated in Fig. 128, it will be noted that these factors are numerically highest while reading blank verse and lowest while reading fiction, with a few minor exceptions. The investigations of Gilliand, as summarized by Vernon,[39] indicate that if the same number of words were printed in different sizes of type, readers with normal eyesight and normal eye-movements showed little variation between 6-point and 36-point type. Obviously the lines would differ greatly in length. On the basis of these data, it appears that the characteristics of eye-movements are not criteria by which the relative visibility and readability of different sizes of type might be appraised. The same conclusion seems warranted with respect to variations in the configuration of type-faces. How-

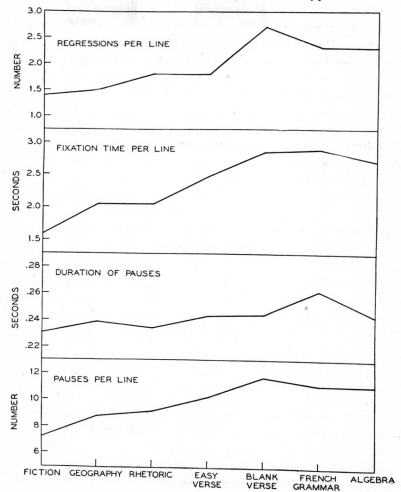

FIG. 128.—Characteristics of the eye-movements of high-school children while reading various kinds of material. (After Buswell.)

ever, these considerations do not include the possible influence on the characteristics of the eye-movements which might result from prolonged reading. In fact, conclusions are too often drawn from researches involving a short period of time with the tacit assumption that they hold after long periods of performance.

The results of the investigations of Erdman and Dodge relating the characteristics of eye-movements with the kinds of material read are given in Table LXXIV. These data clearly reveal the relative severity of proofreading, as a visual task, in comparison with other kinds of reading. In this case, it will be noted that the number of fixational-pauses per line is about three times as great as the number of pauses in ordinary reading. In addition, the pauses in proofreading are also much longer than those in ordinary reading. It is probable that many critical visual tasks of the work-world, such as various kinds of inspection tasks, also involve unusual eye-movements.

TABLE LXXIV

The Characteristics of the Eye-Movements Associated with Reading Various Kinds of Material

Kind of Material	Pauses Per Line	Angular Displace- ment	Total Duration of Pauses in Sec.	Total Duration of Moves in Sec.	Per Cent of Time Taken by Movement
Familiar	4.45	4° 56′	1.70	.090	6.1
Unfamiliar	5.27	4° 11′	1.93	.105	6.1
Proofreading	15.00	1° 50′	3.77	.300	8.1
Native language	4.74	4° 35′	1.58	.095	6.7
Foreign language	5.04	4° 31′	2.18	.101	5.3
Average	5.78	4° 13′	2.01	.116	6.4

The data of Buswell [176] given in Table LXXV show the relationship between age and the characteristics of the eye-movements. These results clearly reveal the influence of training in reading and in mental development as the child grows older. It will be noted that the number of pauses per line decreases until the high-school age is reached, and thereafter, that the number remains substantially constant. Similar changes in the duration of the pauses will be noted. However, the number of regressions per line decreases progressively throughout this range in age. In general, it may be assumed that these changes in the character of the eye-movements with age are largely due to mental rather than to visual factors.

TABLE LXXV

The Effect of Age Upon the Characteristics of the Eye-Movements

Age of Reader	Average Number of Pauses Per Line	Average Duration of Pauses	Average Number of Regressions Per Line
6	18.6	0.660	5.1
7	15.5	.432	4.0
8	10.7	.364	2.3
9	8.9	.316	1.8
10	7.3	.268	1.4
11	6.9	.252	1.3
12	7.3	.236	1.6
13	6.8	.240	1.5
14	7.2	.244	1.0
15	5.8	.248	0.7
16	5.5	.224	0.7
17	6.4	.248	0.7
18 and over	5.9	.252	0.5

Electromyograms. Recently the authors have extended their studies of ocular muscle phenomena by recording the action currents generated by these muscles during reading. This technique involves the placing of electrodes near the eye to be examined and amplifying and recording the currents flowing between the two electrodes. In accomplishing this, an estimated amplification of about two million to one was achieved. Due to the high amplification required, it was found necessary to completely shield the subject, by means of a wire-screen cage, from various extraneous electrical disturbances. Many records have already been obtained in search of important new facts and correlations.

The records shown in Fig. 129 were obtained with the electrodes placed at the right temple and on the forehead just above the nose, respectively. Thus it may be assumed that these records pertain very largely to the activities of the muscles of the right eye. The upper record of Fig. 129 was obtained while the subject read rather large type under an illumination of five footcandles.

The lower record is for a level of 0.25 footcandle. In both cases the speed of the oscillograph drum bearing the photographic film was the same. Furthermore, the two recordings were made in rapid succession and with the same degree of amplification. A critical comparison of these records indicates that the frequency

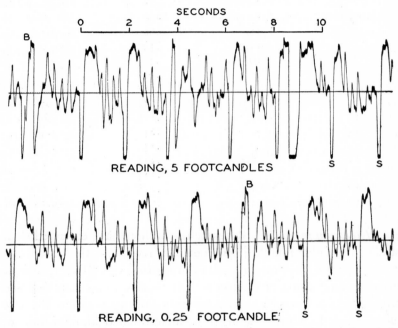

FIG. 129.—Electromyograms showing chiefly the activity of the muscles of the right eye while reading ordinary material with binocular vision under 5 footcandles and 0.25 footcandle, respectively. These records were taken with the electrodes placed, respectively, at the right temple and on the forehead just above the nose. The indicated muscular activity at points *B* is produced by blinking; and at points *S* by shifting fixation from the end of one line to the beginning of the next line.

of the eye-movements in reading a single line is greater when the reading is done under the lower level of illumination than it is under the higher level. The sharp peaks *S* of these records indicate the muscular activity as the point of fixation shifts from the end of one line to the beginning of the next. The peak at *B* is characteristic of that produced by a blink. It will also be noted

from the records of Fig. 129 that the rate of reading was slower
under the low level of illumination than under the higher level
of illumination. Actually, the time required to read a single line
was 2.43 seconds and 2.00 seconds for levels of illumination of
0.25 footcandle and 5 footcandles, respectively.

The fact that rather small differences in the frequencies of the
eye-movements were obtained under these lighting conditions is not
surprising in view of the researches of Israel [177] on the accuracy
of accommodation and convergence. Israel found that under a
level of illumination as low as 0.01 footcandle the average error
for accommodation alone is only about four per cent of the total
distance. When both accommodation and convergence are considered, the error is less than two per cent of the total distance.
Thus it appears that the brain demands and obtains accurate fixation and accommodation even under unfavorable conditions for
seeing. However, it is to be expected that the eye-muscles will
eventually fail to achieve these demands when they have become
fatigued from prolonged effort under unfavorable conditions for
seeing. These considerations reveal the potential source of error in
appraising conditions for seeing from the results of brief tests of
visual function.

The two electromyograms shown in Fig. 130 were taken at
the beginning and end of a two-hour period of continuous reading.
In this case, the reading was done under an illumination of about
two footcandles. Furthermore, the records were made in the late
afternoon and hence it might be supposed that the eye-muscles
were somewhat fatigued at the beginning of the experiment due to
the performance of clerical work for several hours preceding the
period of reading. However, this may not be an extremely important factor since it has been shown that the effects of muscular
fatigue, as indicated by a decrease in convergence reserve, are dissipated within a relatively short time after the cessation of the
critical visual work. [40] The latter conclusion is based upon the
results obtained in a research in which the visual task was not unusually difficult or prolonged. In obtaining the records of Fig.
130, the electrodes were placed in the region of the right eye

and in the same positions as previously described. An examination of the records of Fig. 130 shows that the time required for reading three consecutive lines of print was 0.140 minute and 0.155 minute at the beginning and end of the two-hour period of reading,

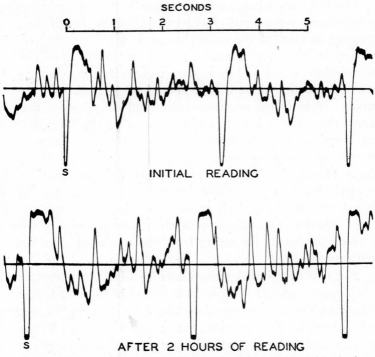

FIG. 130.—Electromyograms showing ocular muscle activity at the beginning and the end, respectively, of a two-hour period of reading. These records reveal the changes in muscle activity due to the performance of a prolonged and critical visual task. The positions of the electrodes were the same as those for the records in Fig. 129.

respectively. In other words, the speed of reading decreased about ten per cent during this period. Obviously these records provide a highly precise means for determining the time required to read a given amount of material, since the interval between the first and last fixational pause is sharply defined. In fact, this method is an excellent one for investigating the influence of the nature of the material read upon the speed of reading and the character of the eye-movements.

The records of Fig. 130 also show that ocular muscle activity, as indicated by the sharp peaks of the action currents during the reading of a single line, increased from 9 to 13 from the beginning

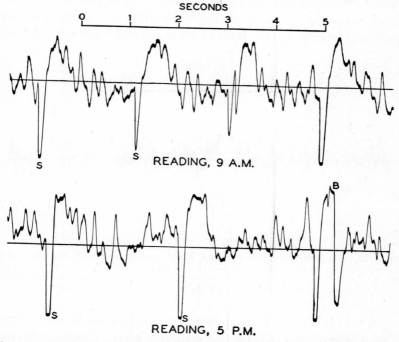

FIG. 131.—Electromyograms showing ocular muscle activity while reading at the beginning and end of a work-day, respectively. The experimental conditions were the same as those for Fig. 130.

to the end of the period of reading. In addition, the amplitudes of these currents also appear to increase with fatigue. These ocular muscle effects of fatigue are to be expected. For example, every rifleman is aware of the fact that the wavering of the muzzle of the rifle increases as the period of aiming is prolonged and the muscles of the arms and shoulders become fatigued. It may also be significant, from the viewpoint of ocular hygiene, that similar records

[477]

taken for a period of one hour of reading indicated only slight changes in muscular activity.

The records shown in Fig. 131 were taken under the same experimental conditions as those of Fig. 130 except that the recording was done at the beginning and the close of the work-day. In this case, the time required for reading three lines of print varied from 0.100 minute to 0.137 minute. The frequency of the fixational pauses occurring during the reading of a single line also increased from 7 to 11. Both of these differences in muscular ac-

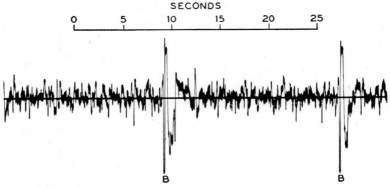

FIG. 132.—An electromyogram obtained while reading and with the electrodes placed directly above and below the right eye, respectively. It will be noted that the records of the line to line fixations are suppressed, in comparison to those produced by blinking, *B*, for these positions of the electrodes.

tivity will be obvious from an inspection of the records of Fig. 131.

These records indicate that relatively severe visual conditions, either in low visibility or prolonged visual effort, must be imposed to isolate differences in the behavior of the ocular muscles. For example, it has been demonstrated that persons with normal vision are often able to read as fast under unfavorable conditions for seeing as under more favorable conditions for short periods of time. In such cases, the adaptability of the visual mechanism is such that it is able to overcome visual handicaps through increased effort. As a result, unfavorable conditions for seeing may be tolerated by the individual merely because he is able to compensate for them through an increased expenditure of human energy. Hence it follows that appraisals of the readability of types, as a function of the physiological effects from reading, will probably necessitate rather extreme visual conditions in order to overcome the tendency of adaptability. These considerations emphasize the necessity for establishing correlations between such effects and measurements of visibility for the purpose of advancing typographical design.

The electromyogram shown in Fig. 132 was obtained with the electrodes directly above and below the right eye. The major peaks indicate blinks. Thus it appears possible to emphasize the activity of certain muscles through a proper location of the electrodes.

In general, this method for investigating visual phenomena appears most promising. The results which we have presented are to be considered only as preliminary to an extensive study of vision and seeing using this method applied to a variety of problems and conditions.

PERCEPTUAL FACTORS

Perceptual span. As the point of central fixation advances by discrete steps along a line of printed or written material, the amount perceived at each fixation determines the rate of reading. The investigations of Cattell indicate that the average reader, for a tachistoscopic exposure of 0.01, could perceive three of four single letters, two disconnected words containing as many as twelve letters, or a sentence of four words. Since the average fixational pause in reading is of the order of magnitude of 0.2 second, it is obvious that the results obtained by Cattell pertain to a single fixational pause. Furthermore, Cattell found that it took longer to name single letters than single words. We have also found that it requires several times as much light on numerals such as stock-market quotations to make their visibility the same as that of words printed in the same size of type and upon the same sheet of paper. These results indicate the influence of the central processes in perception and indicate the impossibility of defining readability completely in terms of the physical characteristics of the objects of regard.

During such fixational-pause, a few letters are seen clearly by foveal vision. Since visual acuity decreases rapidly towards the periphery of the retina, the letters outside the foveal region become less distinct. Furthermore, since visual acuity in the outer regions of the macula is only one-tenth of that in the fovea, it seems probable that the recognition of letters or words is generally limited to those letters or words whose images fall within these regions. Hence it is of interest to determine the number of letters, for various sizes of type, which could be encompassed by foveal and macular vision, respectively. In computing the data of Table LXXVI, it has been assumed that the average fovea and macula subtend visual angles of 70 minutes and 12 degrees, respectively; and that the reading distance is 14 inches.

TABLE LXXVI

Approximate Number of Letters in a Single Horizontal Line Which May Be Seen by Foveal and Macular Vision at a Reading Distance of 14 Inches

	Type Size			
	6-Point	8-Point	10-Point	12-Point
Foveal	6	5	4	3.5
Macular	66	51	45	38

Functional perceptual spans. Since the size of the field of acute vision varies among individuals, it might be assumed that the speed of reading and the number of fixational pauses per line would be correlated with this factor. However, there is no evidence available which indicates such a correlation. Vernon concludes that the speed of perception in reading is independent of retinal sensory functions and must depend upon central nervous processes. Hence it might be assumed that the effective perceptual span might be increased through training. However, according to Mills,[107] persistent attempts to enlarge the perceptual span by flash and speed training often lead to potential and actual deviations of the eyes. Furthermore, exophoria (outward deviation of the eyes) more often results in the nervous child with an active mind, and esophoria (inward deviation) in the deeply intense child from such training. Thus Mills concludes that mental habits are the chief factors in determining the form of ocular deviation.

Apparently the persistent seeking of mass effects and speed, rather than accuracy, may gradually result in a predominant use of peripheral vision. The latter is accompanied by muscular over-action in eyes physically capable of so yielding. It is also believed by some that poor memory is associated with excessive peripheral vision. Thus it would seem that the possible advantages of enlarging the perceptual span, through various methods of flash training, may be discounted by the possibility of accompanying ocular anomalies. This does not mean that increasing the speed of reading is necessarily detrimental to the eyes when such changes are obtained through improved reading habits.

Visibility versus perceptual span. In many cases, and particularly in those involving defective vision, it may be desirable to obtain higher degrees of visibility through the use of larger type-sizes. Obviously, this expedient results in a decrease in the number of letters which may be recognized during a single fixational-pause. In practice the relative influence of each factor should be determined for the individual. For example, it will be noted from Table XLIX that visibility is the all-important factor for the pupils with nystagmus. In these cases, vision is so low that perceptual factors would seem to be of relatively minor importance. On the other hand, the pupils with medium myopia and with visibility ratings comparable with the normal subject, do not require extremely large types. Hence it would appear that the use of either 18-point or 24-point type would impose unnecessary perceptual handicaps. In general, it would seem better to obtain the desired degree of visibility by means of higher levels of illumination rather than by unusually large type when the former is possible. This is an example of the situation in which size and brightness, as complementary factors of the visual threshold, are not equally effective from the viewpoint of seeing as distinguished from visual function.

It will be noted from Table XLIX that all pupils were able to achieve the same degree of visibility with 18-point type as they did with 24-point type when the illumination on the former was increased. For the group as a whole, 18-point type under 20 footcandles was as visible as 24-point type under 10 footcandles. Thus from a consideration of perceptual factors, the augmentation of visibility by means of light seems preferable to achieving the same result with larger type. However, it is not improbable that many of these children need the visual assistance which may be given through an adequate use of all factors.

OCULAR DEFICIENCIES

As stated by Eames,[178] difficulty in learning to read was once regarded as being due to word-blindness or mental deficiency. Later advances in educational psychology caused the viewpoint to shift from the pathological to the psychological extreme. More recently, the relationship between reading deficiencies and visual anomalies has been recognized as an important cause of reading difficulties. A survey of 10,000 school-children under the direction of Morse-Peckham,[179] for example, established definite correlations between rate of reading and visual efficiency. In this investigation, the school-children were classified into the following three visual groups:

Group I. Those with 90-per cent (20/22) distant-vision or better with both eyes; with 80-per cent (20/25) vision or better with both eyes at 14 inches; and who promptly and unequivocally passed all binocular tests.

Group II. Those with between 80-per cent and 90-per cent distant-vision with both eyes; those with 80-per cent vision with one eye and 90-per cent vision or better with the other eye; those with less than 80-per cent vision at 14 inches with one or both eyes even though they had better than 90-per cent distant-vision; and those who failed on some of the binocular tests even though monocular distant-vision with either eye was 90 per cent or better.

Group III. Those with 70-per cent (20/30) distant-vision or less with both eyes; those with less than 70-per cent vision with one eye even though vision in the other eye was 90-per cent or better; and those with 100-per cent vision or better at 14 inches and less than 70-per cent distant-vision.

The results of this survey are summarized in Table LXXVII. It will be noted that (1) the greatest percentage of the faster readers were those with the highest visual rating and (2) that the percentage of the faster readers decreased and the percentage of slower readers increased as the seriousness of the visual handicap increased. These conclusions apply to both boys and girls.

TABLE LXXVII

Percentages of Each Visual Group Among the Fast and Slow Readers

Percentages of Children in Each Visual Group	Fast Readers	Slow Readers
3031 Boys		
Group I, 48 per cent	57 per cent	43 per cent
Group II, 33 per cent............	52	48
Group III, 19 per cent	43	57
2886 Girls		
Group I, 43 per cent	64 per cent	36 per cent
Group II, 35 per cent	57.5	42.5
Group III, 22 per cent	56	44

The improvement in reading ability in cases involving defective vision following correction of the eye-defects has been studied by Eames.[178] From an original group of 114 cases of reading disability, 28 were selected which had been tested at comparable intervals with the same standard reading test. The reading test was administered at the beginning of the school year and a complete eye-examination was made soon afterward. All eye-defects discovered were corrected or treated according to the nature of the difficulty. The same reading test was given again seven

[483]

months later. As a control group, an equal number of unselected cases was taken from the school records. These children had been tested at the same times with the same test and by the school psychologist who had tested the greater part of the other group. The results of the psychological tests are expressed in terms of reading age. For example, a theoretically normal child would be expected to obtain an increment of seven months of reading age from seven months of instruction. A comparison of the results obtained from the two groups follows:

	Median reading-age increment
Reading-disability group	7.8 months
Unselected group	5.33 months

Eames offers an explanation of the greater increment for the reading-disability group on the basis that this group was retarded below the normal reading ages before treatment. When the impeding conditions were removed or lessened,[180] these children were able to approach the normal reading age more rapidly because of greater relative maturity in relation to the work to be done. In general, Eames concludes that poor readers may be expected to make normal monthly progress in reading following correction of eye-defects and fusional deficiencies.

CHAPTER XIII

Eyesight and Seeing

One cannot be intimately associated with diverse researches in vision and seeing without being convinced of the general inadequacy of conditions for seeing. Furthermore, one cannot avoid the conclusion that the usual subjective appraisals of visual function are unreliable and incomplete. On the other hand, such investigations as we have described reveal so many deeply-rooted psychophysiological effects of seeing that it becomes obvious that objective considerations of the visual mechanism or physical conditions for seeing are also inadequate. For example, the diagnosis of visual anomalies involves much more than geometrical optics. Hence the lack of precision and reliability of subjective measurements does not alter the fact that these data are highly significant in appraising the visual ability and efficiency of the individual. Thus the present approach to some phases of ophthalmology is for the purpose of improving rather than criticizing subjective techniques. In brief, the methods which we have used to determine quantitatively the effects of external physical variables upon visibility are now applied to determine quantitatively the effects of biological variables upon visibility.

SENSITOMETRIC MEASUREMENTS

As a matter of definition, we have generally considered visibility as an attribute of the object of regard and sensitivity as an attribute of the visual organs, although the two are inseparable from a formal sensory viewpoint. In the measurement of visibility it is obviously expedient to assume normal vision; and for similar reasons, we assume a standard test-object for the appraisal of the relative sensitivities of human eyes. Thus a combination of our visibility meter and a suitable standard test-object may be

[485]

regarded as one form of an ophthalmic sensitometer. The former has been described in detail in Chapter V. The latter is reproduced in Fig. 133. This object consists of a black biconcave bar, upon a white background, 60 minutes in length and 1.5 and 3.75 minutes in width at its center and extremities, respectively. These configurational characteristics were determined empirically and are such that the visibility of the bar is uniform with respect to its longitudinal dimension. The design of this test-object was suggested by the observation that an elongated object, such as a rectangular bar, tends to fade into invisibility towards its ends as the visual threshold is approached. Since the ends of a rectangular object are first to disappear, the shape shown in Fig. 133 tends to offset this effect.

FIG. 133.—The biconcave test-object used in conjunction with the ophthalmic sensitometer. In practice, this object is 60 minutes in length and 1.5 and 3.75 minutes in width, respectively, at its center and extremities. The configuration of this object is such that it is of uniform visibility, under threshold conditions, with respect to its longitudinal dimension.

In order to investigate the relative merits of the biconcave test-object and a rectangular one of uniform width throughout its entire length, it was assumed that the magnitude of the mean variation of a series of measurements, the time required to make the measurements and the introspective reports of the subjects on the "definiteness" of the visual threshold represent appropriate criteria. In Table LXXVIII are presented the average results

TABLE LXXVIII

Comparative Results Obtained for Two Simple Test-Objects

	Rectangular	Biconcave
Mean variation of a series of 5 measurements	7.4 per cent	4.9 per cent
Average time for a series of 5 measurements	1.19 minutes	1.04 minutes
Number of subjects preferring particular test-object *	1	13

* One subject indicated no preference.

of this investigation, involving a total of 600 observations on each test-object made on four different days by 15 subjects having normal or near-normal vision. It will be noted from these data that the variability of a group of measurements, made under identical physical conditions, was decreased 35 per cent, and the time required for measurement was decreased 13 per cent by modifying the configuration of a rectangular bar to that shown in Fig. 133.

The relative visibility of the biconcave test-object, as determined by many measurements by eight subjects possessing socalled

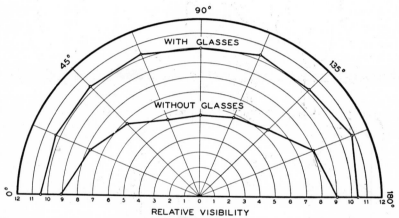

FIG. 134.—The relative visibility obtained with the biconcave test-object in various meridians as measured with and without eyeglasses.

normal vision, is approximately nine under the standardized illumination of ten footcandles. In other words, this test-object should be of threshold visibility to a subject having a visual efficiency rating of about 25 per cent as will be noted from Fig. 77. Hence it may be used as a single standard test-object in a wide variety of cases of defective vision. Since the diameter of the average fovea subtends a visual angle of about 70 minutes, the length of the retinal image of this test-object is comparable to the diameter of the fovea. Hence if the object is rotated about its center, it follows that substantially the entire foveal area is thus surveyed. The data plotted in Fig. 134 represent such a survey of retinal sensitivity by meridians. In this case, the results indicate astigmia. If a sharp depression in this meridional visibility curve is obtained for a particular meridian, it is possible that such a result would indicate a retinal lesion. Thus the sensitometric method may be of value in diagnosing certain pathological anomalies.

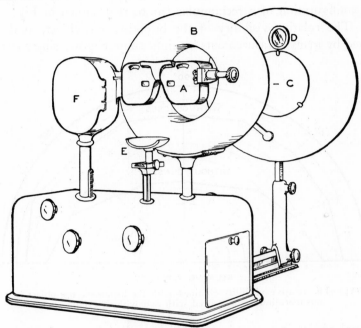

FIG. 135.—The Luckiesh-Moss Ophthalmic Sensitometer showing: *A*, the visibility meter; *B*, the annulus reflector for illuminating the target-field *C*; *D*, a light-sensitive cell for determining the level of illumination; *E*, the chin rest, and *F*, an automatic recording device.

It also should be obvious that this new subjective method is equally applicable and precise in determining visual efficiency under both static and dynamic conditions. This is not a characteristic of the usual Snellen Chart technique. In the latter case, the relatively small details which are required are difficult to reproduce with accuracy. Thus it is reasonable to expect that the use of the sensitometric method in clinical practice would greatly enhance the value of subjective appraisals of visual efficiency taken under dynamic conditions. In fact, an accurate determination of the ratio of dynamic to static visual efficiency might lead to a better understanding of visual anomalies associated with stimulus-distance phenomena.[47] For example, such ratios determined from time to time have been shown to be of value in diagnosing the progress made in treating pseudo-myopia.

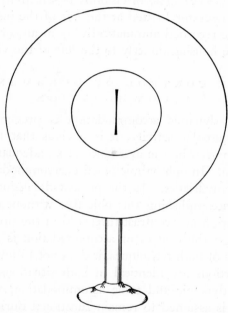

Fig. 136.—The distant-vision target-field and the biconcave test-object which may be placed in any desired meridian by means of electrical control.

The ophthalmic sensitometer, as developed by the authors, is illustrated in Figs. 135 and 136. Fig. 135 shows *A*, the visibility meter which may be operated by turning the knob at the right; *B*, the annulus reflector for illuminating the near-vision targets; *C*, the near-vision target-field consisting of a uniform white disc with the test-object at its center; *D*, a cell near its periphery for determining the level of illumination upon the target; *E*, a chin-rest for positioning the subject; and *F*, an automatic

[489]

recording device which may or may not be used. These elements are adjustable in height. In addition, the near-vision target is so arranged that it may be rotated downward and out of the line of sight when measurements are to be made upon a similar or other test-object at greater distances. The distance-vision test-object is shown in Fig. 136. The biconcave test-object is placed upon a disc which may be rotated to any desired meridian through electrical control. The measurements of visibility or sensitivity may be noted visually by an operator located at the left of the instrument table or they may be recorded automatically by means of the apparatus mounted in the housing directly to the left of the visibility meter.

THE CONTROL OF DYNAMANIC ACCOMMODATION

Although dynamic accommodation is preventable through paralysis of muscular activity, it is obvious that this result can likewise be achieved by the avoidance of an adequate stimulus for accommodation. In ophthalmic practice, accommodation is readily controlled by mydriatics. In the present discussion, a method is proposed for accomplishing this objective without drugs through the use of a brightness-contrast threshold in the process of refraction. Although the control of accommodation is assumed to be a characteristic of both techniques, it does not follow that the physiological functions are identical in both situations. Cycloplegia inhibits both dynamic and tonic accommodation, while tonic accommodation is assumed to remain functional during the sensitometric measurements. The latter characteristic, regardless of its actual or eventual clinical significance, is recognized rather than emphasized in the present discussion.

Stimuli for accommodation. As the threshold of resolution is approached by the usual visual acuity techniques, it is obvious that the critical details of the test-object gradually become unrecognizable although the object *as a whole* may be perceived readily. For example, it might be impossible for a subject to distinguish between the letter *O* and the letter *C*, of a given line of the Snellen Chart, but in both cases the *presence* of these char-

lens producing maximum visibility should necessarily be prescribed. However, a preliminary investigation indicated that the sensitometric method (based upon a brightness-difference threshold) rather consistently indicates more minus or less plus power than does retinoscopy.

It is possible that the dioptric differential between the two methods is due to tonic accommodation induced by the critical character of the visual task. Critical visual tasks are almost always performed at distances within arm's reach; and hence it is conceivable that the subject might tend to accommodate, for psychological reasons, for some distance less than the actual distance of the test-object from the eyes. Furthermore, the proximity of the hand to the eyes when operating the sensitometer may tend to stimulate accommodation reflexly due to the impression of "nearness" arising from proprioceptor phenomena. However, it seems reasonable to assume that accommodation arising from these causes would be avoided by providing a target, in the plane of the test-object, for stimulating binocular fixation and convergence. Obviously, the characteristics of such a fixation target must be such that dynamic accommodation is avoided.

This has been accomplished by surrounding the biconcave bar test-object with a ring of light, the brightness of which gradually decreased from the center of the band of light towards both its inner and its outer boundaries. In other words, the ring of light was similar in appearance to the image of a projected out-of-focus ring of light. Thus this object provided a minimum stimulus for accommodation and an adequate one for convergence regardless of the density of the sensitometric filters before the eyes. Monocular sensitometric measurements of visual function were made possible by placing an additional filter of a fixed density before the eye not being examined, thus lowering the visual efficiency obtained by that eye below that obtained by the eye under examination. Thus in approaching the threshold condition from the sub-threshold condition, the biconcave bar test-object was seen only by the eye being examined although the diffused ring of light was seen by both eyes.

As a result of these refinements in the sensitometric technique, it has been found that the prescriptions obtained with this method are in better agreement with those obtained by retinoscopy. At present, we are engaged in further refinement of our procedures through minimizing the effects of spherical aberration. In addition to reducing the dioptric differential between the subjective (sensitometric) and objective (retinoscopic) techniques, the use of the binocular fixation target permits the use of this method for dynamic refraction.

It is not implied that the results obtained by the subjective sensitometric method are nearer the "true values" than are retinoscopic findings since, as Sheard states, full corrections in hyperopia, for example, are rarely accepted without some blur. Nature has to be taught new habits, and readjustments to innervations have to be accomplished. However, it seems reasonable to assume that the sensitometric data, in conjunction with retinoscopic findings, will be of considerable value in diagnosis, and particularly in those cases where the results obtained by these two methods are not in agreement. Thus the advantages of the sensitometric method are realized to the fullest extent in those cases which are difficult to diagnose.

A statistical analysis of the sensitometric data from ten subjects for the purpose of appraising the symmetry of the relationship between dioptric power and visibility is presented in Table LXXIX.

The data of Table LXXIX indicate that the average decrements in visibility resulting from over- and under-corrections of one-half diopter, respectively, are about equal, thus denoting a symmetrical relationship between the two variables. The definiteness of the maxima of visibility and the symmetry of the relationships, for the "typical" subject, will be clearly shown by plotting these average values. These data also indicate that the average percentage of maximal visibility obtained with over- or under-corrections of one-half diopter is 77, with a probable error of 0.5. However, this value is apparently a function of the brightness and contrast characteristics of the entoptic stimulus. The latter,

TABLE LXXIX

These Values Are the Percentages of Maximal Visibility Obtained for Corrections of One-Half Diopter, Plus and Minus, Added to the Dioptric Power Corresponding to Maximum Visibility.

| Subject | Left Eye Meridians | | | | Right Eye Meridians | | | |
| | Best Vision | | Worst Vision | | Best Vision | | Worst Vision | |
	+	−	+	−	+	−	+	−
1	68	88	75	81	60	71	78	82
2	69	71	70	70	67	78	68	66
3	80	67	86	84	75	61	77	82
4	80	77	78	84	74	77	77	81
5	65	75	69	77	74	77	83	62
6	77	78	81	76	73	77	76	76
7	87	88	72	73	85	86	86	82
8	68	81	64	68	69	85	54	77
9	83	74	71	71	88	84	83	89
10	89	82	91	80	82	79	70	85
Mean	77	78	76	76	75	78	75	78

therefore, govern the "sensitivity" of the method to changes in dioptric power.

The sensitometric data presented in Fig. 137 involve merely the recognition of the presence of the biconcave bar test-object as a criterion of threshold vision. When a Snellen Chart was substituted for this test-object and the subject required to recognize the individual letters thereon, the resulting relationship between visual function and dioptric power was not only far from symmetrical, but also did not always indicate a definite maximum in visibility. This result is consistent with the hypothesis advanced that such a test-object constitutes a stimulus for accommodation when subliminal conditions for *resolution* prevail.

Introspective considerations. The subjects consistently reported that a series of monocular sensitometric measurements taken over a period of 30 minutes or more did not induce an unusual feeling of ocular fatigue when the visual threshold was approached from the subliminal condition. These experiments involved the measurement of visual function while the subject was looking through various powers of both convex and concave lenses. When similar measurements were made by approaching the threshold from the supraliminal condition, the subjects reported definite strain and fatigue within a relatively short time.

Furthermore, the symmetry of the typical inverted "V" curves, Fig. 137, was seriously distorted when the measurements were made by approaching the visual threshold from the supraliminal condition. In this case the measurement of visual function through each lens begins with a test-object of relatively high visibility and, concomitantly, a strong stimulus for accommodation. As the threshold is approached by gradually reducing the contrast between the test-object and its background, the innervation which may induce or maintain accommodation is progressively reduced and at the absolute threshold becomes nil. Nevertheless, measurements taken by this technique are quite likely to be influenced by accommodative effort since a stimulus for accommodation has been present to some degree during the operation. It may be concluded from these experiences that accommodative effort was not exercised in approaching the threshold from the subliminal condition in the attempt to compensate for the various lenses successively placed before the eye.

It should be emphasized that the purpose of refraction is not merely to study the optical properties of the uninnervated eye, for as Southall states,[182] "The important question after all is as to how the individual patient actually focuses his eye for distinct vision, and so far as clinical methods are concerned, the ultimate decision will probably have to depend upon the subjective investigation." This does not exclude the possibility that the accidental error of the subjective method may exceed the systematic error of the objective method employed. Measurements at any particular distance and at any one time obviously give no definite assurance of what the patient will do, or can do, at some other distance or at another time.

Summary. The sensitometric method possesses the following indicated characteristics: dynamic accommodation is controllable without the use of drugs and without inhibiting tonic accommodation; and the significance of subjective refraction is enhanced due to the precision and reliability of the subjective data obtainable. Obviously much additional clinical research is necessary to evaluate the clinical significance of these conclusions. The major purpose of this discussion is to suggest such researches.

VISUAL EFFICIENCY AND OCULAR COMFORT

Clinical experience indicates that the results obtained from subjective and objective methods of refraction are in reasonable agreement in the majority of cases. However, in a very significant number of cases, the two methods may yield quite different diagnoses. In still other cases, the methods may be in agreement for one eye and not for the other. Thus the refractionist must prescribe corrections in accordance with the findings of one method or the other or perhaps effect some sort of a compromise. In either case, he must depend upon the patient to determine the suitability of the prescribed lenses. This the patient is able to do when the corrections given to him are in serious error and asthenopia develops. However, in the absence of extremely deleterious effects, the patient may be quite inaccurate in his appraisal of the correctness of his glasses since he does not have a reliable conception of how clearly or easily he should see. It is obvious that clinical tests which would appraise these factors, *even approximately*, would be of great value to the refractionist.

In discussing certain criteria which appear to be favorable for these purposes, it is recognized that any clinical procedure, applied at the time when the corrections are given to the patient, may serve only as an approximate basis for prognosis. As before stated, the human seeing-machine has to be taught new habits, and readjustments to innervations have to be established. However, it is equally obvious that new and independent criteria of clearness of vision and comfort in seeing, considered as supplementary clinical criteria, will be of assistance in prescribing lenses of the most probable correctness. As a mathematical analogue, the advisability of using an arithmetic, geometric or harmonic mean in summarizing a series of data is determined by comparing these means, respectively, with other statistical criteria such as the median and the mode.

Maximum visual sensitivity. It will be assumed that different ophthalmic corrections may be indicated by subjective and objective methods of refraction. Obviously, the two possible prescriptions thus obtained may be appraised on the basis of (1) producing maximum clearness of vision or (2) providing optimum visual comfort for the patient. In some cases, the two criteria may indicate the same corrections; that is, the lenses which will result in maximum clearness of vision will also provide optimum comfort in seeing. However, without quantitative measurements with respect to these two criteria, this fact may be ascertained only by the method of trial which is subject to all the errors resulting from human vagaries. If the two criteria indicate different corrections, the problem of ascertaining the best correction, through the introspective reports of the patient, is even more difficult. As clinical tests for determining the corrections best suited to the patient we propose (1) to measure visual clearness by the sensitometric technique, and (2) to appraise ease of seeing by appropriate means such as the frequency of the reflex blink which we have definitely correlated with strain and fatigue in seeing as shown in Chapter VI.

The sensitometric method possesses the following advantages as a clinical means for appraising the factor of clearness of vision:

1. Dynamic accommodation is controlled without the use of cycloplegics.

2. Repeated measurements of visual function are possible under identical physical conditions. Hence the clinical results may possess a high degree of reliability. This fact may be verified by accepted statistical methods of analysis.

3. The method involves the characteristic of precision due to the fact that the intensity of the stimulus is directly controlled by the patient while the latter performs a critical task. Furthermore, the patient is required to respond only to the presence or absence of the stimulus in the visual field thus minimizing extraneous psychological factors.

In practice, a series of five measurements or more is made by the patient while wearing, respectively, the subjectively and objectively determined prescriptions. These data are averaged and the probable errors [183] of these averages may be determined from the formula,

$$PE_M = 0.8453 \, \frac{\Sigma d}{n\sqrt{n-1}} \qquad \text{(Equation 1)}$$

where Σd = sum of the arithmetic deviations from the mean; and n = number of observations. The magnitudes of the probable errors which are usually obtained in practice are shown in Tables XXV and XXVI.

Assuming that the two average values of sensitivity are different in magnitude, the statistical significance of this difference may be determined from the formula,

$$PE_D = \sqrt{(PE_1)^2 + (PE_2)^2} \qquad \text{(Equation 2)}$$

where PE_1 and PE_2 are the probable errors, respectively, of the two average values of relative visibility derived from Equation 1. In general, if the difference between the two average values of relative visibility obtained with the subjective and objective prescriptions is five or six times as great as the probable error of the difference, the former may be regarded as real and significant. When the appraisal of clearness of vision is based merely upon the introspective reports of the patient, the refractionist is by no means *certain* of the reliability of the conclusions thus formed. In fact, the patient may not be able accurately to report a difference although such a difference may exist in fact. Obviously, there can be little doubt when the diagnosis is based upon biometric analyses. Although this method of analyzing clinical data may appear somewhat tedious, it is probable that much of it may be eliminated when the refractionist gains experience in thus analyzing his findings.

Optimum ocular comfort. From the neurological viewpoint there are several reasons for supposing that the frequency of the reflex blink is related to physiological conditions such as strain and tenseness. Furthermore, the data of Table XXXIV definitely correlate the frequency of the reflex blink with conditions which are known to be unfavorable for seeing. Thus this phenomenon may serve as a useful criterion of ocular comfort as the latter is influenced by ophthalmic corrections. A summary of the corrections indicated by the criterion of visibility and frequency of the reflex blink, is presented for 30 subjects in Table LXXX.

TABLE LXXX

The Frequency of the Reflex Blink as a Criterion for Determining the Efficacy of Ophthalmic Corrections Prescribed According to the Usual Techniques. These Data Denote the Number of Blinks Occurring During Five Minute Periods of Reading While Wearing Corrections of +.50 Diopter and —.50 Diopter, Respectively, in Addition to the Corrections Usually Worn

Subject	Frequency of Blink			Subject	Frequency of Blink		
	+.50	0	—.50		+.50	0	—.50
1	38	27	30	16	60	36	48
2*	30	22	30	17	35	26	31
3*	77	64	83	18	25	14	19
4	28	17	21	19*	40	30	52
5	93	70	82	20*	28	27	37
6*	16	12	14	21*	17	13	20
7	17	12	12	22*	112	78	92
8	40	20	33	23*	49	36	40
9	38	28	46	24*	25	14	18
10	7	10	12	25	60	24	39
11*	18	10	16	26*	6	8	10
12*	30	24	30	27*	43	33	100
13*	9	6	9	28	16	15	12
14*	25	14	22	29	42	24	34
15*	33	25	25	30*	57	48	56
*Correction Worn				Arithmetic Mean	37.1	26.2	35.8

Considering the subjects as a group, it will be noted that the minimum rate of blinking occurred when the subjects wore plano lenses in addition to their usual corrections, if any. Obviously, this conclusion involves only a consideration of the spherical components of the lenses worn. However, it also is obvious that the criterion of the reflex blink is applicable for appraising the probable correctness of other components of the ophthalmic prescriptions. The *average values* presented in Table LXXX are considered significant only to the extent that they indicate that this new method of diagnosis yields results which are in general agreement with present refractive diagnoses.

An analysis of these data with respect to individual cases shows that additional corrections are needed by six of the thirty subjects when appraised by the method of the reflex blink. Subjects 7, 10, 15, 20, 26 and 28 are included in this group. Among these subjects, it will be noted that three subjects did not wear glasses although such corrections are indicated by the criterion of the reflex blink. It is also emphasized that these data were obtained from a group of subjects not possessing, in general, unusually severe visual disorders. Hence it seems reasonable to assume that this new diagnostic criterion, added to the armamenta of the refractionist, would be of considerable value in the diagnosis of difficult cases. Finally, it represents the first direct physiological criterion, objectively determinable, for the clinical appraisal of ocular comfort.

At this point it may be of interest to refer to Fig. 143 which illustrates graphically some average rates of blinking due to reading under various visual conditions. The reader is also referred to Table XXXIII.

SENSITOMETRIC CRITERIA IN REFRACTION

As a result of the gradual transition in clinical practice from subjective to objective techniques for measuring refractive errors, it is probable that the advantages of subjective measurements as criteria of *seeing* have been relinquished in order to obtain the advantages of precision, reliability and speed which are inherent to objective methods. However, it is axiomatic that the complete visual sensory process is not adequately appraisable in terms of the variables measurable by objective methods. On the other hand, the usefulness of the usual subjective methods is often limited not only by the ambiguity of the data, but also by reason of the limitations of interpretation. As an example of the latter, it should be obvious that sensitivity to brightness-difference is a variable in seeing which may be quite as important as visual acuity. Nevertheless, it is seldom measured in clinical practice. Although the subjective and objective techniques are often considered to be competitive methods for revealing and measuring refractive errors, it would seem more appropriate to regard one as supplementary to the other. Thus if the two methods yield significantly different prescriptions, this fact may be considered as an indication of the need for further clinical study of the case.

Since it has been adequately demonstrated in Chapter V that the effects of external physical variables upon visual function may be measured with unusual precision by the sensitometric method, it may be assumed that this technique is also precise in measuring the effects of biological variables upon visual functions. If this assumption is justifiable, this method presents a means for greatly increasing the precision of subjective data and for augmenting the significance of subjective methods of refraction. However, it is emphasized that this discussion is presented from the viewpoint of the potentialities of a new method, rather than as a description of a technique already thoroughly established by clinical experience. The method is proposed as a means for providing an additional criterion for the diagnosis of difficult cases and at present is not considered as a substitute for present methods of refraction or as a desirable one for the diagnosis of simple and more or less routine cases. As a foremost refractionist has stated: "In perhaps three-fourths of my cases the present methods of refraction are adequate and satisfactory, but in the remainder the entire science of refraction seems to be inadequate." From this viewpoint, new criteria should facilitate the advancement of ophthalmic science.

In the sensitometric method, quantitative measurements of visual function are made possible by a technique which involves a series of observations under identical and controllable physical conditions. Since these data are quantitative in character, they may be presented in simple graphical form which so greatly aids the analyst. Thus relationships between various visual factors are clearly revealed. Many of these relationships may remain undetected when the ocular diagnosis is based upon qualitative verbal reports of the patient, as is the case in the usual subjective examination. Also the significance of the sensitometric data is augmented by the fact that these measurements of visual efficiency correspond to threshold conditions, the physical characteristics of which are directly controlled by the patient.

Laboratory experience indicates that a subject is able to adjust apparatus for threshold conditions much better than he can direct someone else in making the manual adjustments for him.

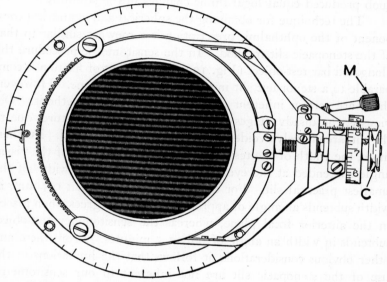

Fig. 139.—The Ives-Cobb crossed-grating visual acuity apparatus. The width of the parallel lines may be gradually altered by the turning of a handwheel by the subject. The shaft of the handwheel is connected to the apparatus by a belt to the pulley at *C*. The parallel lines may be set in any meridian by means of the adjustment screw at *M*.

A fortiori, no photometrist would consider operating a visual photometer in the latter manner. However, such a procedure is not unusual in clinical practice. For example, the refractionist may adjust the Ives-Cobb crossed-grating test-object (Fig. 139) until the patient indicates that he can no longer resolve the parallel lines. In such a case, the visual acuity rating obtained is likely to involve the vagaries of the refractionist as well as the visual acuity of the patient. For example, if the width of the lines is decreased

[505]

rapidly or by irregular steps, the threshold size will be larger than it will be when approached more slowly and regularly. Furthermore, it is a well-known fact in physiological optics that the intensity of the stimulus should be varied uniformly and geometrically if the maximum precision is to be obtained. These characteristics of operation are approximated when the subject operates the sensitometer since equal degrees of rotation of the controlling knob produced equal logarithmic changes in the stimulus.

The technique for obtaining the spherical and cylindrical component of the ophthalmic prescription is somewhat similar to that of the stenopaeic slit method. In the sensitometric procedure the elongated bar test-object (Fig. 133) as the point of fixation is comparable to a stenopaeic slit in the anterior focal plane. However, there are certain inherent differences in the two methods. Obviously, the disadvantages of restricted pupillary aperture, due to the slit, are entirely avoided in the sensitometric method. Furthermore, the width of the test-object, expressed in terms of the visual angle subtended at the eye, is only a fraction of the width of the smallest practical slit. For example, a stenopaeic slit 0.5 mm. in width subtends an angle of approximately two degrees when placed in the anterior focal plane, whereas the sensitometer test-object subtends in width an angle of only 1.5 minutes. From these and other obvious considerations, it follows that the limitations in the use of the stenopaeic slit are not inherent to our sensitometric method, although the latter involves similar basic principles.

The sensitometric method of refraction, in the absence of heterophoria, involves the following determinations:

Principal meridians. The principal meridians are determined from the relationships between relative visibility and angular position of the concave-bar test-object. The results, plotted on polar coordinates in Fig. 134, show the visual sensitivity in various meridians without glasses and with glasses, respectively. Obviously, the flattened part of the curve for the uncorrected eye in the region of the 90 degree meridian indicates astigmia. When glasses are worn, the curve relating visibility and angular position is substantially a semi-circle, thus indicating the correction of the astigmatism. In addition, the increased radius of the curve with glasses as compared to that without glasses indicates the effectiveness of the spherical component of the ophthalmic prescription. In Fig. 140 the relationship between visibility and angular position of the test-object is plotted on rectangular coordinates in order to facilitate determination of the principal meridians. It will be noted that the data of Fig. 134 and 140 do not pertain to the same subject.

Spherical and cylindrical corrections. With the test-object in

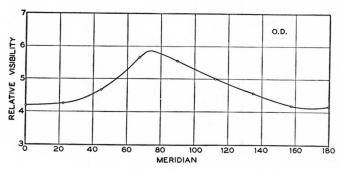

FIG. 140.—The relative visibility of the biconcave test-object in various meridians as determined by a patient having astigmatism.

the meridian corresponding to the highest degree of visibility, a series of measurements is made for each of several powers of spherical lenses. This procedure is repeated with the test-object in the meridian of least visibility. The data thus obtained are plotted in Fig. 141. In accordance with the theory of the stenopaeic-slit method, the spherical correction is determined by the dioptric power corresponding to maximal visibility in the meridian of best vision; and the cylindrical correction, by the algebraic difference in dioptric powers producing maximal visibility in the meridians of best and worst vision, respectively. Usually measurements made for four different dioptric powers, two less and two greater than that corresponding to maximum visibility, will be sufficient to accurately define the dioptric power producing maximum visibility. Actually the latter is usually found by extrapola-

[507]

tion as is indicated in Fig. 141. Approximate subjective methods or retinoscopy may be used to determine the approximate power corresponding to maximum visibility. Of course, the latter could be found by taking sensitometric measurements over a wide range

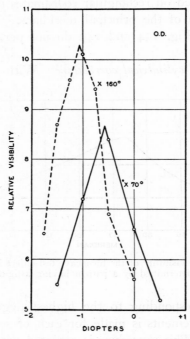

FIG. 141.—The relative visibility of the biconcave test-object placed in the meridians of best vision (solid-line) and worst vision (broken-lines), respectively, and observed by the patient through lenses of various dioptric powers.

of powers. This is usually inadvisable since it unnecessarily tires the subject. Obviously, data obtained in previous sensitometric examinations would be very helpful in minimizing the number of measurements required in the determination of the lens-power corresponding to maximum visibility.

It will be noted that each measurement of visibility contributes to the specification of the final lens since it influences the form of the curve relating visibility and dioptric power. In either subjective or objective refraction by the usual methods the individual

[508]

observations of patient or refractionist are not involved in the final diagnosis since they are qualitative in character. Furthermore, since the sensitometric data are quantitative in character and describe definite relationships, it is possible to detect and eliminate occasional erratic data. Thus precision is an inherent characteristic of the sensitometric method of refraction, and it is obvious that it is well adapted for the prescription of lenses of fractional dioptric power.

The sensitometric method of refraction appears to be particularly well adapted for the diagnosis of lenticular astigmatism due to its precision and to the fact that dynamic accommodation is controlled. In addition, it should be a valuable aid in refracting cases involving small pupils, cataracts, opacities, cloudy media, scissor movements, high refractive errors and others in which retinoscopy is difficult. It is obvious that these factors do not present a serious handicap in sensitometry since their effect upon visibility may be counteracted, if necessary, through the use of a larger test-object or higher levels of illumination.

Although the sensitometer has been developed primarily for purposes of refraction and for the appraisal of physical factors in seeing, it may be used in certain fields of pathology. For example, it is well known that retardation in the rate of dark-adaptation is symptomatic of night-blindness and glaucoma. Hence this phase of visual function may be investigated quantitatively by observing the time required for the retinae to become adapted to a low level of illumination after a definite exposure to a much higher one. Since such measurements involve brightness-difference threshold as a criterion, and the sensitometer is designed to measure this variable, the sensitometer seems appropriate for the purpose. It may also be possible to appraise the course of treatment of traumatic retinal conditions by a comparison of the degree of visibility obtained with the test-object image coinciding with and adjacent to, respectively, the retinal area under consideration.

Since the sensitometric method provides a means for precisely determining the dioptric characteristics corresponding to maximal sensitivity with dynamic accommodation controlled and tonic accommodation in force, the results obtained by subjective and objective methods of refraction may be critically compared. A comparison of this kind is obviously impossible when the subjective examination is made by means of the usual visual-acuity techniques.

Binocular measurements. In general, our binocular sensitometric measurements indicate that the monocular findings should be reduced approximately ¼ diopter in minus power or increased by the same amount in plus power in some cases. However, this dioptric datum is based upon the results obtained in relatively few cases. It is presented as an illustration of (1) the rather close agreement between monocular and binocular sensitometric tests; and (2) the precision with which small refractive differences may be detected. Thus emphasis is placed upon the method rather than upon the values obtained. In addition, the subjects examined did not possess severe visual disorders of a muscular character.

In comparing the results obtained by monocular and binocular refraction account must be taken of the interrelation of convergence and accommodation and of the effect of age on this interrelation. The subject will have at any instant a "rest position" of the extrinsic muscles and a degree of accommodation correlated with this. In the absence of any stimulus for either convergence or accommodation, this should determine the results of refractive tests. It should, however, be borne in mind that the stimulus for convergence may be subjective, i.e., the patient may expect the test-object at some particular distance and make a more or less successful attempt to converge at that distance.

The tightness of bonding between convergence and accommodation may be expected to vary widely among subjects. One subject may have a large accommodation reserve, but practically no power to dissociate it from convergence. Another subject may have a small accommodation reserve, but be able to exercise it regardless of convergence. It may be expected as the lens stiffens that the accommodation coupled with convergence will become inadequate, as the same innervation will produce less and less refractive effect. This will tend to obscure systematic errors in objective refraction due to the position of the plane of emergent

[510]

light, since a lens correct for distance vision will not have enough plus at shorter range, and most people do little critical work at great distances. With a young subject in whom the automatic accommodation is already excessive such a neglect would compound the error in refraction at close range.

ORTHOPTIC TRAINING

If the binocular coordination of the eyes may be functionally compared to the paralleling of two direct-current generators, it follows from the electrical analogue that the monocular visual stimuli must be equalized if the eyes are to function normally in the perception of solidity and depth, just as the voltages of the two electrical machines must be equalized for an equal division of the load. In the biological situation, the intensities of the monocular stimuli and ocular dominance are considered analogous, respectively, to the voltages and loads of the two electrical machines operating in parallel. Since the balancing of visual efficiency has long been recognized as of fundamental importance in orthoptics, the significance and value of the electrical analogue is in emphasizing the essentiality of a precise balancing of monocular vision.

Clinical experience indicates that stereopsis is dependent upon balanced visual stimuli, but is independent of the intensity level of the latter. For example, it has been possible to obtain complete stereopsis in cases of congenital amblyopia involving visual acuities as low as 20/100 by carefully balancing the visibility of the two targets. Furthermore, it has been observed that such a balancing is also an important factor in the functioning of the convergence mechanism. For example, in some cases involving low adductive ability, as measured by base-out prism tests, the balancing of the visual stimuli immediately increased the apparent amplitude of convergence.

The usual procedure for balancing the visibility of the binocular test-objects used with orthoptic apparatus is to control the target illumination. As a result, these methods not only involve certain practical difficulties, such as providing an adequate range in visibility, but also possess the inherent disadvantage of often requiring extremely low levels of illumination. It is a well-known fact that large changes in objective illumination are required to produce relatively small changes in visual efficiency as appraised by the criterion of visual acuity. This relationship will be noted from Fig. 37. For example, it will be noted that a hundredfold change in retinal illumination must be made to reduce visual acuity from 1.0 to 0.2 or from the Snellen rating of 20/20 to 20/100. Such a reduction in the visibility of one of the test-objects is not infrequently necessary in treating amblyopia-ex-anopsia.

It is obvious that the alteration of visibility by means of brightness changes involves concomitant changes in the size of

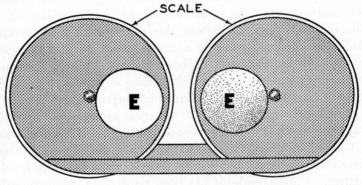

Fig. 142.—The Luckiesh-Moss Visibility Control as adapted for use with the Rotoscope. The letters "E" are shown behind the circular gradients for the purpose of indicating the independent control of monocular visibility.

the pupil and also in the state of retinal adaptation. Furthermore, it seems reasonable to assume that the introduction of these variables in the orthoptic problem is undesirable, particularly in cases where rather large changes in pupil size and retinal sensibility are involved. In addition to these physiological objections to altering visibility by brightness changes alone, there may be practical difficulties involved such as stray light and restricted ranges in illumination. These difficulties are minimized by controlling visibility through simultaneous changes in both brightness and contrast. In this manner, large changes in visibility may be accomplished with relatively small changes in illumination.

[512]

Apparatus and technique. The clinical apparatus consists essentially of two circular colorless filters with precise gradients of density, which may be placed before the apertures of the orthoptic instrument and in any desired angular position. These gradient filters are similar to those used in our visibility meter. The following technique, which a collaborator has used extensively for several years in clinical practice,[184] has proved to be effective in obtaining single binocular vision and in the treatment of orthoptic cases.

1. The angular deviation having been approximated and corrected (Duane) two dissimilar targets of equal brightness are exposed to the patient. Suppression of the object before the squinting or non-dominant eye usually follows. The gradient filter is then interposed before the dominant eye and rotated slowly (approaching absolute threshold) until suppression of that eye occurs and fixation is transferred.

2. Slight adjustments may then be made by varying: (1) the size of the targets, (2) the target illumination, (3) the amounts of prismatic power, and (4) the density of the filter before the dominant eye. At the present time, this fourth means of control appears to be of marked clinical advantage since simultaneous binocular vision has been established in a number of cases which had failed to respond to the first three methods of control.

3. The targets are then set in motion (technique of Stereo-Orthopter and Rotoscope) and the treatment continued in the usual manner. As the visual efficiency of the non-dominant eye increases, the density of the filter is progressively reduced.

Since the filters placed before the apertures of the orthoptic instrument are of the gradient type, it is obvious that the density of the interposed filter changes as the line of visual fixation changes with the motion of the targets. This effect is illustrated in Fig. 142 by placing a black object directly behind the gradient filters. However, clinical experience indicates that this characteristic of the method is a favorable one. For example, in cases involving extremely low visual acuity and a correspondingly dense filter for equalizing the visibility of the two targets, it has been observed that the target before the dominant eye will occasionally disappear as the target rotates. This is due to the fact that the line of vision passes through different portions of the gradient filter while following the movement of the target. Thus the advantages of the "make and break" method of treatment are obtained without the necessity of prismatic adjustment.

Diagnosis of progress in training and treatment. The data of Table LXXXI indicate the progress made in treating a case of pseudo-myopia as determined from sensitometric measurements. These data indicate that vision is approximately normal at 14 inches and far below normal at 20 feet. Many measurements of the visibility of the biconcave test-object by subjects with normal vision empirically establish the fact that a relative visibility value of about 9 is normal when the test-object is illuminated to 10 footcandles. Obviously the same level of illumination is used in both the near- and distant-vision measurements. These data in conjunction with those obtained by retinoscopy, indicate that the apparent myopia is in excess of the true dioptric error. The improvement, the eventual goal, and the necessity for bifocal glasses were readily appreciated by this patient from a plot of these data.

TABLE LXXXI

Diagnosis of Progress in the Treatment of Pseudo-Myopia. The Sensitometric Measurements of Relative Visibility Were Taken Binocularly and Without Eyeglasses. Each Measurement of Visibility Represents the Average of a Series of Five Observations. The Probable Errors of These Data Are Expressed in Per Cent.

Tests	Distant-Vision		Near-Vision		Ratio	P.E. of Ratio
	R.V.	P.E.	R.V.	P.E.		
Initial values......	2.0	1.9	8.7	2.8	0.23	3.4
After 3 months..	3.7	1.4	9.5	2.4	0.32	2.8

In this particular case, it will be noted that distant-vision, as compared with near-vision, was increased from 23 to 32 per cent, respectively. This is equivalent to an improvement in distant-vision of approximately 40 per cent. Since the probable error of these data is of the order of three per cent, the improvement may be regarded as real and significant from a statistical viewpoint. If the improvement or impairment in vision is several times as great as the probable error, the change may be regarded as real. This mathematical analysis of clinical data is obviously of value in orthoptic diagnosis.

VISUAL EFFICIENCY

Since the regulation of visual tasks in accordance with the visual ability of the individual is an important phase of ocular hygiene, the characteristics of the criteria for appraising visual ability or efficiency are correspondingly important. In ophthalmological practice, visual efficiency is usually expressed as a definite function of visual acuity as will be noted from Fig. 77. However, resolving power is but one characteristic of visual function, and in many situations it is not the primarily important one. As an extreme example, seeing at night outdoors depends largely upon the ability to discriminate brightness-differences. Furthermore, it can be shown that the latter criterion is the critical one in visual situations involving test-objects which are large in comparison with the spatial characteristics of the retinal mosaic. This fact is emphasized quantitatively in Fig. 42. Although the criterion of visual acuity involves the factor of retinal sensitivity, the influence of this variable upon the acuity threshold is relatively slight when high-contrast test-objects are used. In general, acuity is a rather insensitive criterion for revealing differences in retinal sensitivity among various subjects. Certainly the available knowledge of seeing proves that individuals with the same test-chart rating are not necessarily equivalent in efficiency or efficacy as human seeing-machines.

The data of Table LXXXII indicate the differences in efficiency ratings obtained among a group of low-vision subjects by the criteria of (1) visual acuity and (2) minimum perceptible brightness-difference as described in connection with Table XLIX. These data emphasize the insensitiveness of acuity as a criterion

[515]

of retinal sensitivity. The relative visibilities of 24-point type printed with black ink on white paper and illuminated by ten foot-candles were determined by means of the visibility meter.

TABLE LXXXII

The Values in the Second and Third Columns Were Determined with the Snellen Chart and Those in the Fourth Column by Means of the Visibility Meter.

Subject	Vision Uncorrected	Vision Corrected	Visibility of 24-Point Type
1	6/60	6/6	6.03
2	6/60	6/6	9.06
3	1/60	6/6	6.43
4	6/60	6/6	13.10
5	counts fingers	6/7.5	3.55
6	6/60	6/7.5	4.06
7	6/30	6/7.5	5.03
8	6/60	6/7.5	6.55
9	6/60	6/7.5	7.38
10	6/60	6/20	4.84
11	6/60	6/20	6.40
12	6/60	6/20	7.76
13	Nil	6/30	2.78
14	Nil	6/30	6.40

Although the vision of the first group was brought to 6/6 by eyeglasses, it will be noted that the individuals of this group are far from equal when appraised by means of brightness-difference thresholds. For example, Subjects 1 and 4 differ by more than a factor of two in the size of object just visible under threshold brightness-contrasts. Similar results are obtained for the other three groups. Since the probable errors of the values presented in the fourth column are of the order of three per cent, these data are quite reliable from a statistical viewpoint. However, it might be argued that this difference in "visual efficiency" may be due to perceptual rather than visual phenomena, since the visibility measurements involved ability to read as a criterion in contrast with ability to recognize single characters. This hypothesis may account for some but not for all of the difference observed, since rather large differences are obtained when single test-objects are used in both cases. Furthermore, if perceptual phenomena are important in these measurements, they are likewise important in performing customary visual tasks.

In clinical practice the contrast between the test-object and its background is generally that obtained with a "black" object upon a "white" background which is illuminated to a constant but often unknown brightness. Thus the various characters of the Snellen Chart, for example, could be represented, approximately and from an objective basis, by points along the abscissa of 100 per cent contrast in Fig. 37. Obviously, test-objects of lower contrasts could be specified with equal justification from the viewpoint of physiological optics. In fact, a test-chart developed by the authors which involves a series of test-objects of various contrasts but identical in size appears to be more precise than the usual form. At least, the introspective reports of the subjects indicate that the threshold condition is more sharply defined in the case of the graded-contrast chart. In other words, the same change in dioptric power of a lens before the eye apparently produces a more noticeable difference on the latter type of chart. In the world of seeing, high contrasts are involved in reading and similar tasks and hence an appraisal of visual efficiency with test-objects of maximal contrast is correspondingly appropriate. On the other hand, many visual objects or tasks involve low and even extremely low contrasts. These are found throughout the work-world. In a fairly extreme case, such as objects to be seen on the highway at night, an appraisal of visual efficiency by the criterion of minimum perceptible brightness-difference is a far more appropriate one.

The relative thresholds of size for a group of subjects having socalled normal vision, when appraised with test-objects of various contrasts illuminated to the same brightness, are indicated by the data of Table LXXXIII. In this case, the criterion of visual efficiency involves the resolution of space-intervals. It will be noted, for example, that Subjects 2 and 3 possessed approximately the same "visual acuity" (reciprocal of the values in the table) when the appraisal was made with black test-objects upon a white background (contrast = 100 per cent). However, the "visual acuity" of Subject 2 was more than twice as great as that of Subject 3 for very light gray test-objects upon a white background (contrast = 2 per cent). For the group of nine subjects the mean variation from the mean visual efficiency increased from 6 to 32 per cent, respectively, when the contrast of the test-objects was lowered from 100 to 2 per cent. Hence it may be concluded from both theoretical and empirical considerations that the term "visual acuity" is ambiguous as a criterion of visual efficiency except as it is used in the science of refraction.

TABLE LXXXIII

The Threshold Sizes of Objects in Minutes Visual Angle for Contrasts of 100, 10 and 2 Per Cent, Respectively. The Last Column Gives the Per Cent Mean Variation in Size of the Threshold Stimulus for the Nine Subjects. The Probable Errors of These Threshold Values Are of the Order of 1 Per Cent. Brightness-Level, 20 Millilamberts.

Per Cent Contrast	1	2	3	4	Subjects 5	6	7	8	9	Per Cent Variation
100	0.83	0.79	0.77	0.74	0.85	0.78	0.70	0.91	0.75	6.0
10	1.83	1.59	2.11	1.80	1.98	2.83	1.67	2.24	1.68	14.4
2	8.50	5.44	14.00	7.15	13.80	14.70	6.90	9.40	6.20	32.1

The duration of the stimulus has not been considered in this discussion of visual thresholds since it is governed *ad libitum* by the subject and the same temporal conditions prevail in the various techniques described. To this extent they are not representative of the conditions which obtain in most actual cases, e.g., reading and automobile driving.

An analysis of a series of measurements obtained through the use of our sensitometer leads to a similar conclusion. The data of Table LXXXIV, in addition to the agreement with the results presented in Table LXXXIII, are of interest since the sensitometric method does not involve a check upon the threshold values obtained, whereas the results in Table LXXXIII represent definitely checked thresholds. In other words, the accuracy of each threshold observation was checked in order to eliminate guessing.

TABLE LXXXIV

The Mean Variation in Relative Visibility Among a Group of 14 Adult Subjects Possessing Average Vision as Determined with the Sensitometer. These Values Were Determined from 25 Separate Measurements of Visual Function for Each Subject and for Each Test-Object. Brightness-Level, Ten Millilamberts.

Size of Threshold Test-Object in Minutes	3.95	2.50	1.66
Mean Variation in Relative Visibility Among Subjects in Per Cent	27	19	12

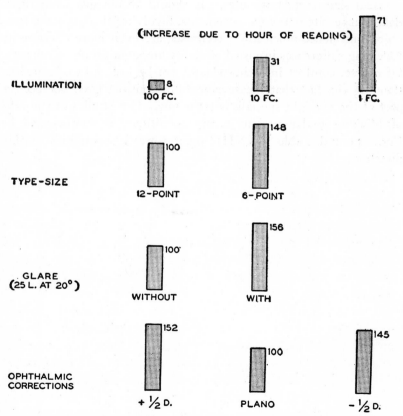

FIG. 143—Changes or differences in the frequency of blinking while reading under various visual conditions.

It will be noted from Table LXXXIV that the mean variation in relative visibility, as a criterion of the differences in visual
efficiency among the subjects, is a function of the physical characteristics of the test-object.   For example, these data indicate that
the mean variation in visual efficiency among these subjects was
12 per cent when appraised by measurements of the visibility of
a test-object of relatively high contrast and a visual size of 1.66
minutes.   However, the variation in visual efficiency among the
same group of subjects was found to be 27 per cent when the
measurements involved a test-object of relatively low contrast and
a visual size of 3.95 minutes.   It should be obvious from these
data that sensitometric measurements, involving the biconcave test-
object and hence much lower contrasts, are even more effective in
revealing differences in visual efficiency among a group of subjects.
Of course, comfort in seeing should not be lost sight of notwithstanding the fact that measurements of comfort have not been a
part of the eyesight specialist's technique.   Our studies of the rate
of blinking under various seeing conditions, as summarized in
Fig. 143 and Table XXXIII, point toward possibilities in this
direction.

References

1. "Seeing—A Partnership of Lighting and Vision," M. Luckiesh and Frank K. Moss, Williams and Wilkins Co., Baltimore, 1931.

2. "Seeing and Human Welfare," Matthew Luckiesh, Williams and Wilkins Co., Baltimore, 1934.

3. "The Relative Potency of Color and Form Perception at Various Ages," C. R. Brian and F. L. Goodenough, *Jour. Exper. Psych.*, 12, 1929, 197.

4. "Visual Illusions," M. Luckiesh, D. Van Nostrand Co., New York, 1922.

5. "Light and Work," M. Luckiesh, D. Van Nostrand Co., New York, 1924.

6. "The New Science of Seeing," M. Luckiesh and Frank K. Moss, *Trans. I. E. S.*, 25, 1930, 15.

7. "The New Science of Lighting," M. Luckiesh and Frank K. Moss, *Trans. I. E. S.*, 29, 1934, 641.

8. "The Human Seeing-Machine," M. Luckiesh and Frank K. Moss, *Jour. Frank. Inst.*, 215, 1933, 629; *Trans. I. E. S.*, 27, 1932, 699.

9. "Visibility—Its Measurement and Significance in Seeing," M. Luckiesh and Frank K. Moss, *Jour. Frank. Inst.*, 220, 1935, 431.

10. "The Applied Science of Seeing," M. Luckiesh and Frank K. Moss, *Trans. I. E. S.*, 28, 1933, 842.

11. "Seeing and Highway Safety," M. Luckiesh, *National Safety News*, 28, 1933, 33.

12. "Changes in Visual Acuity Through Simultaneous Stimulation of Other Sense Organs," G. W. Hartman, *Jour. Exper. Psych.*, 16, 1933, 393.

[521]

13. "The Concept of the Threshold and Heyman's Law of Inhibition," L. T. Spencer, *Jour. Exper. Psych.*, 11, 1928, 194.

14. "Reaction of the Eye to Light," P. Reeves, *Transactions of the Optical Society*, 22, 1920-1921, 1.

15. "Do Movements Occur in the Visual Cells and Retinal Pigment of Man?" L. B. Arey, *Science*, 42, 1915, 915.

16. "The Increase in Visual Acuity in One Eye Through Illumination of the Other," G. W. Hartman, *Jour. Exper. Psych.*, 16, 1933, 383.

17. "Dietary Deficiency and Ocular Disease," *Archives of Ophthalmology*, 8, 1932, 580.

18. "The Dark Adaptation of Retinal Fields of Different Size and Location," Selig Hecht, *Jour. Gen. Physiol.*, 19, 1935, 321.

19. "Intermittent Stimulation by Light," Selig Hecht and E. L. Smith, *Jour. Gen. Physiol.*, 19, 1936, 979.

20. "The Adaptation of the Eye: Its Relation to the Critical Frequency of Flicker," R. J. Lythgoe and K. Tansley, *Medical Research Council Report No. 134, His Majesty's Stationery Office*, London, 1929.

21. "Light and Shade and Their Applications," M. Luckiesh, D. Van Nostrand Co., New York, 1916.

22. "Neutral Value Scales," A. E. O. Munsell, L. L. Sloan and I. H. Godlove, *Journal of the Optical Society of America*, 23, 1933, 394.

23. "The Relation Between Visual Acuity and Illumination," Selig Hecht, *Jour. Gen. Physiol.*, 11, 1928, 255.

24. "The Principles of Psychophysiology," Vol. II, L. T. Troland, D. Van Nostrand Co., New York, 1930.

25. "Starling's Principles of Human Physiology," Lea and Febiger, Philadelphia, 1933.

26. "Clinical Physiology of the Eye," F. H. Adler, The Macmillan Co., New York, 1933.

27. "The Visibility of Radiation and Dark Adaptation," R. A. Houston, *Philosophical Magazine and Journal of Science*, 7th Series, 10, 1930, 416.

[REFERENCES]

28. "Some Experiments on Eye-Movements," R. J. Lythgoe and D. Corkill, *Brit. Jour. Ophth.*, 13, 1929, 433.

29. "A Demonstrational Test of Vision," M. Luckiesh and Frank K. Moss, *Amer. Jour. Psych.*, 45, 1933, 135.

30. "Berger Rhythm—Potential Changes in. the Occipital Lobes of Man," E. D. Adrian and B. H. C. Matthews, *Brain*, 57, 1934, 355.

31. "Electrical Potentials of the Human Brain," A. L. Loomis, E. N. Harvey and G. Hobart, *Jour. Exper. Psych.*, 19, 1936, 249.

32. "The Response of the Average Pupil to Various Intensities of Light," P. Reeves, *J. O. S. A.*, 4, 1920, 35.

33. "Area and Brightness of Stimulus Related to the Pupillary Light Reflex," M. Luckiesh and Frank K. Moss, *J. O. S. A.*, 24, 1934, 130.

34. "The Influence of Pupillary Diameter on Visual Acuity," P. W. Cobb, *Amer. Jour. Physiol.*, 36, 1915, 335.

35. "On the Variation of the Diameter of the Pupil with Age," Nitsche and Gunther, *Mitteilungen*, December, 1930, 117.

36. "Size of Pupil as a Possible Index of Ocular Fatigue," M. Luckiesh and Frank K. Moss, *Amer. Jour. Ophthal.*, 16, 1933, 393.

37. *Zeitschr. f. Sinnesphysiol.*, 45, 1911, 307.

38. "The Fixation Pause of the Eyes," P. W. Cobb and Frank K. Moss, *Jour. Exper. Psych.*, 9, 1926, 359.

39. "The Experimental Study of Reading," M. D. Vernon, Cambridge University Press, 1931.

40. "Fatigue of Convergence Induced by Reading as a Function of Illumination Intensity," M. Luckiesh and Frank K. Moss, *Amer. Jour. Ophthal.*, 18, 1935, 319.

41. "Corresponding Retinal Points, The Horopter and Size and Shape of Ocular Images," A. Ames, G. H. Glidden, and K. N. Ogle, *J. O. S. A.*, 22, 1932, 575.

42. "Individual Variations in Retinal Sensitivity and Their Correlation with Ophthalmologic Findings," P. W. Cobb, *Jour. Exper. Psych.*, 5, 1922, 227.

43. "Binocular Summation in Scotopic Vision," D. Shaad, *Jour. Exper. Psych.*, 18, 1935, 391.

44. "Binocular and Monocular Vision," E. M. Lowry, *J. O. S. A. and Review of Scientific Instruments*, 18, 1929, 29.

45. "Physiological Optics," W. D. Zoethout, The Professional Press, Chicago, 1927.

46. "Intensity of Light in Relation to the Near-Point and the Apparent Range of Accommodation," C. E. Ferree and G. Rand, *Amer. Jour. Ophthal.*, 18, 1935, 307.

47. "The Dependency of Visual Acuity upon Stimulus-Distance," M. Luckeish and Frank K. Moss, *J. O. S. A.*, 23, 1933, 25.

48. "Speed of Accommodation as a Practicable Test for Fliers," L. E. Tefft and E. K. Stark, *Amer. Jour. Ophthal.*, 5, 1922, 339.

49. "The Effect of Ocular Fatigue on Sensitiveness to Differentiation," T. B. Schubova, *Amer. Jour. Ophthal.*, 17, 1934, 178.

50. "The Basis of Sensation," E. D. Adrian, Christophers, London, 1934.

51. *Journal de Physiologie et de Pathologie Generale*, No. 4, July, 1902.

52. "On the Growth and Decay of Color Sensations in Flicker Photometry," M. Luckiesh, *Physical Review*, 4, 1914, 1.

53. "Color and Its Applications," M. Luckiesh, D. Van Nostrand Co., New York, 1921.

54. "A Quantitative Investigation of the Purkinje After-Image," D. B. Judd, *Amer. Jour. Psych.*, 38, 1927, 507.

55. "Visual Illusions," M. Luckiesh, D. Van Nostrand Co., New York, 1922.

56. "The Principles of Psychophysiology," Vol. I, L. T. Troland, D. Van Nostrand Co., New York, 1929.

57. "A Quantitative Formulation of Color Vision," Selig Hecht, University Press, Cambridge, 1932.

58. Letter Circular LC-454, National Bureau of Standards, Washington.

[REFERENCES]

59. "Studies Based on Spectral Complementaries," R. H. Sinden, *J. O. S. A. and R. S. I.*, 7, 1923, 1123.

60. "The Measurement of Visual Acuity," R. J. Lythgoe, *Medical Research Council Report No. 173, His Majesty's Stationery Office*, London, 1932.

61. "Attention (Summary of Literature)," K. M. Dallenbach, *Psychological Bulletin*, 23, 1926, 1.

62. "An Analysis of the Literature Concerning the Dependency of Visual Functions Upon Illumination Intensity," L. T. Troland, *Trans. I. E. S.*, 26, 1931, 107.

63. "The Four Variables of the Visual Threshold," P. W. Cobb and Frank K. Moss, *Jour. Frank. Inst.*, 205, 1928, 831; also *Jour. Exper. Psych.*, 10, 1927, 350.

64. "Some Experiments on Speed of Vision," P. W. Cobb, *Trans. I. E. S.*, 19, 1924, 150.

65. "An Experimental Determination of the Visual Thresholds at Low Values of Illumination," J. P. Conner and R. E. Ganoung, *J. O. S. A.*, 25, 1935, 287.

66. "A View of the Cortical Integrational Process Through Liminal Visual Stimuli," M. Luckiesh and Frank K. Moss, *Jour. Exper. Psych.*, 17, 1934, 449.

67. "The Role of Form in Perception," H. Helson and E. V. Fehrer, *Amer. Jour. Psych.*, 44, 1932, 79.

68. "The Effect of One Border in the Visual Field Upon the Threshold of Another," G. A. Fry and S. H. Bartley, *Amer. Jour. Physiol.*, 112, 1935, 414.

69. "The Relation Between Visual Acuity and Illumination," Selig Hecht, *Jour. Gen. Physiol.*, 11, 1928, 255.

70. "Anomalies of Visual Acuity in Relation to Stimulus-Distance," Ellis Freeman, *J. O. S. A.*, 22, 1932, 285.

71. "The Minimum Radiation Visually Perceptible," P. Reeves, *Astrophysical Journal*, 46, 1917, 167.

72. "Study of Light Signals and Navigation," I. Langmuir and W. F. Westendorp, *Physics*, 1, 1931, 273.

73. "The Effect on Foveal Vision of Bright Surroundings—IV," P. W. Cobb, *Jour. Exper. Psych.*, 1, 1916, 540.

74. "A Correlation Between Pupillary Area and Retinal Sensibility," M. Luckiesh and Frank K. Moss, *Amer. Jour. Ophthal.*, 17, 1934, 598.

75. "Elements of Physiological Psychology," Ladd and Woodworth, 1911.

76. "The Perception of Lights of Short Duration at Their Range Limits," Blondel and Rey, *Trans. I. E. S.*, 7, 1912, 625.

77. "Physiological Optics," Charles Sheard, Cleveland Press, Chicago, 1918.

78. "Tests for the Efficiency of the Eye Under Different Systems of Illumination and a Preliminary Study of the Causes of Discomfort," C. E. Ferree, *Trans. I. E. S.*, 8, 1913, 40.

79. "Effects of General Distraction on the Higher Thought Processes," H. B. Hovey, *Amer. Jour. Psych.*, 40, 1928, 585.

80. "The Concept of the Threshold and Heyman's Law of Inhibition," L. T. Spencer, *Jour. Exper. Psych.*, 11, 1928, 88 and 194.

81. "The Effects of Distractions on Reaction-Time," J. E. Evans, *Archives of Psychology*, 25, 1916, 15.

82. "A Visibility Meter," M. G. Bennett, *Journal of Scientific Instruments*, 8, 1931, 122.

83. "The Effect of Dark Surroundings Upon Vision," P. W. Cobb and Frank K. Moss, *Jour. Frank. Inst.*, 206, 1928, 827.

84. Report of Committee on Compensation for Eye Injuries, Section on Ophthalmology, A. M. A., 1925, 368-377.

85. "A Critical Study of the Snellen Letters and the Illiterate 'E' Tests," J. M. McCallie, *American Journal of Physiological Optics*, 4, 1923, 371.

86. "Studies in Illumination," U. S. *Public Health Bulletin*, *No. 181*.

87. "Muscular Tension Resulting from Glare," M. Luckiesh and Frank K. Moss, *Jour. Gen. Psych.*, 8, 1933, 455.

[REFERENCES]

88. "Eye Fatigue and Its Relation to Light and Work," P. W. Cobb and Frank K. Moss, *Jour. Frank. Inst.*, 200, 1925, 239.

89. "Glare and the Four Fundamental Factors in Vision," P. W. Cobb and Frank K. Moss, *Trans. I. E. S.*, 23, 1928, 1104.

90. "A Correlation Between Illumination Intensity and Nervous Muscular Tension Resulting from Visual Effort," M. Luckiesh and Frank K. Moss, *Jour. Exper. Psych.*, 16, 1933, 540.

91. "The Effect of Visual Effort Upon the Heart-Rate," M. Luckiesh and Frank K. Moss, *Jour. Gen. Psych.*, 13, 1935, 131.

92. "The Heart-Rate," E. P. Boas and E. F. Goldschmidt, Thomas, Baltimore, 1932.

93. "Die Frequenz des Herzschlages," *Hdbk. d. norm. u. path. Physiol.* Springer, Berlin, 1926.

94. "Organic Changes and Feeling," J. F. Shepard, *Amer. Jour. Psych.*, 17, 1906, 522.

95. "The Relative Influence of Mental and Muscular Work on the Pulse Rate and Blood Pressure," R. D. Gillespie, *Jour. of Physiol.*, 58, 1924, 425.

96. "On the Act of Blinking," E. Ponder and W. P. Kennedy, *Quarterly Journal of Experimental Physiology*, 18, 1927-1928, 89.

97. "Recording of Winking as a Method of Study of Ocular Fatigue in Children Resulting from Reading," G. A. Litinky, *Sovet. vestnik optal.*, 4, 1934, 275.

98. "Controls of the Eye-Wink Mechanism," J. Peterson and L. W. Allison, *Jour. Exper. Psych.*, 14, 1931, 144.

99. "The Rate of Visual Work on Alternating Fields of Different Brightnesses," M. Luckiesh and Frank K. Moss, *Jour. Frank. Inst.*, 200, 1925, 731.

100. "Some Factors Influencing Voluntary and Reflex Eyelid Responses," C. W. Telford and N. Thompson, *Jour. Exper. Psych.*, 16, 1933, 524.

[527]

101. "Measurement of the Fatigue of the Ocular Muscles," L. Howe, *Journal of the American Medical Association*, 49, 1912, 1024.

102. "Studies in Ocular Fatigue. III. Fatigue of Accommodaiton," C. Berens and E. K. Stark, *Amer. Jour. Ophthal.*, 15, 1932, 216.

103. "Studies in Ocular Fatigue. VI. Convergence Fatigue in Practice," Berens, Hardy and Pierce, *Transactions of the American Ophthalmological Society*, 24, 1926, 262.

104. "The Effect of Intensity of Illumination on the Near Point of Vision and a Comparison of the Effect for Presbyopic and Non-Presbyopic Eyes," C. E. Ferree and G. Rand, *Trans. I. E. S.*, 28, 1933, 590.

105. "Modified Broca Pupillometer," Frank K. Moss, *J. O. S. A.*, 22, 1932, 735.

106. "Light and Sight—First Aid for Safety and Production," R. E. Simpson, *Trans. I. E. S.*, 21, 1926, 54.

107. "Functions of Eyes in the Acquisition of Education," Lloyd Mills, *J. A. M. A.*, 93, 1929, 841.

108. U. S. Public Health Bulletin No. 182.

109. "What Schools Do for Children's Eyes and Ears," E. A. Pratt, *Hygeia*, 9, 1931, 813.

110. "Variations in Visual Acuity Among College Students," R. E. Boyton, *Sight-Saving Review*, 6, 1936, 263.

111. "Functions of An Industrial Eye Clinic," Industrial Health Series, No. 4, Metropolitan Life Insurance Company.

112. "The Consequences of Myopia as an Industrial Disease of the Eyes," H. N. Bishop, *Journal of Industrial Hygiene*, 4, 1923, 371.

113. "Eye Health Study of Texas School Children," Jones, Hemphill and Pinckney, Bureau of Nutrition and Health Education, University of Texas, Extension Division.

114. "Eyesight Conservation Survey," Bulletin 7, Eyesight Conservation Council of America.

115. "Influence of School Lighting on Scholarship," Willard Allphin, *Trans. I. E. S.*, 31, 1936, 739.

116. "A Procedure for Balancing Parallel Groups," Rulon and Croon, *Journal of Educational Psychology*, 24, 1933, 585.

117. "Visual Tasks in Sight-Saving Classes, M. Luckiesh and Frank K. Moss, *Amer. Jour. Ophthal.*, 19, 1936, 992.

118. "The Effect of Brightness on the Precision of Visually Controlled Operations," P. W. Cobb and Frank K. Moss, *Jour. Frank. Inst.*, 199, 1925, 507.

119. "Data Pertaining to the Desired Illumination Intensities," Luckiesh, Taylor, and Sinden, *Jour. Frank Inst.*, 192, 1921, 757.

120. "Humanitarian Footcandles," M. Luckiesh and Frank K. Moss, *Proceedings of the International Illumination Congress*, 1, 1931, 76.

121. "Improvement in Highway Safety," A. R. Lauer, *Proceedings of the 12th Annual Meeting of Highway Research Board*, December 1932, 389.

122. "Determination of Visibility on Lighted Highways," K. M. Reid and H. J. Chanon, *Trans. I. E. S.*, 32, 1937, 187.

123. "Visual Requirements for Automobile Drivers," M. F. Weymann, *California Western Medical Journal*, 35, 1931, 101.

124. Lectures, Detroit Congress of American Optometric Association, 1936.

125. "The Relation Between the Magnitude of the Stimulus and the Time of Reaction," S. Froeberg, *Archives of Psychology*, 1, 1907.

126. "Reaction Time to Photometrically Equal Chromatic Stimuli," J. L. Holmes, *Amer. Jour. Psych.*, 37, 1926, 414.

127. "Correlation of Reaction and Coordination Speed with Age in Adults," W. R. Miles, *Amer. Jour. Psych.*, 43, 1931, 377.

128. "Psychological Research in Aviation in Italy, France, England and the American Expeditionary Forces," F. C. Dockeray and S. Isaacs, *Journal of Comparative Psychology*, 1, 1921, 115.

129. "Reaction to Multiple Stimuli," J. W. Todd, *Arch. Psych.*, 3, 1912, 1.

130. "Quality of Lighting," Matthew Luckiesh and Frank K. Moss, *Trans. I. E. S.*, 30, 1935, 531.

131. *Journal of the Optical Society of America; Transactions of the Illuminating Engineering Society.*

132. "Prescribing Light and Lighting," M. Luckiesh and Frank K. Moss, *Trans. I. E. S.*, 32, 1937, 19.

133. "A Brightness-Meter," M. Luckiesh and A. H. Taylor, *J. O. S. A.*, 27, 1937, 132.

134. "Measurement of Diffuse Reflection-Factors and a New Absolute Reflectometer," A. H. Taylor, *J. O. S. A.*, 4, 1920, 9; *Trans. I. E. S.*, 15, 1920, 811.

135. "Physiological Eye-Strain," H. Hartridge, *Jour. Physiol.*, 53.

136. "Recommended Footcandles," M. Luckiesh and Frank K. Moss, *Trans. I. E. S.*, 26, 1931, 1061.

137. "Lighting Plus Vision Equals Seeing," M. Luckiesh and Frank K. Moss, *Trans. I. E. S.*, 25, 1930, 807.

138. "General Lighting Plus," M. Luckiesh and Frank K. Moss, *Trans. I. E. S.*, 24, 1929, 233.

139. "Lighting Fixtures and Lighting Effects," M. Luckiesh, McGraw-Hill Book Co., New York, 1925.

140. "Glare and Visibility," M. Luckiesh and L. L. Holladay, *Trans. I. E. S.*, 20, 1925, 221.

141. "The Fundamentals of Glare and Visibility," L. L. Holladay, *J. O. S. A.*, 12, 1926, 271.

142. "Glare—Its Manifestations and the Status of Knowledge Thereof," P. S. Millar and S. McK. Gray, *Proc. Int. Com. Illum.*, 1928, 239.

143. "What Is Wrong with Our 50-Footcandle Installations?", Ward Harrison, *Trans. I. E. S.*, 32, 1937, 208.

144. "Chromatic Aberration and Visual Acuity," Louis Bell, *Elec. World*, 57, 1911, 1163.

145. "Monochromatic Light and Visual Acuity," M. Luckiesh, *Elec. World*, 58, 1911, 450; *Trans. I. E. S.*, 7, 1912, 135.

[REFERENCES]

146. "Spectral Distribution of Radiation from High and Low Pressure Hg Arcs," B. T. Barnes, *J. O. S. A.*, 24, 1934, 147.

147. "Spectral Distribution of Energy in Common Illuminants," A. H. Taylor, *G. E. Review*, 37, 1934, 410.

148. "The Color of Daylight," A. H. Taylor, *Trans. I. E. S.*, 25, 1930, 154.

149. "Seeing in Tungsten, Mercury and Sodium Lights," M. Luckiesh and Frank K. Moss, *Trans. I. E. S.*, 31, 1936, 655.

150. "The Effect on Visual Acuity of Shortening the Spectrum in the Blue End," M. Luckiesh and Frank K. Moss, *J. O. S. A.*, 10, 1925, 275.

151. "Comparison of the Light from High-Intensity Mercury Vapor Lamps and Incandescent-Filament Lamps for Visual Tasks," C. S. Woodside and Harris Reinhardt, *Trans. I. E. S.*, 32, 1937, 365.

152. "Visual Acuity and Sodium-Vapor Light," M. Luckiesh and Frank K. Moss, *Jour. Frank. Inst.*, 215, 1933, 401.

153. "Seeing in Sodium-Vapor Light," M. Luckiesh and Frank K. Moss, *J. O. S. A.*, 24, 1934, 5; also *Trans. I. E. S.*, 31, 1936, 655.

154. "Glare from Sodium Light," M. Luckiesh and Frank K. Moss, *Trans. I. E. S.*, 30, 1935, 602.

155. "Degree of Contrast of Sodium, Mercury and White Light," P. J. Bouma, Phillips Laboratories, Einhoven, Holland, *De Ingenieur*, 49, 1934, 290.

156. "Artificial Daylight—Its Production and Use," M. Luckiesh and F. E. Cady, *Trans. I. E. S.*, 9, 1914, 839.

157. "Filters for Artificial Daylighting, Their Grading and Use," H. P. Gage and Norman Macbeth, *Trans. I. E. S.*, 31, 1936, 955.

158. "Handbook of Colorimetry," A. C. Hardy, Technology Press, M. I. T., Cambridge, Mass., 1936.

159. "Light and Color in Advertising and Merchandising," M. Luckiesh, D. Van Nostrand Co., New York, 1923.

160. "The Visibility of Airplanes," M. Luckiesh, *Jour. Frank. Inst.*, 187, 1919, 29 and 409. Also "Aerial Photometry," M. Luckiesh, *Astrophys. Jour.*, 49, 1919, 108.

161. "Relative Glare in Moderately Colored Lights," Luckiesh, Holladay and Taylor, *J. O. S. A.*, 11, 1925, 311.

162. "Energy Density in the Eye-Media," M. Luckiesh, *Elec. World*, 66, 1915, 576.

163. "Infrared Radiation and Visual Function," M. Luckiesh and Frank K. Moss, *J. O. S. A.*, 27, 1937, 69.

164. "The Eyelid Reflex as a Criterion of Ocular Hygiene," M. Luckiesh and Frank K. Moss, *Jour. Exper. Psych.*, 20, 1937, 589.

165. "The Dark Adaptation of the Human Eye," Selig Hecht, *Jour. Gen. Physiol.*, 2, 1920, 499; also *Jour. Gen. Physiol.*, 19, 1935, 321.

166. "Artificial Sunlight," M. Luckiesh, D. Van Nostrand Co., New York, 1930.

167. "Psychology," E. G. Boring, H. S. Langfeld and H. P. Weld, John Wiley and Sons, Inc., New York, 1933.

168. "Studies of Typographical Factors Influencing Speed of Reading," M. A. Tinker and D. G. Patterson, *Journal of Applied Psychology*, 16, 1932, 605.

169. "The Relative Legibility of Different Faces of Printing Types," B. E. Rothlein, *Amer. Jour. Psych.*, 23, 1912, 1.

170. "The Visibility of Various Type Faces," M. Luckiesh and Frank K. Moss, *Jour. Frank. Inst.*, 223, 1937, 77.

171. "Studies of Typographical Factors Influencing Speed of Reading," M. A. Tinker and D. G. Patterson, *Jour. Applied Psych.*, 13, 1929, 205.

172. "Critical and Experimental Studies in Psychology from the University of Illinois," Madison Bentley, *Psychological Monographs.*, 30, 1921, No. 3.

173. "Hygiene of the Eye," W. C. Posey, J. B. Lippincott Co., Philadelphia, 1918.

174. "Reading Disabilities and Their Correction," E. A. Betts, *Elementary English Review*, 12, 1935, Nos. 3 to 6.

175. "Silent Reading: A Study of Various Types," C. H. Judd and G. T. Buswell, *Psychol. Monog.*, 1922, No. 23.

·176. "Fundamental Reading Habits: A Study of Their Development," G. T. Buswell, *Supplementary Educational Monographs*, 1922, No. 21.

177. "Accommodation and Convergence Under Low Levels of Illumination," H. E. Israel, *Jour. Exper. Psych.*, 6, 1923, 223.

178. "Improvements in Reading Following the Correction of Eye-Defects of Non-Readers," T. H. Eames, *Amer. Jour. Ophthal.*, 17, 1934, 324.

179. "An Investigation of the Visual Efficiencies of 10,000 School Children and the Correlation of Vision and Scholarship," R. Morse-Peckham, *American Journal of Optometry*, 13, 1936, 321.

180. "Bibliography on Analysis, Prevention and Correction of Reading Difficulties," E. A. Betts, Keystone View Co., Meadville, Pa., 1935.

181. "A Subjective Method of Skiascopy," Charles Sheard, *Amer. Jour. Physiol. Optics*, 7, 1926, 76.

182. "Optical Theory of Skiascopy," J. P. C. Southall, *J. O. S. A.*, 13, 1926, 245.

183. "The Theory of Measurements," L. Tuttle and J. Satterly, Longsman, Green and Co., London, 1925.

184. "On the Attainment of Simultaneous Binocular Vision in Orthoptic Training," M. Luckiesh, Frank K. Moss, and R. M. Hall, *Jour. Amer. Optom. Assn.*, 8, 1937, 268.

Index

Proofreading, 472
Proprioceptor phenomena, 495
Pseudo-myopia, 514
Psychophysiological factors, 46
Pupillary area versus retinal sensitivity, 156
Pupillometer, 395
  Luckiesh-Moss, 237
Pupillomotor,
  fibers, 78
  influence, 68
Pupil size, related to,
  accommodation, 90
  age, 92
  emotional state, 90
  fatigue, 93, 237, 240
  light stimulus, 87, 89, 156
  physiological state, 87
  psychological state, 85
  quality of lighting, 375, 395
  refractive errors, 376
  visual efficiency, 92, 156
Purkinje effect, 62, 68, 373
Purples, 433

Quality of lighting,
  appraisal in practice, 394
  basic considerations, 360
  brightness and adaptation, 366, 370
  empirical practices, 297
  general lighting plus, 346
  glare, 211, 320, 366, 383, 443
  highlights and shadows, 311, 313
  illumination and brightness, 306
  influence of surroundings, 377
  light and lighting, 296
  negative factors, 383
  psychological aspects, 381
  pupillary criteria, 373
  reflection of light, 314
  for seeing and for rest, 301
[544]

Quality of light, spectral, 399
  chromatic aberration, 403
  color-contrast, 39, 43, 309, 432
  color-discrimination, 426
  colored eyeglasses, 440
  common illuminants, 409
  fundamental characteristics, 399
  glare and colored lights, 448
  psychological effects, 433
  seeing in mercury light, 415
  seeing in sodium light, 422
  selectivity of atmosphere, 437
  ultraviolet and infrared, 451
Quantity of light
  for defective vision, 268, 353
  effectiveness, 334
  footcandle eras, 332
  footcandle prescriptions, 343
  introspectively chosen, 351
  level of illumination, 303, 305, 341
  for reading, 347
  recommended footcandles, 345
  for various tasks, 344, 467

Radiant energy, 4, 400, 410, 427, 430
Radiation, 6
Reaction-time, 159, 286
  effect of age on, 286
  inhibition and facilitation of, 164
Readability, 455
Reading, 49, 266, 454
  in bed, 469
  disability, 484
  distance, 469
  eye-movements in, 97, 470, 473
  footcandles for, 50, 234
  influence of ocular defects, 482
  psychophysiological effects of, 224
  rate of, 209, 271, 483
  while drowsy, 469